GERMAN WEAPONS OF
WORLD WAR II

Edited by
Chris Bishop and Adam Warner

Grange
BOOKS

This edition first published in 2001 for Grange Books
An imprint of Grange Books plc
The Grange
Kingsnorth Industrial Estate
Hoo, nr Rochester
Kent ME3 9ND
www.grangebooks.co.uk

ISBN: 1-84013-421-6

Jacket design by
Amber Books Ltd
Bradley's Close
74–77 White Lion Street
London N1 9PF

This material was previously published as part of the reference set *Hitler's Third Reich*.

Contributors: Chris Bishop, Kurt Steiner, Adam Warner, William Wilson

Illustrators: Peter Harper, Chris Bishop

Picture credits: Aerospace, AKG, Bundesarchiv, Deutsches Museum, EWWF,

Koblenz, John Weal, TRH Pictures

Printed in Italy

CONTENTS

U-BOAT
WOLFPACKS
Hunters of the Atlantic

Ranging far out into the Atlantic and preying on sea-borne British trade, the Kriegsmarine's U-boat fleet was the biggest threat to Britain's survival during World War II, and in the early years at least offered Germany's best chance of winning the war.

IN 1939, half the food eaten in the United Kingdom came from overseas. Two-thirds of the raw materials required by Britain's war industries were imported too. If German U-boats could stop this flow of goods by sinking Allied merchant ships, Hitler would win the war.

After the French surrender in 1940, the bulk of the U-boats were based on France's Atlantic coast in vast reinforced-concrete submarine pens. To reach the shipping lanes they had to cross the Bay of Biscay. Travelling on the surface to get into action as quickly as possible, they often submerged by day to hide from British long-range aircraft.

WAR PATROL

Once in the Atlantic, the hunt began. From his headquarters ashore, Doenitz exercised tight control over his U-boats. By radio direction finding, aerial reconnaissance and the cracking of certain British naval codes, Doenitz enjoyed some success at predicting the course of the convoys. U-boat 'Wolf packs' were assembled, patrolling in long lines with the submarines at intervals of 10 to 20 km.

Once a convoy was located, Doenitz assigned one U-boat as 'shadower'. This followed the convoy, reporting its course and speed to the U-boat HQ while the other boats moved in for the kill. The first attacks were made underwater, but ace skippers quickly learned that night surface attacks were more effective, trusting to their low silhouette to avoid detection and to the U-Boat's ability to outpace most escorts. More cautious skippers remained submerged and fired fans of torpedoes at the columns of merchant ships. The top commanders each sank over a hundred thousand tonnes of Allied shipping.

Standard defence against a U-boat attack was to fire starshell; the sudden burst of light occasionally revealed a U-boat on the surface. Any nearby escorts would open fire with their main armament: really aggressive escort commanders would try to ram their opponent. Curiously, if a U-boat submerged it became easier to detect. These were the days before effective radar had been widely deployed aboard escorts, but they all had ASDIC detection gear, which used sound waves to search for submerged boats. If a U-boat was detected a deadly game of cat and mouse would follow in which the submarine, with its low underwater speed and limited submerged range, was at a distinct disadvantage. The crew listened as the 'ping' of enemy sonar echoed around them. If full speed on the electric motors and rapid alterations in course failed

The Battle of the Atlantic was an epic struggle, during which the German U-boat arm sank 150 Allied warships and 2,850 merchantmen of more than 14 million tonnes. But it was at considerable cost: although over 1100 U-boats were built only 830 managed to get into operation, and 817 of those were sunk.

BENEATH THE WAVES
Inhuman conditions of U-boat life

Life aboard a U-Boat was hard. The boat was packed with weapons, engines, batteries, equipment and supplies, and there was little room for the crew, who could be at sea for up to 60 days.

The bow compartment was 'home' to 24 men, who had to share it with the torpedoes. At least half were on duty at any one time, and they took turns to sleep in collapsible bunks or hammocks. There was no privacy, nor were there any real washing facilities, so the atmosphere reeked of body odours, motor oil and stale food.

The captain, his three officers and five senior petty officers shared the next compartment aft. The captain's bunk was on the port side: the other side of the central passageway were the radio and sonar rooms. The officers' com-

partment also housed the toilet, shared by the whole crew. There was another aft, near the galley, but this was invariably used to store provisions.

Abaft the control room was a compartment with eight bunks for the petty officers, lockers for the crew's personal possessions and the boat's galley: a three-ring electric hob, two little ovens and a tiny sink.

Food was stored everywhere when the boat put to sea: in the early days of a patrol it was a floating larder, with sausages and mesh bags of bread dangling from the ceiling, cheeses and canned food crammed into every bit of space.

Above: A Type IX U-Boat returns to port after a two-month war patrol far out in the Atlantic.

Below: U-boat crewmen lived in conditions of almost unspeakable squalor – cramped, crowded, damp, unhygenic and usually too hot or too cold for comfort.

Above: The working spaces of a World War II-era submarine were crammed from deck to ceiling with a daunting mass of pipes, dials, valves, hand wheels, levers and other equipment. The men who worked in these quarters had to be able to withstand claustrophobia as well as weeks or even months of very close and increasingly insanitary proximity to his crewmates.

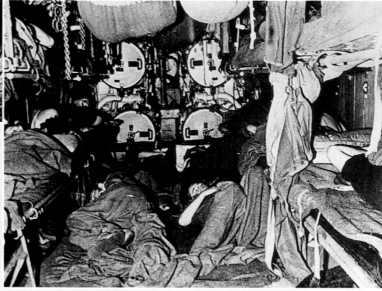

to shake the pursuer, they could try to escape by stealth, but all too often the U-boat men would hear the awful express train sound of a destroyer passing overhead to drop depth charges. The thunderous detonations of the explosive devices reverberated through the submarine. A near miss could smash dials, crack open valves and plunge the boat into darkness.

EVADING DEPTH CHARGES

Bold skippers would take the boat down through the pre-war safety depth of 50 metres, the hull creaking as the pressure increased, down to and even beyond the normal maximum permissible depth of 150 metres.

To escape from a particularly accurate depth-charging attack in 1939, the famous 'ace' Otto von Kretschmer dived U-99 beyond 210 metres, his gamble paying off because early-war British depth charges had a maximum depth setting of 150 metres. If the U-boat men were lucky, the escorts would lose contact or be compelled to abandon the attack and rush to head off an attack on another part of the convoy and the submarine could slink away.

The effect of such an attack was often to leave the U-boat a long way astern of the convoy. As long as the boat was not too seriously damaged, it would creep up to periscope depth after an hour or two. Catching the convoy again would be impossible while submerged, so captains would bring their boats back to the surface as soon as possible, using the U-boat's superior surface speed to regain contact, ready to renew its attack the following night.

Once out of torpedoes a U-boat commander would often be instructed to continue to shadow the convoy, sending position reports for the benefits of fresher boats arriving on the

Type VIIC Unterseeboot

The majority of U-boats that fought the Battle of the Atlantic were Type VIIs. Originally a pre-war ocean-going design, only 10 of the original Type VIIA were built before production switched to the Type VIIB, which was stretched by about 2 metres to allow more fuel and torpedoes to be stowed, and which had more powerful diesels for greater surface speeds. This and the Type VIIC, again enlarged to carry two extra torpedoes, were built in huge numbers. Over 700 Type VIIs were built, construction continuing from 1936 right through the war.

The Type VII had no air conditioning or proper heating. On patrols to the Caribbean the temperature inside often reached 35 degrees C – by contrast, boats wreaking havoc on American shipping off the US east coast in January 1942 recorded internal temperatures of 1 degree C day after day.

TECHNICAL SPECIFICATION

Type VIIC U-boat

Crew: 44 officers and men

Displacement: 769 tonnes surfaced/ 871 tonnes submerged

Length: 66.5 m (218 ft)

Beam: 6.2 m (20 ft)

Draught: 4.7 m (15.5 ft)

Machinery: 2-shaft diesel/electric delivering 2,800 hp on diesel engines and 750 hp on batteries

Speed: 17 knots surfaced/ 7.5 knots submerged

Range: 15750 km (9,785 miles) at 10 knots on surface/ unrecharged underwater range 130 km (80 miles) at 4 knots or less

Armament: 1 x 88 mm gun, 1 x 20-mm AA gun (later fitted with one or two flakvierling quad AA mounts); 14 x 533 mm (21 in) torpedoes fired through four forward torpedo tubes and one aft tube

A Type VII U-boat of the Seventh Flotilla returns to port after a successful cruise. The Flotilla's 'Laughing Bull' insignia adorned the conning towers of some of the most successful U-boat aces.

Type VIIs were driven by twin propellers. Under diesel drive the boat could reach around 17.5 knots on the surface – more than enough to run rings around a slow-moving convoy.

The engine room, a narrow passageway running between two diesel engines, and beyond that, the electric motor compartment. An air pipe ran from the engines up to the top of the bridge structure, keeping the engines' air intake as far above sea level as possible. The diesels propelled the boat on the surface and charged the electric batteries that powered it underwater.

The six-metre-long control room was aft of the officers' compartment. In the middle was a cylindrical tube with a ladder inside, leading up into the cramped conning tower which housed a duplicate helm station, engine telegraph and the attack periscope.

The conning tower opened out to the bridge, where four lookouts were posted when the boat was on the surface. Each man was responsible for one 90-degree segment of the horizon, peering through Zeiss 7 x 50 binoculars. The safety of the boat depended on their vigilance: there was no radar aboard.

Type VIIs had four torpedo tubes in the bow, for which six reloads were carried – the bow compartment (two on the deck plates and four below in the bilges) plus a single torpedo tube in the stern, with one reload.

Above: The bridge of a U-Boat out in the Atlantic was both a refuge and a place of acute danger. Going topside was the only way for a crewman to escape the stinking interior of the boat and get any fresh air, but in rough weather it was often inundated by a green wall of water.

Right: Bad weather was often the merchant sailor's friend, since it made it very difficult for the low-set U-Boats to manoeuvre into position for an attack on a convoy.

Left: U-boat torpedoes were 7 metres long, 533 mm in diameter and weighed nearly two tonnes. They demanded regular maintenance checks to ensure their electrical systems were functioning properly. This was a tiresome job, especially when the reloads below the deck plates had to be winched up for testing.

scene, before receiving the order to return.

Early in the war boats spent a good proportion of their time on the surface. However, the biggest danger to any U-boat was that of surprise attack from the air, and as the war progressed more and more commanders would submerge by day when in range of Allied air bases. Even so, many were caught by surprise.

A well-trained crew could submerge a Type VII boat in under 30 seconds, the bridge lookouts hurling themselves down the ladder. Minor injuries were frequent, and terrible mistakes sometimes occurred. The first watch officer of U-451, accidentally left on the bridge when the boat crash-dived to escape a British aircraft, was

rescued by a British warship. The submarine and the rest of the crew were never seen again.

Back in the submarine pens, the crew would emerge into daylight, filthy, bearded, bedraggled and malodorous. But the captain would have a white cover on his cap, the battle ensign would be snapping in the wind and everyone would be looking forward to leave. U-boat men partied hard in Paris, where wine and women were never in short supply for these much fêted but ultimately doomed warriors of the Reich.

Battle of the North Atlantic

British survival in the early years of the war depended upon a steady flow of supplies being maintained by convoys plying between the New World and the Old. The primary German weapon in the attempt to strangle this flow was the U-Boat, and the Kriegsmarine's submarine supremo, Admiral Karl Doenitz, well understood his priorities. An experienced World War I submarine commander, he had developed theoretical group tactics – the 'wolfpack' – even before his appointment in 1935, and once in charge of the German submarine force he was able to define the types of boat best suited to near and distant operations as well as the number required to beat a fully-organised convoy system. However, even after the Anglo-German Naval Agreement of 1935 had allowed the Germans quite generous limits to submarine construction, the Kriegsmarine's grandiose capital ship plans prevented their realisation. As a result, in place of the 300 boats Doenitz considered necessary, only 56 were in service at the beginning of the war, of which only 22 were of types capable of ocean service. For a time, losses exceeded commissioning so that, as late as February 1941, only 22 boats were actually operational. An unrestricted sinking policy was, Doenitz considered, legally justified with merchantmen escorted, armed and given instructions to ram on opportunity. The declared war zone first extended to 20 degrees West, about 500 miles west of Ireland. In the first months of the war, pickings were rich with merchantmen returning individually to the UK, while the major routes from the UK to Halifax and Sydney, Nova Scotia saw convoys escorted through only 15 degrees longitude from either end, due to lack of suitable escorts.

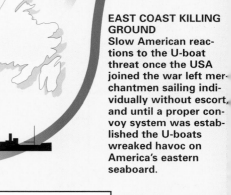

EAST COAST KILLING GROUND
Slow American reactions to the U-boat threat once the USA joined the war left merchantmen sailing individually without escort, and until a proper convoy system was established the U-boats wreaked havoc on America's eastern seaboard.

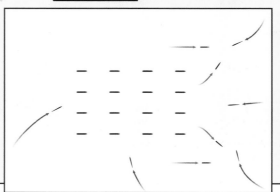

3 In the early days of the war, convoys were only lightly escorted. The first boats to attack drew off the escorts, leaving later arrivals, often attacking from a wide arc, a free run in on the hapless merchantmen.

1 Once the FW 200s found a convoy, the big aircraft were used as orbiting beacons. By transmitting continuously they provided course data both to the high command and for the wolfpacks, which could home in on their transmissions.

2 The Kriegsmarine kept tight control of its boats, maintaining regular radio contact. Allocated, position reports were sent to operational boats in the Atlantic, and the wolfpack gathered to attack.

RECONNAISSANCE LOOP
The FW 200s of KG 40 flew a giant loop from their base in France out over the convoy routes to their northern bases in Norway.

NORTHERN ROUTE
In an attempt to evade the marauding wolfpacks, British convoys were routed as far north as possible as they crossed the Atlantic. Convoys also followed zig-zag routes, radical changes of course in the night being designed to lose shadowing U-Boats.

U-BOAT HQ
Operational control of the U-boat fleet was maintained from Wilhelmshaven, though Doenitz also had a forward headquarters at Kerneval, overlooking Lorient

OCEAN HIGHWAYS
Convoy routes were linked like a network of ocean highways, each with its own identification code. The most important routes were those to and from Halifax in Nova Scotia, which were given OB/ONS and HX/SC designations.

U-BOAT PATROL LINE
Doenitz deployed his forces in patrol lines across the likely convoy routes, covering the maximum amount of sea to ensure that Allied merchant vessels did not slip through the net.

MARITIME RECONNAISSANCE
A key element in German plans were the Focke-Wulf FW 200 Kondors of I/KG40 based at Bordeaux-Merignac. These long-range aircraft could not only sink stragglers but also reported convoys to available submarines.

Below: A Kondor belly gunner's view of an Atlantic U-boat rendezvous.

4 Early attacks were made from outside the convoy, with boats firing a fan of torpedoes. The best U-Boat commanders quickly discovered that a more lethal process was to get inside the convoy itself, attacking selected ships individually.

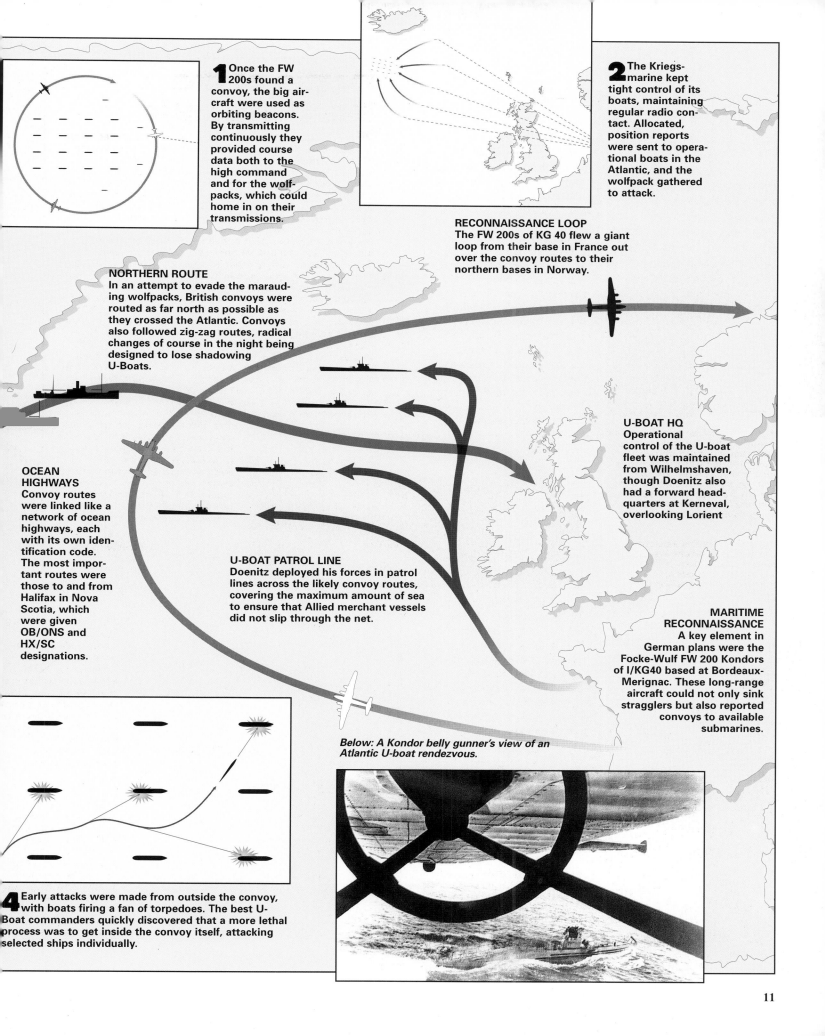

ACE ATTACK ON CONVOY SC 7

Otto Kretschmer was the most successful U-boat ace of World War II, and one of the top submarine commanders of all time. He was the originator of many of the surface-attack night fighting tactics with which a few daring captains cut a swathe through Britain's Atlantic convoys. In the first 18 months of the war Kretschmer sank over 265,000 tonnes of Allied shipping before his own U-99 was damaged and forced to surrender in March 1941.

1 The attack on the eastbound transatlantic convoy SC 7 was one of the most devastating of the war. On 18 October 1940 U-93 made a general signal giving the position, course and speed of a large convoy it had spotted. It tried but failed to shadow the convoy while all other U-Boats within range converged on the area. The convoy was next spotted by U-48 on the afternoon of 17 October; but by intercepting signal traffic the British knew SC 7 was being followed. The convoy made several violent course alterations, and U-48 lost contact too.

2 Doenitz promptly ordered his U-boats to deploy into an 'interception stripe' across the probable course of the convoy. SC 7 eventually brushed the northern edge of the line, and as darkness fell the wolfpack pounced. Six U-boats, including Kretschmer's U-99 and Schepke's U-100 attacked at dusk. Kretschmer manoeuvred to aim at a ship on the edge of the convoy when the target suddenly exploded, torpedoed by another member of the wolfpack. A destroyer appeared just as U-99 and the nearby U-123 were closing in, and Kretschmer sped off into the darkness, returning to attack at 10pm.

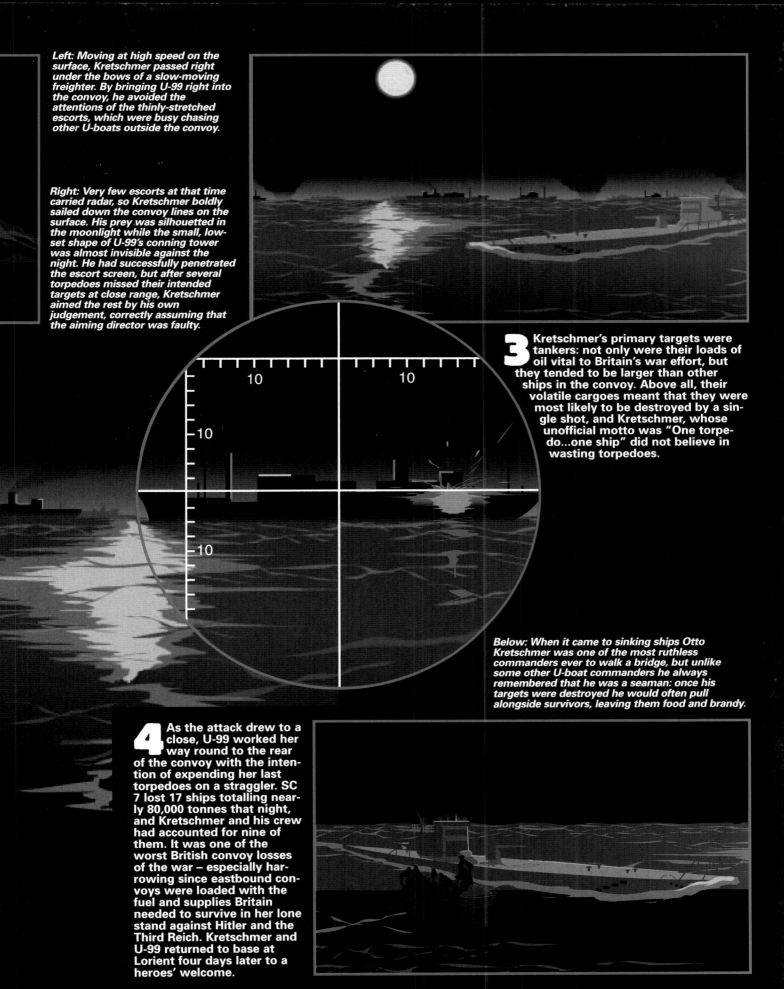

Left: Moving at high speed on the surface, Kretschmer passed right under the bows of a slow-moving freighter. By bringing U-99 right into the convoy, he avoided the attentions of the thinly-stretched escorts, which were busy chasing other U-boats outside the convoy.

Right: Very few escorts at that time carried radar, so Kretschmer boldly sailed down the convoy lines on the surface. His prey was silhouetted in the moonlight while the small, low-set shape of U-99's conning tower was almost invisible against the night. He had successfully penetrated the escort screen, but after several torpedoes missed their intended targets at close range, Kretschmer aimed the rest by his own judgement, correctly assuming that the aiming director was faulty.

3 Kretschmer's primary targets were tankers: not only were their loads of oil vital to Britain's war effort, but they tended to be larger than other ships in the convoy. Above all, their volatile cargoes meant that they were most likely to be destroyed by a single shot, and Kretschmer, whose unofficial motto was "One torpedo...one ship" did not believe in wasting torpedoes.

Below: When it came to sinking ships Otto Kretschmer was one of the most ruthless commanders ever to walk a bridge, but unlike some other U-boat commanders he always remembered that he was a seaman: once his targets were destroyed he would often pull alongside survivors, leaving them food and brandy.

4 As the attack drew to a close, U-99 worked her way round to the rear of the convoy with the intention of expending her last torpedoes on a straggler. SC 7 lost 17 ships totalling nearly 80,000 tonnes that night, and Kretschmer and his crew had accounted for nine of them. It was one of the worst British convoy losses of the war – especially harrowing since eastbound convoys were loaded with the fuel and supplies Britain needed to survive in her lone stand against Hitler and the Third Reich. Kretschmer and U-99 returned to base at Lorient four days later to a heroes' welcome.

PANZERKAMPFWAGEN VI
TIGER

T O THE unknowing eye, the two German tanks lumbering purposefully towards the village of Malinava were heading for a trap. Malinava, north of the town of Dunaberg (now known as Daugavpils) in Latvia, had been occupied by advanced elements of the elite Soviet 4th Shock Army. It was a reconnaissance in force, with a battalion of T-34/85 tanks led by a single example of the brand-new Josef Stalin or JS-1 heavy tank, which with its 122-mm gun was one of the most powerfully-armed fighting vehicles in the world.

The huge 1944 summer offensive in the south had caught

When it appeared in 1942 the Tiger was the most powerful tank in the world. It was to be a dominant force on the battlefield right up to the end of the World War II.

the Germans completely by surprise, and whole German armies were in the process of being wiped out. Here in the north, armoured columns of the Second Baltic front were heading for the port of Riga with the aim of cutting off the divisions of the German Army Group North.

However, the men in the tanks approaching Malinava knew exactly what they were doing. If it was a trap, then when it closed, the Soviets would find themselves with a Tiger by the tail. More accurately,

they would have two Tigers – Panzerkampfwagen VI Tiger heavy tanks, to be precise. The most powerful and hardest-hitting armoured fighting vehicle of the war – and these two had veteran crews, led by tank 'aces' Carius and Kirschner.

Flame belched from the Tigers' long-barrelled 88-mm guns before the T-34s could turn their turrets, instantly exploding two Soviet tanks. Only the single JS-1 had any chance of taking them on, but it was burning before it could engage as the Tigers continued to fire. In a short but fierce battle through the ruins, the two German panzers destroyed 17 Soviet tanks in under 20 minutes. The action of the two Tigers managed to blunt the main Soviet attack for several days.

It was big, it was slow, and its crews cursed its unreliability. But when it came to a fight, the Tiger's armour and gun made it almost unbeatable.

The Tigers were from the Wehrmacht's *schwere Panzer Abteilung* (heavy tank battalion) 502, which had been the first to take the powerful vehicle into action two years before. The fight outside Dunaberg was a perfect example of why the Tiger was probably the most feared armoured vehicle produced by any side in World War II.

FIGHTING POWER

The combination of unparalleled protection and superior fire power meant that in the right circumstances and with experienced crews, it was almost unbeatable, and could have an effect on the battlefield out of all proportion to its numbers.

The Tiger concept dated back to 1937 and a specification for a new heavy tank issued by the German Armaments Ministry to Daimler-Benz, Henschel, MAN and Porsche. At that stage it was envisaged as a heavy tank which could break through defenses like the French Maginot line.

Work on the project was shelved when the PzKpfw III and IV proved satisfactory in Europe, but in May 1941 a new requirement was issued for a 45-tonne tank armed with a modified 8.8-cm Flak gun.

THE FÜHRER STEPS IN

Hitler had been impressed by the heavy armour of the British Matilda I and French Char B1 bis in 1940 and with the invasion of Russia imminent saw a need for a heavy tank, with the heaviest armour possible. The Führer's intervention meant that the new design got much heavier. Prototypes of the PzKpfw VI were to be ready for demonstration at Rastenburg in East Prussia on the Führer's birthday – 20 April – in a year's time.

Henschel and Porsche each submitted a vehicle, the latter being powered by a complex diesel-electric drive. The Henschel design was judged more practical and economical to buiild, though the 90 Porsche

Right: Ninety of the complex Porsche Tiger chassis were built before the Wehrmacht decided to concentrate on the simpler Henschel design. The Porsche Tigers were completed as self-propelled guns, known as Ferdinands (after the designer, Doctor Ferdinand Porsche).

"We will be victorious, thanks to our Tiger!"

Adolf Hitler, Before the battle of Kursk

Main picture: Tigers move across the Russian steppes during the Battle of before Kursk, kicking up dust as their turrets nose round in the quest for enemy tanks.

Right: The burning remains of a Red Army T-34 show what happens in a long-range duel with a Tiger. Even with its thick, well-sloped front armour, the Soviet tank is vulnerable to the Tiger at ranges of up to 1400 metres: conversely, it has to close to almost point-blank range to have a chance of destroying the big German tank.

Above: A German army Tiger passes the Victor Emmanuel monument in Rome late in 1943. Germany had occupied Italy following the overthrow of Mussolini and Italy's armistice with the Allies.

chassis were converted into tank destroyers. They were known as Elefants or Ferdinands.

The Tiger's operational career lasted less than three years. The first tanks to see action were deployed in small numbers with *sPzAbt* 502 on the Leningrad front in August 1942. It was an inauspicious beginning: several were lost as they advanced in single file over marshes, unable to manoeuvre when engaged from the flank by Soviet artillery.

Later that year, Tigers were shipped to the Afrika Korps, going into action in Tunisia in December. It quickly became a bogeyman to British and American troops, the thick front armour making it almost invulnerable to Allied tank guns, while its powerful cannon could destroy any Allied tank at ranges of two kilometres or more.

As the tide turned against the Axis in North Africa, 17 Tigers of *sPzAbt* 504 were retained in Sicily, where they were attached to the Hermann Goering Panzer Division. They attacked the American beachhead when the Allies landed in July 1943, but were driven off by heavy naval gunfire from destroyers operating close inshore. Sixteen out of the 17 tanks were lost in the next few days, most being destroyed by their crews to prevent capture.

ACTION IN ITALY

Tigers were heavily involved in the fighting in Italy, the reconstituted 504th losing three quarters of its tanks in the fighting after the battle of Monte Cassino in June 1944. The 508th *Abteilung* was sent to Italy at about the same time, tasked with destroying the Allied Bridgehead at Anzio. However, they were unloaded nearly 200 km from the battle, and the approach march through twisty, mountainous Italian terrain cost the unit nearly 30 Tigers due to mechanical failure. The survivors mounted an attack, alongside PzKpfw V Panthers and the heavy Tiger-based assault guns known as Ferdinands, but were driven back by naval gunfire.

The bulk of Germany's Tigers were deployed to the Eastern Front, but until 1944 there were rarely more than 150 tanks available, and of these less than 50 per cent were serviceable at any one time. During the battle of Kursk 147 Tigers were assembled, and by an almost superhuman effort over 120 were actually ready to fight. They acquitted themselves well in battle, only 18 being lost.

Above: A Tiger from the 508th schwere Heeres Panzer Abteilung heads towards Anzio early in 1944. The long approach march to the Anzio front – nearly 200 kilometres from the railhead – put great strain on the battalion's tanks: only about 15 of 45 Tigers actually reached the battle without breaking down.

Left: The heavy Panzer company of SS Panzer Regiment Das Reich had received its first 10 Tigers by January 1943, and was heavily involved in the Kharkhov counter-offensive of March. Tank S13 nearest the camera has taken a hit in the side: note the pierced and buckled mudguard over the tracks and the field repairs to the hull just above and partially obscuring the Balkenkreuz.

INSIDE THE TIGER

Teamwork the key to success

Combat reports from the summer of 1943 indicated that Tiger units destroyed at least 20 enemy tanks, 15 anti-tank guns and four artillery pieces for every one of their own that was lost

LACK OF RANGE

The big tank's complexity, unreliability and low endurance meant that it was at a disadvantage over the vast expanses of Russia. Even so, in a situation which played to the type's strengths it was almost unbeatable. And it could fight at very long range: in July 1944 a tank commanded by the CO of *sPzAbt* 506 destroyed a Soviet T-34 at a range of nearly four kilometres. Individual Tiger commanders ran up huge scores: Michael Wittmann of the SS was the most successful ace of the war, he and his crew destroying more than 100 enemy tanks in the east alone. He was closely followed by Wehrmacht experts like

Pre-war tanks tended to have two-man turrets, with the commander and gunner often loading and manning machine guns, their multiple tasks having a detrimental effect on efficiency.

The Tiger followed the standard German practice from the Panzer III onwards of having a three-man turret, which enabled each man to concentrate on his most important task. The commander directed the tank and found targets, the gunner located the targets

in his sight and engaged them, the loader making sure that the correct ammunition – armour-piercing or high-explosive – was loaded for each specific target. At its best, a well-drilled Tiger crew made the Tiger an even more formidable fighting machine.

COMMANDER
Right: The most important member of the crew who directed the vehicle in action also served as the primary means of locating targets. Seated at the left rear of the turret, the commander had a rotating cupola equipped with vision blocks, giving limited all-around vision even when the tank was fully 'buttoned up'.

RADIO OPERATOR
Right: Seated in the right front of the Tiger's hull, the radio operator also manned the machine gun mounted in the front plate of the hull. This was primarily used as an anti-infantry weapon.

DRIVER
Left: Seated next to the radio operator in the left front of the hull, the driver was tasked with driving the heavy vehicle as smoothly as possible, and was often the oldest, most mature member of the crew.

Killing from a Distance

The Tiger's superb 8.8-cm gun could outrange and penetrate more armour than almost every other tank gun, with the exception of the Anglo/American hybrid Sherman.

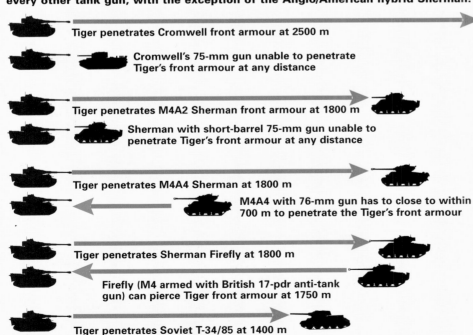

Tiger penetrates Cromwell front armour at 2500 m

Cromwell's 75-mm gun unable to penetrate Tiger's front armour at any distance

Tiger penetrates M4A2 Sherman front armour at 1800 m

Sherman with short-barrel 75-mm gun unable to penetrate Tiger's front armour at any distance

Tiger penetrates M4A4 Sherman at 1800 m

M4A4 with 76-mm gun has to close to within 700 m to penetrate the Tiger's front armour

Tiger penetrates Sherman Firefly at 1800 m

Firefly (M4 armed with British 17-pdr anti-tank gun) can pierce Tiger front armour at 1750 m

Tiger penetrates Soviet T-34/85 at 1400 m

T-34 with 85-mm gun has to get within 500 m to have a chance of destroying a Tiger

GUNNER
Above: Sitting in the left of the turret immediately in front of and below the commander, the gunner controlled turret traverse and used a Turmzielfernrohr 9B or 9C sight to acquire targets.

LOADER
Above: Located in the right of the turret, the loader was responsible for choosing and loading the type of ammunition specified by the gunner.

SUPER TIGER

The shock received by the Wehrmacht on encountering the superb Soviet T-34 spurred German designers to produce much more powerful, harder-hitting tanks. First to incorporate combat lessons was the PzKpfw V Panther medium tank, which had well-sloped armour and a long, high-velocity gun.

Introduced in 1944, the very powerful Tiger II resembled a scaled-up Panther. Known as the *König* or 'King' Tiger, it was mechanically similar to the original PzKpfw VI, but with sloping armour of greater thickness it was even harder to kill – though its weight of around 70 tonnes made it even less mobile than the earlier model.

The 8.8-cm gun had a longer barrel than that of the original Tiger, and with it the Tiger II could outrange and destroy any other tank in service.

The King Tiger first saw action on the Eastern Front, and was also involved in France, Belgium (supporting the Ardennes offensive) and in the final defence of the Reich. Only 485 were ever completed.

Below: A Tiger II of the 503rd sPzAbt moves through the outskirts of Budapest early in 1945 as Army and SS troops attempt to relieve the 9th SS Korps trapped in the city: the King Tigers almost broke through the encircling Red Army, but stiffening Soviet resistance drove them back, and only 785 out of 45,000 German soldiers escaped the Hungarian capital.

Oberleutnant Otto Carius.

The Tiger's great strength was in the protection it offered its crew, and the immense striking power of its gun. The thick, slab-sided armour lacked the good ballistic shape found on contemporary designs like the Panther and the Soviet T-34, but with a thickness which ranged from 63 to 102 mm on the hull and 82 to 100 mm on the turret of the Ausf H, (increased to 110 mm on the Ausf E) it hardly needed to.

'EIGHTY-EIGHT'

Main armament was the 8.8-cm KwK 36 L156, adapted from the anti-tank version of the superb 'eighty-eight' Flak gun. It was the most powerful anti-tank gun then in use by any army, capable of penetrating 112 mm of armour at 1400 metres. The Tiger carried 92 rounds of main gun ammunition in stowage bins, lockers in the turret floor and anywhere else that was handy.

Self-defence against infantry was provided by two MG34

Right: It might have weighed the best part of 60 tonnes, but the Tiger's wide tracks gave it mobility in the worst of the mud and snow encountered in Russia.

7.92-mm machine guns, one mounted co-axially with the main gun and one in a flexible mount in the front of the hull.

In spite of its immense power, the Tiger had several bad flaws. The turret traverse was slow, which meant that a fast-moving (and brave) enemy tank crew might be able to manoeuvre for a flank or rear shot. Tigers were slow, and the big tank's limited range meant that in a mobile battle it was at a considerable disadvantage.

Tigers were complex vehicles, needing experienced crews and maintenance personnel to keep operational under field conditions. All too often bogged-

down or broken-down Tigers had to be destroyed, the tank's massive weight making it an impossible load for standard Wehrmacht recovery vehicles.

WIDE TRACK

The Tiger needed a track with a width of 72.5 cm to spread the load. This was too wide for conventional railway flat cars, and so for transport the outer road wheels had to be removed and a narrower 52-cm track fitted. It took considerable effort to refit the outer wheels and wide tracks for combat.

Ride comfort was good – the interleaving road wheels helped to spread the massive weight

evenly, and the torsion bar suspension gave a smooth ride over rough terrain. However, if an inner road wheel was damaged by a mine, field repairs were a major problem. In the East, mud freezing between the wheels overnight could immobilise the tank.

By the summer of 1944, Tiger strength was reaching its peak, with over 300 in service in the East (with around 250 being operational), and a further 98 deployed in France and 76 in Italy. However, the massive battles of that summer against overwhelming enemy strength saw heavy Tiger losses (more than 240 in three months on the Eastern Front alone).

Production of the Tiger was never high. Initially 12 vehicles were completed per month, but by November 1942 this had increased to 25. It went through various modifications during its

Muzzle Brake: The Tiger's KwK L/56 gun was fitted with a muzzle brake, which reduced muzzle velocity to just under 1000 m/sec with armour-piercing rounds.

two-year production run; early models had smoke projectors and pistol ports in the turret side, but these were removed in later vehicles. Those that were destined for Africa and Russia were fitted with air filters against dust and sand. Eventually 1,355 Tigers were completed. The last operational Tigers were used to defend the centre of Berlin in April 1945.

There were few Tiger variants: around 80 were completed as *Befehlswagen* with extra radios giving commanders improved control of their units. Some recovery versions were improvised out of necessity – the standard Wehrmacht recovery vehicle was the SdKfz 9 18-ton half track, but two or even three might be needed to handle a Tiger. The field solution to recovering a damaged or bogged-down Tiger I was to use two more Tigers to tow it clear.

Escape hatch: Early Tigers had a pistol port in the right rear of the turret, but from the 46th turret this was replaced by an escape hatch as seen here.

Air filters: The four large bottle-like attachments on the rear of the hull are Feifel air filters, fitted to tanks designed for tropical or desert service.

Cupola: Early Tiger cupolas – a mini-turret on the main turret just for the commander – had simple vision slits like this example: later versions had a rotating hatch and were fitted with periscopes with a greater field of view.

Heat shields: Operational use showed that glowing exhausts could be seen from a long distance away at night. sPzAbt 501 was the first unit to fit sheet metal shields around the exhaust stacks in the rear of the hull.

Front armour: Tigers were heavily protected, the armour plate in the front of the turret and in the front of the hull being more than 100-mm thick.

Pistol port: The *MP Klappe* or machine pistol port next to the storage bin allowed the commander to fire a sub-machine gun against attacking infantry.

Tracks: The Tiger's *Geländeketten* or cross-country tracks were 72.5- cm wide, and distributed the Tiger's 58 tonnes to produce an effective ground pressure of around 0.73 kg per square cm.

Stowage bin: A large stowage box was fitted to the rear of all Tiger turrets from the 56th built.

Engine: Early Tigers were powered by a 23-litre Maybach HL 210 P45 Vee-12 petrol engine, which delivered 522 kW (700 hp) through a Maybach transmission with eight forward and four reverse gears.

PzKpfw VI Tiger I Ausf E
Schwere Heeres Panzer Abteilung 501
Tunisia, December 1942

TECHNICAL SPECIFICATIONS
PzKpfw VI Tiger Ausf E

Crew: Five

Weight: 55000 kg (121,250 lb)

Dimensions: Length (including armament) 8.24 m (27 ft 0 in); length (hull) 6.20 m (20 ft 4 in); width 3.73 m (12 ft 3in); height 2.86 m (9 ft 3.25 in); combat track width 71.5 cm (28.1in); travelling track width 51.5 cm (20.3in)

Armour thickness: 100-mm hull and turret front; 80 mm turret walls; 60-80mm hull sides and rear; 25 mm top and belly

Powerplant: One Maybach HL 230 P 45 12-cylinder petrol engine developing 700 hp (522 kW)

Performance: Maximum road speed 45 km/h (28 mph); normal maximum speed 38 km/h (24 mph); maximum cross-country speed c.18 km/h (11 mph); maximum road range stated to be 195 km (121 miles) but

under operational conditions rarely more than 100 km (62 miles); fording 1.2 m (3 ft 11 in); gradient 60 per cent; vertical obstacle 0.79 m (2 ft 7 in), trench 1.80 m (5 ft 11in)

Main armament: One KwK 36 L/56 88-mm cannon with 92 rounds

Ammunition: Armour-piercing, armour-piercing tungsten core, high-explosive and hollow-charge (HEAT)

Muzzle velocity: 600m/sec (HE); 773 m/sec (AP); 930 m/sec (AP/tungsten core)

Effective range: 3000 m with armour piercing and 5000 m with HE rounds

Armour penetration: 171 mm at close range and 110 mm at 2000 m using AP tungsten-core rounds

Secondary armament: One 7.92-mm MG 34 mounted coaxially and one MG 34 flexibly mounted in hull front

Tiger Ace
Michael Wittmann

The most successful armoured 'ace' of World War II found an ideal platform in the fighting power of his Tiger tank.

As an NCO Michael Wittmann had commanded armoured cars and assault guns in Poland, France and Greece, serving with the *Leibstandarte-SS* as it evolved from Hitler's bodyguard to a fully-fledged armoured division. Sent to the *SS-Junkerschule* at Bad Tolz in Bavaria, he returned to the division as an officer in 1943. There he was made a section commander in the Tiger-equipped *schwere SS-Panzer Abteilung* or heavy SS Panzer Battalion 13. He quickly turned his regular crew – Woll, Berger, Kirschner and Pollmann – into a lethal team, knocking out 30 Soviet tanks, 28 anti-tank guns, and two artillery batteries during the Battle of Kursk.

By 9 January 1944 when he was awarded the Knight's Cross, Wittmann's score stood at 66 tanks and, as if to celebrate the award of the decoration, he shot up 19 T-34s and three heavy assault guns. On the 20th he was promoted to *SS-Obersturmführer* and ten days later added the Oakleaves to his Knight's Cross. By the time he was transferred to France Wittmann's score stood at 117 tanks and assault guns.

Right: Tigers of the 101st heavy SS Panzer Battalion pass through the French countryside near Rouen as they advance toward the Normandy invasion front. Wittmann commanded one of the battalion's Tiger companies.

On the morning of 13 June 1944 he took four Tigers from *sSSPzAbt 101*, (the heavy tank unit of the 1st SS Panzer corps) and, with a solitary Panzer IV flanked a column of the British 7th Armoured Division moving out of Villers-Bocage, near Hill 213 on the road towards Caen.

Wittmann brought his own tank forward and in an astonishing feat destroyed 25 British tanks, 14 half tracks and 14 Bren gun carriers. Wittmann then entered the town where his tank knocked out three Cromwell cruiser tanks – a fourth escaped by reversing out of sight into a side road. He continued down the hill through the town but when he rounded a corner was confronted by a squadron of Cromwells with at least one Sherman Firefly armed with the powerful 17-pounder gun. Wittmann's Tiger took a hit from the Sherman and was forced to move back through the town. Here he met the surviving Cromwell from the earlier

Above: Michael Wittmann poses on his Tiger after being awarded Swords to add to the Oakleaves of his Knight's Cross.

encounter, which managed to land two hits before it was destroyed.

In subsequent close-range fighting in the town Wittmann's Tiger had a track blown off and he was obliged to bail out. Nine

ONE AGAINST AN ARMY
The battle of Villers-Bocage

The British movement through Villers-Bocage was intended to take the 7th Armoured Division around the flank of the German Panzer Lehr and 12th SS Panzer Divisions. As the leading British tanks reached Hill 213 behind the German lines, they and their supporting infantry stopped nose to tail down the road, the men dismounting to brew tea and stretch their legs.

Michael Wittmann's Tiger emerged from a small wood to the south of the road. He destroyed the rear tanks of the leading British unit, (A Squadron, 4th County of London Yeomanry), then motored down the column at a range of about 80 metres, shooting up the half tracks and Bren-gun carriers of the 1st Battalion, the Rifle Brigade. The leading British tanks were trapped in the sunken lanes typical of this part of France, unable to turn or climb the banks on either side of the road.

Wittmann then drove into the village, knocking out 4 CLY's reconnaissance troop and then its headquarters troop. While he was doing this, three more of his Tigers had attacked the British tanks on Hill 213, forcing them to surrender. However, Wittmann was now in trouble, being in a built-up area without infantry support, and coming under increasingly heavy attack. A British anti-tank gun managed to disable the Tiger, and Wittmann and his crew baled out and escaped back to German lines.

Wittmann's action stopped the entire British 7th Armoured Division as it attempted to fight its way around the German defences of Caen, and may have extended the Normandy campaign by several weeks.

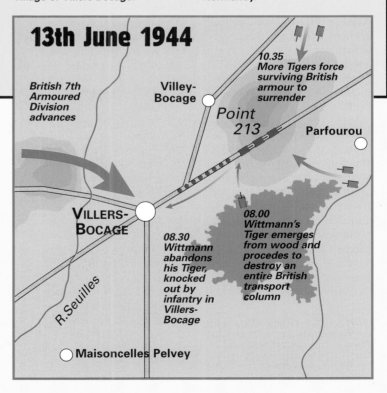

Left: One of four Cromwells from the County of London Yeomanry's Headquarters Troop which was knocked out by Wittmann in the village of Villers Bocage.

Above: A Tiger from the 101st passes a schwimmwagen – an amphibious Volkswagen – as they move through a small town in Normandy.

days later he was awarded Swords to his Knight's Cross.

Michael Wittmann died in action south of Caen on 8 August 1944. Initially the kill was thought to have been made by five Shermans and Sherman Firefly tanks which surrounded the lone Tiger, and Wittmann's scalp was claimed by Polish, Canadian and British armoured troops. However, the best evidence indicates that the tank was destroyed by rocket-firing Typhoon ground-attack fighters.

In less than two years commanding a Tiger Wittmann's score reached 138 tanks and assault guns and 132 anti-tank

guns, making him the top tank ace of World War II, and possibly of all time.

After Wittmann's action at Villers-Bocage the already profound British respect for the Tiger developed to new heights. A general if unofficial rule was formulated by British tankers, which went something like "If one Tiger is reported, send four Shermans or four Churchills to deal with it – and expect to lose three of them!".

Right: Villers-Bocage is a small but strategically important village southwest of Caen. The small hill known as Point 213 dominates the flat country around and can be seen for miles.

13th June 1944

British 7th Armoured Division advances

Villey-Bocage

Point 213

Parfourou

10.35 More Tigers force surviving British armour to surrender

VILLERS-BOCAGE

08.30 Wittmann abandons his Tiger, knocked out by infantry in Villers-Bocage

08.00 Wittmann's Tiger emerges from wood and procedes to destroy an entire British transport column

R. Seuilles

Maisoncelles Pelvey

JUNKERS JU 87 STUKA

Most military aircraft have a streamlined elegance quite at odds with their deadly purpose. Not so the Junkers Ju 87 *Sturzkampfflugzeug* – possibly the ugliest warplane ever to turn the tide of battle.

'STUKA' entered the world's vocabulary in May 1940. The mere appearance of its angular silhouette in the summer sky triggering 'Stuka fright' among the columns of soldiers and refugees fleeing across France. Ordered to attack road junctions, and especially bridges, to hinder the movement of Allied ground forces, the Stukas often found their targets packed with escaping civilians. With sirens ('Jericho Trumpets') fitted to terrorise their victims, the bombers attacked with surgical precision—and then returned to strafe the survivors with their machine guns.

REARMAMENT

Under the terms of the Versailles Treaty, Germany was not allowed to have an air force, but within months of coming to power Hitler announced he would no longer be bound by this restriction. The Stuka was designed by Hans Pohlmann the following year and the first prototype, ironically powered by an imported Rolls Royce Kestrel engine, flew in 1935. Junkers had manufactured all-metal monoplane ground attack aircraft towards the end of World War I. (In March 1918 the future commander of the Luftflotte 6,

Robert Ritter von Greim carried out the first aerial anti-tank sortie over the Somme). The Ju 87 built on that experience, but Pohlmann added a new feature: the Stuka would be built to dive vertically on to its target. This offered far greater accuracy than was possible with level bombing. Japan, the USA and Britain ordered dive bombers for their naval air arms, because level attacks were not accurate enough to hit a moving warship.

The Luftwaffe's first dive bomber unit was created in 1937, and a handful of Ju 87A-1s were sent to Spain where Germany was providing military aid to the Nationalist forces. Many senior Luftwaffe officers were unimpressed with the Stuka, criticising it for being too slow, too cumbersome and an easy target for enemy fighters. However, its performance in Spain was considered excellent.

DIVE BOMBERS

It gained the whole-hearted approval of Ernst Udet, the World War I fighter ace and aerobatic pilot now drinking his way to oblivion while in charge of the Luftwaffe's technical branch. (He was so impressed, he insisted on all future bombers having dive bombing capability, a decision that killed off some promising designs and imposed serious delays on the Heinkel He

177 heavy bomber programme).

There were over 300 Stukas in service by the invasion of Poland and they performed well enough.But it was over France and the Low Countries in 1940 that they stunned the world. The British, French, Belgian and Dutch armies had more men and more tanks than the Germans, but the Luftwaffe achieved air superiority. As the panzer divisions debouched from the Ardennes forest, their way was barred by the French 9th Army.

Main picture: Stukas sounded terrifying in the attack, thanks to the wind-driven 'Trumpets of Jericho' sirens attached to the main landing gear which emitted a piercing screech as the aircraft dived on its target.

Above: Armourers load a Ju 87B-1, probably from 3./StG1. This was the unit which made the first attacks on Polish soil in the early morning of 1 September, 1939.

Right: An artillery battery smashed by Ju 87 attacks May 1940. Stukas could attack with deadly precision – as long as they were unmolested by fighters.

"Stukas existed to carry a heavy bomb a short distance and deliver it with great accuracy; all other design considerations were subordinated to this aim."

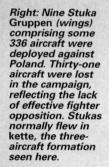

Right: Nine Stuka Gruppen (wings) comprising some 336 aircraft were deployed against Poland. Thirty-one aircraft were lost in the campaign, reflecting the lack of effective fighter opposition. Stukas normally flew in kette, the three-aircraft formation seen here.

It was a weak formation, but held the line of the Meuse, heavy guns ranged in on likely crossing points. French artillery positions were silenced by 120 Stukas, their front-line positions bombed to oblivion, and the German ground troops forced their way across.

The Stukas were like flying artillery, but with far greater range and flexibility. They struck at Allied divisions behind the front, catching French heavy tanks still on their railway cars. In World War I it had proved impossible to break through the Western Front until 1918, largely because the defenders could always bring up reinforcements to seal a gap faster than the attackers could advance over the shell-torn ground. The Stuka reversed the process: now the German army could keep on the move, but the Allies could never react fast enough, their divisions slowed to a crawl by repeated air attacks behind the lines.

However, the Ju 87 did rely on German air superiority. Even over France, there were a number of disasters. One *staffel* (flight) was wiped out by five French fighters on 12 May. With a 100 mph speed advantage and armed with 20-mm cannon, the French fighters made short work of the lumbering and unmanoeuvrable Stukas. The Ju 87's defensive armament consisted of two fixed forward-firing 7.9-mm machine guns and one or two more, operated by the observer, on a flexible mounting in the cockpit rear. It was not enough to beat off a determined fighter pilot.

VULNERABILITIES

This became cruelly obvious in the Battle of Britain. Early in August 1940, the Stukas attacked airfields in Kent, radar sites along the south coast and the naval base at Portsmouth. If co-ordination broke down between the Ju 87s and their Bf 109 escorts, the Stukas were cut up by RAF fighters. Four Stuka *gruppen* attacked Gosport, Thorney Island, Ford and the radar station at Polling on 18 August. Their escorts were nowhere in sight as Spitfires of

Above: Although the battles of 1940 showed that Stukas were vulnerable to modern fighters, they were still effective in other theatres. Ju 87B-2s like these wrought havoc on British ships in the Mediterranean in 1941.

Below: The Ju 87D was a cleaned up version of the Stuka, but it was still a sluggish beast – the escorting Bf 109 seen here over Russia would have had difficulty flying slowly enough to stay with the lumbering dive bombers.

No. 152 Squadron and Hurricanes of No. 43 Squadron caught them as they reformed for the flight back across the Channel. In the greatest 'Stuka Party' Fighter Command staged that summer, 30 Stukas were lost or badly damaged, including 18 of StG.77's 28 aircraft. The *Stukaverbände* were withdrawn from the battle.

The Battle of Britain was a salutary reminder of the Ju 87s limitations, but the Luftwaffe dominated other skies over other battlefields for several years to come. Stukas sank a number of British warships off Malta, and in May 1941, German air superiority over the eastern Mediterranean was good enough that Luftwaffe paratroops were able to seize Crete. It was an admittedly Pyrrhic victory, but the Royal Navy was obliged to evacuate British and Commonwealth ground forces without air cover, losing nine warships in the process. British casualties might have been even heavier had not the timetable for 'Barbarossa' demanded the transfer of VIII Fliegerkorps and its Stukas to Poland on 1 June.

SERVICE IN THE EAST

Limited numbers of Stukas served in North Africa and the Italian campaign, but it was in Russia that the Ju 87 had its greatest impact. In 1941 the Soviet air force was effectively wiped out by the Luftwaffe, and the 290 Stukas sent to the Eastern Front could attack without fear of interception.

Hans-Ulrich Rudel, Hitler's favourite pilot and Germany's most highly-decorated flier, crippled the battleship *Marat* in an attack on Kronstadt. It was he who later pioneered the 'tank busting' Ju 87G with its 37 mm guns, and claimed 519 tank 'kills' by the end of the war. Shot down 30 times, he truly bore a charmed life.

It was not until mid-1943 that German bombers were seriously menaced by Soviet fighters.

Stukas continued to operate in large numbers – over 500 of them attacked the Soviet bridgehead near Novorossiysk in April 1943. Ju 87s were supplied to allied air forces of Romania, Italy, Hungary and Bulgaria. Stuka production peaked that year, at 1,814 units. Some 5,700 were completed before production ceased in 1944.

DANGEROUS SKIES

By then, the Soviets had radar coverage of the battlefront and thousands of modern fighters with which to intercept the dwindling number of German bombers. Even those twin- engined stalwarts, the Heinkel He 111 and Junkers Ju 88, found it dangerous to operate in daylight. Stukas were relegated to night harassment missions, their airbrakes removed and 20 mm cannon fitted for strafing attacks.

Most Luftwaffe Stuka squadrons were converted to Focke Wulf FW 190 fighter-bombers during 1944-45, but Rudel stayed with his trusted Ju 87G. He was shot down by Soviet flak in February 1945, had his right foot amputated, but was back in action with his die-hard Stukas until the last day of the war in Europe.

STUKA IN OPERATION

Most dive bombers give their pilots the sensation of diving vertically, but the Stuka did genuinely plummet earthwards at a true 90 degree dive angle. Indicator marks on the starboard side of the cockpit side screen ran from 30 to 90 degrees to enable the pilot to judge the angle correctly. From its level flight speed of 255 mph (410 km/h) the Stuka accelerated to 335 mph (540 km/h) as it dived some 4,500 ft (1,370 m). Its maximum permitted speed was 373 mph (600 km/h).

The Stuka's acceleration was progressive, its fixed undercarriage providing additional drag to that provided by the dive brakes. Less awkward

Ju-87 G-1 Stuka
10 (Pz) Staffel, II Gruppe, Schlachtgeschwader 3

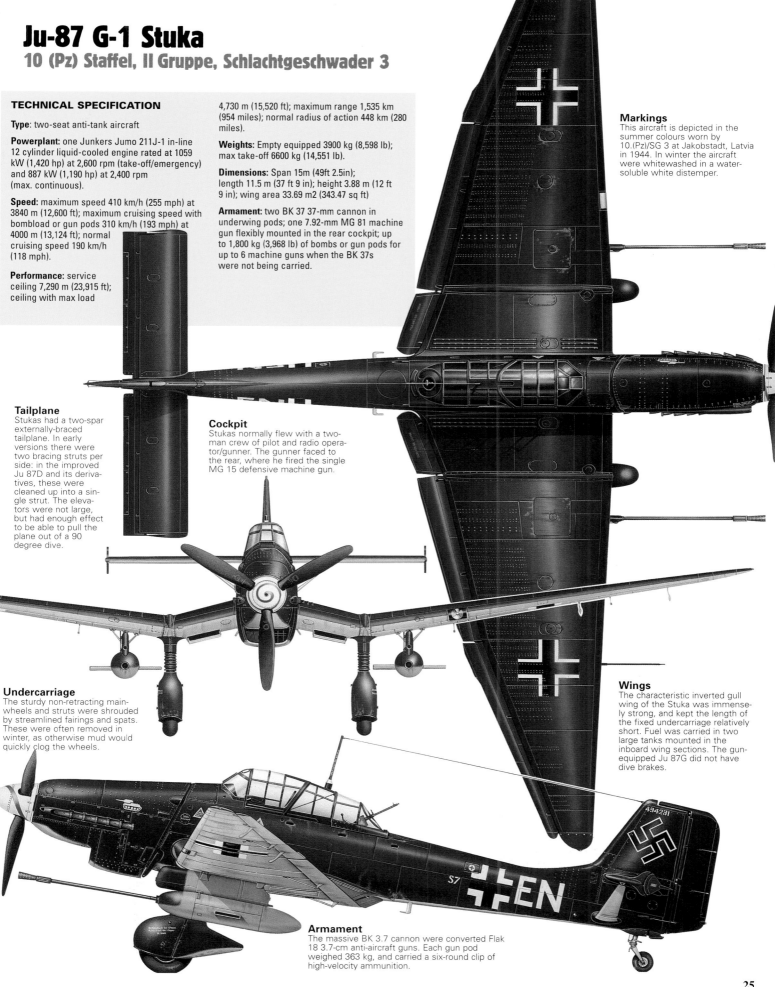

TECHNICAL SPECIFICATION

Type: two-seat anti-tank aircraft

Powerplant: one Junkers Jumo 211J-1 in-line 12 cylinder liquid-cooled engine rated at 1059 kW (1,420 hp) at 2,600 rpm (take-off/emergency) and 887 kW (1,190 hp) at 2,400 rpm (max. continuous).

Speed: maximum speed 410 km/h (255 mph) at 3840 m (12,600 ft); maximum cruising speed with bombload or gun pods 310 km/h (193 mph) at 4000 m (13,124 ft); normal cruising speed 190 km/h (118 mph).

Performance: service ceiling 7,290 m (23,915 ft); ceiling with max load 4,730 m (15,520 ft); maximum range 1,535 km (954 miles); normal radius of action 448 km (280 miles).

Weights: Empty equipped 3900 kg (8,598 lb); max take-off 6600 kg (14,551 lb).

Dimensions: Span 15m (49ft 2.5in); length 11.5 m (37 ft 9 in); height 3.88 m (12 ft 9 in); wing area 33.69 m2 (343.47 sq ft)

Armament: two BK 37 37-mm cannon in underwing pods; one 7.92-mm MG 81 machine gun flexibly mounted in the rear cockpit; up to 1,800 kg (3,968 lb) of bombs or gun pods for up to 6 machine guns when the BK 37s were not being carried.

Markings
This aircraft is depicted in the summer colours worn by 10.(Pz)/SG 3 at Jakobstadt, Latvia in 1944. In winter the aircraft were whitewashed in a water-soluble white distemper.

Tailplane
Stukas had a two-spar externally-braced tailplane. In early versions there were two bracing struts per side: in the improved Ju 87D and its derivatives, these were cleaned up into a single strut. The elevators were not large, but had enough effect to be able to pull the plane out of a 90 degree dive.

Cockpit
Stukas normally flew with a two-man crew of pilot and radio operator/gunner. The gunner faced to the rear, where he fired the single MG 15 defensive machine gun.

Undercarriage
The sturdy non-retracting main-wheels and struts were shrouded by streamlined fairings and spats. These were often removed in winter, as otherwise mud would quickly clog the wheels.

Wings
The characteristic inverted gull wing of the Stuka was immensely strong, and kept the length of the fixed undercarriage relatively short. Fuel was carried in two large tanks mounted in the inboard wing sections. The gun-equipped Ju 87G did not have dive brakes.

Armament
The massive BK 3.7 cannon were converted Flak 18 3.7-cm anti-aircraft guns. Each gun pod weighed 363 kg, and carried a six-round clip of high-velocity ammunition.

Stuka Variants

Ju 87A-0	pre-production aircraft
Ju 87A-1	production version 1937
Ju 87A-2	introduced Jumo 210 supercharged engine
Ju 87B-0	pre-production series of re-designed Ju 87B
Ju 87B-1	standard version 1939, introduced 1,200 hp Jumo 211
Ju 87B-2	improved version, available with ski or tropical fits; supplied to Italy, Bulgaria, Hungary and Romania.
Ju 87R1-4	anti-ship versions of Ju 87B-1 with provision for drop tanks but armed with only one 260 kg (551 lb) bomb
Ju 87C	carrier version for Graf Zeppelin (also recorded as Ju 87T)
Ju 87D-1	introduced revised layout, new canopy and uprated 1,410 hp Jumo engine
Ju 87D-2	glider tug version, used in North Africa
Ju 87D-3	additional armour plating
Ju 87D-4	equipped to carry a torpedo
Ju 87D-5	level attack version: no divebrake but extended wings
Ju 87D-7	night intruder with no dive brakes, flame-dampened exhausts, night flying equipment and twin 20 mm cannon
Ju 87D-8	definitive production version of Ju 87D-7
Ju 87G-1	anti-armour version of Ju87D-5, armed with twin 37 mm cannon
Ju 87H	Ju 87D trainer

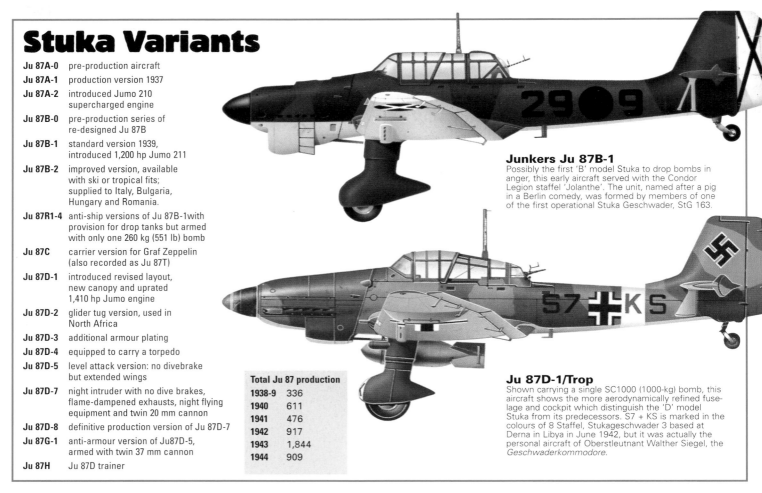

Junkers Ju 87B-1
Possibly the first 'B' model Stuka to drop bombs in anger, this early aircraft served with the Condor Legion staffel 'Jolanthe'. The unit, named after a pig in a Berlin comedy, was formed by members of one of the first operational Stuka Geschwader, StG 163.

Ju 87D-1/Trop
Shown carrying a single SC1000 (1000-kg) bomb, this aircraft shows the more aerodynamically refined fuselage and cockpit which distinguish the 'D' model Stuka from its predecessors. S7 + KS is marked in the colours of 8 Staffel, Stukageschwader 3 based at Derna in Libya in June 1942, but it was actually the personal aircraft of Oberstleutnant Walther Siegel, the *Geschwaderkommodore*.

Total Ju 87 production	
1938-9	336
1940	611
1941	476
1942	917
1943	1,844
1944	909

dive bombers such as the Douglas Dauntless accelerated like a rocket when they dived with a full bombload. It was this ability to make such a controlled vertical dive that enabled the Stuka to deliver heavy bombs with greater precision than any other aircraft of the war.

As he dived, the pilot kept an eye on the contact altimeter. It had an indicator which lit up when it was time to initiate the automatic pull-out. This brought the Stuka back to level flight at 6g (six times the force of gravity), descending another 1,475 ft (450 m) in the process.

The control column had a safety device, limiting it to 5 degrees of movement from neutral, stopping the pilot from pulling too much g during a pull-out. This could be overridden in an emergency – a hard tug on the control column brought the Stuka out of its dive. The minimum authorised altitude for starting a dive bombing attack was 800 m (2,624 ft): a lower cloud base restricted the Ju 87 to level attacks.

BOMBLOAD

If a target was close enough, the Stuka could deliver a formidable bombload. The Ju 87 could carry a 1,800 kg (3,968 lb) bomb for a short range mission: the sort of bombload carried by twin-engined aircraft throughout

World War II, and not far off that carried by American four-engine bombers during the strategic bombing of Germany.

Combat experience in Russia demonstrated that hitting a tank with a heavy bomb was next to impossible, even for a Stuka. On the Russian front, the standard anti-tank weapon was the SD-4-H1, a 4 kg hollow-charge bomblet. Seventy eight were carried inside a 500 kg bomb case. The bomblets could penetrate the thin top armour of any Allied tank – even the massive JS-2s usewd by the Red Army's in 1945.

More spectacular, but fraught with danger for the aircrew, was one of the final Stuka models: the Ju 87G-1. Introduced in 1943, this carried a pair of 37-mm cannon which could also penetrate the top armour of a tank, but the weight and drag further reduced the Stuka's already marginal performance.

Left: The Stuka's normal load was a 1,000 kg (2,205 lb) bomb beneath the fuselage or a 500 kg (1,102 lb) bomb under the fuselage and four 50 kg (110 lb) bombs under the wings.

Anatomy of the Ju87 Stuka

The Ju 87 was not fast, nor was it pretty. But it was very good at the job for which it was designed: diving vertically down on an enemy and delivering heavy bombs with great accuracy.

Tail wheel: Although free to swivel on the ground, the tail-wheel is locked into a fore-and-aft position on take-off and landing.

Controls: The Stuka was fitted with double-wing flaps and ailerons. A classic design which had been patented by Junkers, this used the outboard section as ailerons for roll control, with the two inner sections being used as flaps.

Markings: This Stuka is marked as an aircraft of StG 2 in use during the Battle of Britain.

Dive brakes: Opening the dive brakes automatically sent the Ju 87 into its dive.

Right: During a dive, the pilot safety mechanism restricted stick movement to 5 degrees to avoid inducing excess g-forces in the pull-up. In emergencies this could be over-ridden by a 27-kg (60-lb) pull on the stick.

Machine gun: The single MG 15 7.92-mm machine gun was hopelessly inadequate as a defence against fighters attacking from behind.

Dive angle: Pilots kept track of the angle at which they were diving by means of red lines painted on the canopy, which they would line up with the horizon.

Structure: The Stuka was designed to stand up to the incredible stresses generated by repeated 6g pull-outs from vertical dives. However, building such strength made the Ju 87 heavy, and its performance was poor.

Dive bombing techniques

Pre-dive checklist:
1. Landing flaps at cruise position
2. Elevator trim at cruise position
3. Rudder trim at cruise position
4. Airscrew pitch set at cruise
5. Contact altimeter on
6. Contact altimeter set to release height
7. Supercharger set to automatic
8. Throttle pulled right back
9. Cooler flaps closed
10. Dive brakes opened

Dive brakes open: This automatically noses the aircraft over into a dive. Red tabs protrude from the upper surfaces of the wing as a visual indicator to the pilot; at the same time the automatic dive recovery system is actuated. The pilot aims the entire aircraft at his target using a simple gun-type sight. Maximum dive speed is around 600 km/h (373 mph)

Bomb release: A light on the contact altimeter comes on to indicate the bomb-release point – usually at a minimum height of 450m. A knob is depressed on the control column to release weapons and to initiate the automatic pull-out mechanism.

Pullout mechanism: Automatically initiates a 6g pullout, returning elevator trim tabs to normal position. Can be overridden by the pilot in emergency. Once nose is above horizon, dive brakes retract, throttle opens and airscrew is set to climb.

Undercarriage: The origins of the Stuka design dates back to the early 1930s, when a fixed undercarriage was not seen as a disadvantage. By the time war broke out, however it was a distinctly old-fashioned feature.

Radiator: Cooling was provided by a radiator carried in an armoured 'bath-tub' mounted beneath the engine.

Weapons: Stukas existed to deliver bombs, and they could deliver them accurately. Most level bombers of the day were very lucky if they could hit within 100 metres of a target – in good hands a Stuka could hit to within 10 metres.

Engine: The Ju 87B was powered by a 12-cylinder liquid-cooled Junkers Jumo 211 engine. This delivered 900 kW (1,200hp) at 2,400 rpm for take off, with a normal maximum power of 825 kW (1,100 hp) at 1500 m (4,920 ft)

MASCHINENGEWEHR MG34/42

The German army's standard general purpose machine-guns during World War II are amongst the most influential infantry small arms of all time.

GERMANY produced many advanced weapons during World War II. Some were successful, some were unreliable, and some were a little too advanced for their own good. But a few German weapons were so good that they changed the face of warfare, and would influence weapons development all over the world for decades after Germany's defeat. Among their number were the MG34 machine-gun, and its successor the MG 42.

The first crude machine-guns were introduced in the 1860s, but they only came to dominate the battlefield during the First World War. By the time World War II broke out, machine-guns in most armies came in a variety of forms.

TYPES OF MG

There were light machine-guns, sometimes little more than automatic rifles: equipped with bipods and generally magazine fed, they were carried and used by infantrymen to provide their own extra firepower.

Then there were medium machine-guns: heavy, often water cooled, and mounted on massive tripods or mountings. These were used to lay down fire in the classic World War I manner: hosing out immense

Left: A German infantry machine-gun team moves through a cornfield in the Ukraine during the summer of 1941. The MG 34 general purpose weapon they carried had no real equivalent in other armies.

quantities of lead for long periods of time. Heavy machine-guns were also support weapons, operating over greater range and with greater penetration, but were even more unwieldy.

The Wehrmacht was different. In the MG34 the Germans had produced the first general-purpose machine-gun, a weapon which could do just about anything. Fitted with a bipod, it could be used as a light machine-gun by infantry in the assault. Mounted on the *MG-Lafatte*, a tripod with a periscope sight, it could be used in defence in the sustained fire role. When the gun fired the recoil moved the gun on the mount so that it automatically swept a beaten zone with fire. The tripod was designed so that the gunner could fire the weapon from below the parapet of the trench - either by using a grip handle which had a mechanical linkage

Below: A German infantry MG 34 team engages Soviet forces holed up in the Red October tractor factory at the height of the Battle of Stalingrad.

Right: On a tripod, the MG 34 was capable of laying down vast amounts of suppressive fire, like the water-cooled weapons used by the Allies.

Above: On a bipod, the MG 34 could be used as a light machine gun for infantry support. This example has a 75-round magazine.

to the trigger – or simply by pulling a cord fixed to the grip. Other mountings included twin and triple for AA use and with a heavier barrel sleeve and a ball mounting it was installed in tanks.

The MG34 was air cooled, doing away with the clumsy water cooling systems which had formerly prevented the barrel from melting under sustained fire. To prevent overheating, it was fitted with a quick-change barrel – MG crews always carried one or more spare barrels. It fired a 7.92 mm round

from a 50-round non disintegrating metal belt. As defensive armament in bombers it used 75-round saddle magazines.

With a bipod the MG34 weighed around 12 kg loaded and 31 kg on its tripod. It was 1219 mm long, with a barrel length of 627 mm. The muzzle velocity was 755 metres a second. The maximum effective or combat range was 2,000 metres and the MG34 had a cyclic rate of fire of 800 to 900 rounds per minute.

The chief drawback of the gun was that it was built to very high standards, mostly with components machined or turned from solid billets of steel. This meant that it was labour intensive and very expensive to produce.

The expansion of the war into Russia saw a huge increase in demand for machine-guns. A team of engineers headed by Dr Grunow, a successful industrialist, was tasked with finding ways of speeding up production of the MG34.

The result was the classic

Left: The angular, pressed-steel form of the MG 42 makes it easily identifiable compared to its more expensive MG 34 ancestor. The newer weapon was less temperamental when used in extreme weather.

MG42, one of the most influential firearms in history. It used plastic in the butt and pistol grip and stamped and diecast metal components instead of expensive machined steel. In place of riveted or screwed joints spot welding was used. When Allied intelligence officers evaluated captured MG42s they assumed that these changes were the result of pressure on the German munitions industry. They did not at first realise that it was a conscious design decision which had so simplified manufacture that machine-guns could be produced at a much greater rate, even with a semi-skilled workforce.

COMBAT EXPERIENCE

The MG42 incorporated lessons hard-won in combat on the Eastern Front. Both the cocking handle and the catch for the top cover to the working parts were designed so that the gunner could operate them wearing mitts – or with a stick or rod. This was vital in the sub-zero Russian winters where contact by bare flesh on cold metal could cause severe injury. The MG42 also functioned well in other climates; dust and dirt in North Africa and Italy was less likely to jam the MG42 than the more temperamental MG34.

Maschinengewehr MG42

Recoil Booster: Designed to trap muzzle gases and increase the weapon's recoil.

Front sight: The MG 42 was fitted with conventional iron sights for use in the light machine-gun role.

Barrel: The MG 42's quick release barrel could be changed by an experience gunner in five or six seconds.

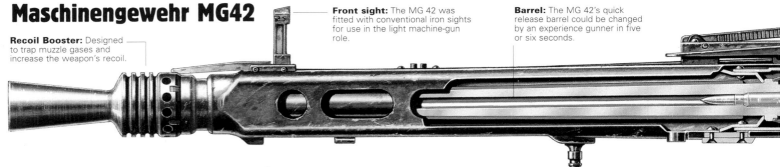

TECHNICAL SPECIFICATIONS MG 34

Type: General purpose machine-gun

Calibre: 7.92 x 57 mm Mauser (0.31-in);

Length: 1219mm

Barrel: length 627 mm; 4 grooves, right-hand twist

Weight: 12.1 kg with bipod; 36kg with Lafette 34 tripod

Muzzle velocity: 755 m/sec

Rate of fire, cyclic: 800-900 rounds/min

Effective range: 800 metres direct fire; 2000-3000 metres indirect fire

Ammunition feed: 75-round saddle drum magazine or 50-round belt (usually clipped in fives to give 250 rounds)

Unit cost: 327 RM (727 RM including tripod)

TECHNICAL SPECIFICATIONS MG 42

Type: General-purpose machine-gun

Calibre: 7.92 x 57 mm Mauser (0.31-in);

Length: 1220mm

Barrel: length 533 mm; 4 grooves, right-hand twist

Weight: 11.5 kg with bipod; 32kg with Lafette 42 tripod

Muzzle velocity: 755 m/sec

Rate of fire, cyclic: 1200 rounds/min

Effective range: 500 metres direct fire; 3500 metres indirect fire

Ammunition feed: 50-round belt (usually clipped in fives to give 250 rounds)

Unit cost: 250 RM (c.550 including tripod)

Left: An MG 34 mounted for the heavy machine-gun role on a Lafette 34 tripod, complete with indirect sights. The tripod was a solidly-machined piece of equipment – it cost as much to manufacture as the machine-gun itself! The two pads on the front leg of the tripod rested on the back of the man who carried iy when folded for transport.

Right: An MG 42 in its light machine-gun guise, without the tripod and resting on the two legs of the weapon's permanently-attached bipod. The legs could be adjusted individually for length, so that the weapon could be used without any problems on uneven ground.

Left: An MG 42 mounted on a Lafette 42 tripod. As with the Lafette 34, the Lafette 42 had extending legs, which was a feature primarily designed to give ground clearance when the gun was used in the anti-aircraft role. At 20.5 kg, the Lafette 42 was about 3 kg lighter than its predecessor.

MG34 ORIGINS

Design of the *Maschinengewehr* MG34 began at the Mauser plant at Obendorf in 1934. The weapon which entered service in 1936 was to change machine-gun design forever and with it infantry tactics. However it had a long gestation period dating back to 1919.

In that year *Rheinische Metallwaren und Maschinenfabrik* set up a subsidiary in Holland mainly to circumvent the Treaty of Versailles. This was followed in 1920 by a secret Russian 'front' company, and then in 1929 by the acquisition of the small Swiss firm of Solothurn.

The latter merger resulted in the 'Solothurn' MG30 of 1929, a box-magazine fed, air cooled machine-gun built to an extremely high standard, which remained in production until 1935.

The Mauser engineers used the MG30 as a starting point for their new weapon and the resulting gun, the MG34, incorporated many of the design features of the earlier machine-gun including the in-line mechanism and trigger arrangement and the rapid barrel change.

Belt-feed cover: The MG 42 did not have a magazine option like the MG 34: it could only fire the standard 50-round ammunition belts.

Bolthead and firing pin: When fitted with a lightweight bolthead, the MG 42 proved capable of achieving rates of fire as high as 1800 rounds per minute.

Bolt: The MG 42 was recoil operated, the working parts being locked at the moment of firing by locking rollers which were forced into sockets by the bolt.

Trigger: Even though the MG 42's trigger release was very well engineered, it took an experienced hand not to waste ammunition as a half-second burst fired 10-12 rounds

Recoil/return spring: This had to be immensely strong to handle the MG 42's potent rate of fire, returning the working parts forwards up to 25 times per second.

Butt: Like the rest of the MG 42's parts, the butt was designed for ease of manufacture. It was largely made of plastic.

The MG42 was lighter and slightly more compact than its predecessor, but used the same operating principal of short recoil assisted by gas pressure from a muzzle booster. The muzzle velocity of the MG42 at 755 metres a second was the same as the MG34, but the most distinctive change was the rate of fire – the MG42 ripped through belted ammunition at a cyclic rate of 1,550 rounds a minute.

BARREL CHANGE

This high rate of fire heated up the barrel of the MG42 even more than the MG34, and so the quick change system was simplified. The gunner had only to reach forward of the working parts, push a retaining catch on the housing forward and the barrel swung out to the right. Taking care, because it was very hot, he then pulled it to the rear and it was free. To replace the new barrel he simply reversed the procedure. A trained machine-gunner could complete the whole process in under 30 seconds.

The high rate of fire could be reassuring to a nervous soldier, but the vibration it produced was a problem; the MG 42 was less accurate than the MG 34 on the bipod. Though soldiers were trained to fire short bursts, this was sometimes hard to remember in the heat of battle. Enthusiastic use of the weapon also got through a lot of rounds, which meant that the three-man crew needed to carry heavy loads of ammunition.

The snarling fire of an MG42 was unmistakeable, often likened by Allied soldiers to the sound of tearing linoleum. One veteran recalled "the hysterical shriek of the MG42's furious rate of fire"... "I remember my first reaction ...was one of amazement at the crushing fire power of these guns. It seemed to me that the German soldier seldom used his rifle. He was a carrier of boxes of light machine-gun ammunition of which they seemed to have an endless supply."

Above: The ability to hose out ammunition made the MG 34 an effective short-range anti-aircraft weapon, especially on multiple mounts.

Below: In the sustained fire role the MG 42 usually operated with a three-man team of spotter, gunner and a loader to the left.

Above: Although the MG 42 was more crudely manufactured than its predecessor, it proved more reliable in harsh conditions. For this reason it was issued primarily to the infantry, while vehicle-mounted troops usually got the older weapon.

Below: Although the MG 42 was designed to fire only the standard 50-round ammunition belts, it was not difficult to modify it to acccept the MG 34's 75-round saddle-drum magazine. The large round fore sight on this example is an anti-aircraft sight.

Right: The only problem with the MG 42 was that its prodigious rate of fire encouraged an equally prodigious use of ammunition. As a result, most members of German infantry squads would carry extra belts of rounds for the machine-gun.

Scharnhorst as originally completed, with a straight stem. Though built as fast battleships, Scharnhorst her sister Gneisenau and were undergunned. Plans were afoot to upgrade their triple 11-inch turrets to twin 15-inch equipment, but Germany was at war before they could be refitted.

KRIEGSMARINE
THE FÜHRER'S NAVY

O N 22 JULY 1939 Grand Admiral Erich Raeder addressed the assembled officers of Germany's U-boat arm. He was there at Hitler's request, to pass on the Führer's assurance that however the international crisis developed, there would not be another war between Germany and Britain. Less than six weeks later, at 1.30 pm on 3 September, German warships received the signal from Naval High Command, "commence hostilities with Britain". It may have been the first time Hitler's

Although it had grown at an explosive rate from the time Hitler came to power, when war broke out in 1939, the Kriegsmarine was far from ready for war with Britain.

strategic decisions left the navy in the lurch, but it was far from being the last.

Hitler's decision to invade Poland found the Kriegsmarine in the early stages of a massive construction programme, intended to create a fleet powerful enough to challenge Britain's Royal Navy by the late 1940s. But the fleet committed to war in 1939 was smaller than the French navy. Its two greatest warships, the battlecruisers *Scharnhorst* and *Gneisenau* were unhappy compromises, armed with nine 28-cm (11-inch) guns; British and French capital ships had 15-inch (381-mm) and 16-

inch (406-mm) weapons.

Two 15-inch gun battleships – *Bismarck* and *Tirpitz* – were under construction, but even when the latter commissioned in 1941 Germany would have four big gun capital ships to Britain's fourteen. The British also had seven aircraft carriers, with at least six more building, while the Kriegsmarine had yet to acquire its first. The *Graf Zeppelin* was still nine months away from completion, and its sister ship *Peter Strasser* would not even be launched until the end of 1940. There were only about 20 ocean-going U-boats ready for operations, while the French had

some 70 submarines in service and the British had 50.

Hitler had inherited a very modest naval force when he came to power in 1933, the Reichsmarine's size and composition having been dictated by the victorious Allies in 1919. With the bulk of the once-feared High Seas Fleet at the bottom of Scapa Flow, where it had been scuttled in a final act of defiance, the most powerful warships left to post-war Germany were eight pre-dreadnought battleships, already obsolete by 1914. U-boats, which had inflicted such terrible losses on British merchant shipping during World War I, were forbidden altogether.

NEW U-BOATS

The navy continued to develop submarine designs in secret, funding the construction of six new boats in Finland and one later in Spain. This clandestine programme was exposed by the German press in 1926, leading to the resignation of the then minister of defence and Admiral Zenker, commander of the Reichsmarine. However, as the political climate changed, the German navy was already poised to break the Versailles Treaty, even before Hitler became Chancellor in January 1933. A construction programme authorised in 1932 envisaged six 'armoured ships', an aircraft carrier, six new heavy cruisers and 16 submarines.

Hitler had a boyish fascination with the minutiae of naval construction, and took a personal interest in the building plans advanced

Far right: Accompanied by Admiral Raeder, Adolf Hitler reviews the tiny Kriegsmarine he inherited on coming to power in Germany.

Right: The only capital ships Germany was allowed were two ancient pre-dreadnoughts, dating back to the early years of the 20th century.

German U-Boats had been a major success in World War I, and in the first half of World War II they were far and away the Kriegsmarine's most successful weapons.

Linienschiff Schlesien

U-Boats or Battleships?

Combat efficiency versus national pride

To people growing up in the first half of the 20th century, naval power meant big ships armed with big guns. Few could foresee a time when the battleship did not rule the waves.

Naval professionals were no different: when the Kriegsmarine high command drew up its expansion plans for the 1940s, they were centred on some of the largest battleships ever projected. They would have been monumentally expensive, and would have soaked up a lot of manpower, but they would certainly have been impressive.

One exception was Karl Doenitz. A submarine man through and through, he wanted lots of U-Boats. With a large submarine force, he felt that any potential maritime enemy could be blockaded and starved into submission. He was nearly right.

A Type VII U-Boat passes the Scharnhorst. *U-Boat commanders argued that for the cost of one capital ship, you could build and crew a whole flotilla of submarines.*

by the Kriegsmarine. However, his exceptional memory, especially for technical data, masked his very uneven grasp of technological issues and an even more limited mastery of maritime strategy.

Determined on a rapid expansion of the navy, he sought a formal agreement with Britain rather than risk immediate confrontation. The result was the 1935 Anglo-German naval agreement, under which

Germany was allowed to build modern capital ships up to a ceiling of 35 per cent of the Royal Navy's battleship tonnage. Incredibly, given the damage they had done 20 years earlier, the British ultimately agreed that Germany could expand its submarine fleet to achieve parity with that of the Royal Navy.

By 1938 Hitler's aggressive foreign policy had triggered a belated but rapid re-armament programme in Britain. Hence the

concern voiced by German naval officers, conscious that their building plans were still far from complete. If war came, they intended to attack British shipping with their modest force of U-boats and 'Deutschland' class *Panzerschiffe* or 'armoured ships'. These were long-range heavy cruisers designed to out-run anything they could not out-fight, and with six 280 mm guns, they were theoretically a match for anything except a full-sized

battleship. Dubbed 'pocket battleships' by the British, these unique warships could have no other purpose than commerce-raiding, with every design consideration subordinated to firepower and endurance. During the war, the *Admiral Scheer* would sail as far as the Indian Ocean and back, steaming 46,000 miles and sinking 100,000 tons of Allied shipping in the process.

Hitler ordered construction of the *Bismarck* and *Tirpitz* to be speeded up, and stepped up plans to replace the 28-cm guns aboard *Scharnhorst* and *Gneisnau* with battleship-calibre 38-cm guns. Increased quantities of every class of warship were authorised. The 'Z-plan', formally adopted in March 1939, called for eight battleships, five battlecruisers, four aircraft carriers, eight heavy cruisers, 68 destroyers and 249 submarines. The programme would be completed in 1948.

SUPER-BATTLESHIPS

At the core of the Z-plan were some of the most magnificent battleships ever designed. Three 35-knot battlecruisers, armed with six 38-cm (15-inch) guns and capable of steaming 14,000 miles at 19 knots, were authorised in 1939. In April 1939 contracts were issued for the first two of six 52,000 ton behemoths shipping eight 40.6-cm (16-inch) guns, the keels being laid in July and September respectively. Even larger monsters were to follow: the H41 design was to top 70,000 tons and mount new 42-cm (16.5-inch) guns, and the projected follow-on class were to displace an astonishing 96,555 tons at full load. The latter were scheduled to receive eight 48-cm (18.9-inch) guns, with the third unit mounting weapons with an unheard-of 51-cm (20-inch) calibre! Lest these be dismissed as disagreeably Freudian fantasies of the German leader, it

Left: Scharnhorst *and* Gneisenau *engage a British convoy during a sortie into the North Atlantic. Both battlecruisers were sunk or damaged beyond repair by the British Navy and Air Force.*

KMS Bismarck

As with most German warships of the 1930s, Bismarck was considerably heavier than the international treaty limits which she was supposed to meet. She was commissioned in August 1940, and after working up in the Baltic, the battleship attempted to break out into the Atlantic in May 1941. After sinking HMS Hood, Bismarck was hunted down and sunk by the British.

Main armament:
Bismarck's 15-inch guns were similar in capability to contemporary French and Italian designs. German armour-piercing shells were of poor quality, however.

Design: Bismarck's internal structure was based on the last battleships of the Imperial navy, but considerably enlarged. As a result its armour protection was not as sophisticated as on contemprary British or American battleships.

Fire control: German fire control was generally excellent. During the battle with HMS Hood, both Bismarck and the accompanying heavy cruiser Prinz Eugen hit the British battlecruiser early in the fight. The Hood blew up soon afterwards.

Colour scheme: Originally painted grey, Bismarck sailed on her only operational sortie sporting a bright dazzle colour scheme. This was toned down considerably before the unsuccessful attempt to break out into the Atlantic.

Conning tower: intended to be proof against battleship shells, the conning tower was in fact penetrated by 8-inch shells from British heavy cruisers.

In most respects identical to Bismarck, but with the addition of torpedo tubes, the Tirpitz had an undistinguished combat career. She was sunk by RAF Lancaster bombers.

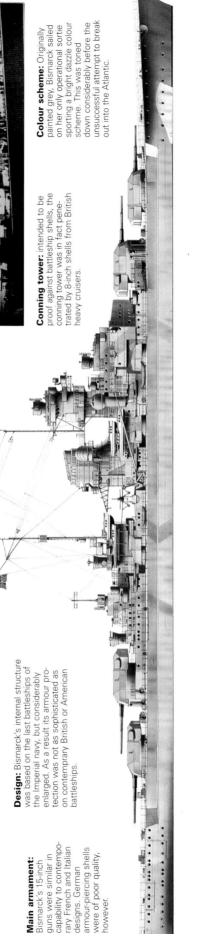

Beam: Bismarck's broad beam meant that the battleship was very stable in all weathers. Coupled with the excellent German fire control optics, this made Bismarck a very good gun platform.

Aircraft: capable of shipping up to five, but normally carried two Arado Ar 196 floatplanes for reconnaissance, light attack and gunnery spotting.

Complement: between 2,100 and 2,200 officers and men.

Armament: Eight K34 38-cm (15-inch) 47-calibre cannon in four twin turrets; 12 K28 15-cm (5.9-inch) 55-calibre cannon in six twin turret; 16 K32 105-mm (4.1-inch) 65-calibre anti-aircraft guns in eight twin turrets; 16 K30 37-mm anti-aircraft guns on eight twin mounts; 12 K30 20-mm anti aircraft guns.

SPECIFICATIONS
KMS Bismarck

Displacement: Nominally 35,000 tons, but actually 41,600 tons normal and 50,150 tons deep load.

Dimensions: Length overall 251 m (823 ft 6 in); waterline length 241.5 m (792 ft 4 in); beam 36 m (118 ft); average draught 9.3 m (30 ft 7 in)

Machinery: 12 Wagner boilers, 3-shaft

Blohm & Voss geared steam turbines delivering 103 000 kW (138,000 shp).

Speed: 29 knots (33.25 mph/53 km/h).

Armour thickness: Main belt 320 mm (12.6 in); decks 50-120 mm (2 in/4.7 in); main turrets 177-362 mm (7-14.25 in); secondary turrets 38-102 mm (1.5-4 in).

Above: The commerce raiders Orion and Komet operate in company in the Pacific. Armed merchant cruisers like these sank more enemy vessels than conventional warships.

should be noted that most of the world's major navies were designing, if not actually building, battleships that would dwarf anything then afloat. (Only Japan would actually complete any, and both would be sunk by carrier aircraft by the end of World War II.)

Curiously, the 249 U-boats scheduled to be in service by 1948 was not enough. Admiral Doenitz, the commander-in-chief of Germany's submarine forces,

calculated that 300 boats were required in order to maintain about 100 on patrol in the North Atlantic at any given moment. This was the number he believed necessary to cut Britain's maritime lifeline, and starve the UK into surrender. Doenitz had another objection to the navy's plans: he wanted to concentrate on building the small Type VII U-boat, in his view the ideal submarine for a second campaign against British convoys. It could carry up to 14 torpedoes, had the endurance to operate in the North Atlantic for a month, yet was able to crash dive in 20 seconds. Larger submarines, such as the

Type IX already developed, were slower to seek the safety of the deep, and in Doenitz's experience this was a significant handicap. Worse, from the point of view of the ongoing arms race, Type IXs took longer to build and required more material.

THE WRONG BOATS

Yet Doenitz was over-ruled; not only were a significant proportion of the new boats to be the less agile Type IXs, but the OKM (*Oberkommando der Kriegsmarine*, or Naval High Command) demanded even larger 'cruiser submarines' with an ill-thought out idea of surface

engagements. The proportion of Type VIIs was further reduced by an equally puzzling order to continue building Type II coastal submarines, of which Germany already had enough to patrol the Baltic and North Sea.

If Hitler's grandiose plans for the Kriegsmarine had been fulfilled, by the end of the 1940s the German navy would have been able to put to sea with two surface action groups, each consisting of an aircraft carrier and four or five of the most powerful battleships in the world. However, the war came too soon, and Admiral Raeder had to make do with what he had.

Above: A flotilla of Type VII U-boats at its moorings. Although fewer than 30 boats were at sea at any one time in the first two years of the war, the U-boat force sank millions of tons of British and Allied merchant shipping.

Below: A high point of the Kriegsmarine's war, as the Scharnhorst, Gneisenau and Prinz Eugen dash through the English Channel fighting off all attempts at interception by the Royal Navy.

Raeder had spent his career in surface ships, serving as Admiral Hipper's chief-of-staff during World War I, and had written the two volumes of the German official history dealing with the exploits of the German commerce raiders. He therefore launched a two-pronged surface attack on the Allied convoy system. Both 'Scharnhorsts', the 'Deutschland' class pocket battleships and 'Hipper' class heavy cruisers sailed on a succession of raids into the Atlantic. Specially-converted merchant raiders soon followed. Externally, they appeared like innocent merchant vessels, but they carried concealed 15-cm (six-inch) guns and had up to four hidden torpedo tubes. Although lacking armour, they could be highly effective in battle: one raider, the *Kormoran*, actually sank the Australian heavy cruiser *Sydney* in a mutually-destructive engagement.

RAIDERS AND ESCORTS

The warships enjoyed some successes, but this was exactly the kind of war for which the British Royal Navy had been preparing. Veteran battleships were attached to important convoys, and more than once *Scharnhorst* and *Gneisenau* were forced to pull back when confronted by the daunting bulk of a World War I dreadnought steaming out to defend its charges. The British escorts were very aggressive, even when hopelessly outgunned: the armed merchant cruisers *Rawalpindi* and *Jervis Bay* sacrificed themselves in battle to win time for their convoys to scatter.

The German campaign started badly: *Graf Spee* was caught off Argentina and destroyed in an action that did nothing for the Kriegsmarine's confidence. The

Small Combatants
Bitter fighting in the Coastal War

Many of the Kriegsmarine's larger vessels spent most of their time at moorings. For smaller combatants, however, it was a much more active war.

There were two main areas of operations for German small craft. They had to escort coastal convoys through the inshore waters of northern Europe, and they also took offensive action against British convoys in the North Sea and the Channel.

The main strike weapon was the *Schnellboot* or S-Boat (known as the E-Boat to its opponents). Larger and slower than British or American boats, S-Boats were better seakeepers, able to sustain their maximum speeds in rougher weather than British MTBs or American PT boats.

Based in heavily fortified concrete pens, S-Boats attacked all around the English coast, but they concentrated on thge area of the Thames Estuary, which became known as 'E-Boat Alley'. However, with increased air patrols and the fitting of radar to British coastal craft the threat had largely been contained by 1944.

Fighting long and hard, the German crews maintained the evil reputation of 'E-Boat Alley', but they became vulnerable to increasingly effective and co-ordinated opponents.

Taken out of context, the effects of German coastal forces were not great in a material sense. Measured in psychological and disruptive terms, however, they were a major nuisance, requiring a large expenditure of scarce resources for the Allies to counter them.

Above: Heavily-armed minesweepers known as R-Boats were also used in the coastal war, primarily as convoy escorts.

Below: A flotilla of S-Boats heads out to sea. Most of their offensive actions took place by night.

Lürssen *Schnellboot*
Late model S-Boats were fitted with armoured bridges. They capable of speeds of 40 knots, and had a range of 1400 km at 35 knots. Their low silhouettes and quiet diesel engines gave them an advantage until the Allies began using radar more widely.

Armament
Typically, S-Boats carried two 533-mm (21-inch) torpedoes with room for two or four reloads. Gun armament varied, but usually comprised 3 or 4 20-mm cannon and a single 37-mm or 40-mm weapon.

Above: U-boats were generally good sea boats. This was a good thing, since they spent most of their time on the surface, and their main operation area was the North Atlantic.

Right: U-Boats were stunningly successful in the first years of the war, sinking millions of tons of Allied shipping. But it came at great cost: U-Boat crews had only a one-in-four chance of surviving the war.

Below: Tirpitz saw very little action, but her existence was a threat to the Russian convoys. The British attacked the battleship many times, finally sinking the great vessel with 6-ton bombs.

'Hipper' class cruisers lacked endurance, and their complex powerplants proved unreliable. And then came the *Bismarck's* disastrous maiden voyage. Although she sank the old battlecruiser *Hood*, pride of the Royal Navy, the Kriegsmarine's largest battleship never even found an Allied convoy before the British intercepted her and smashed her to pieces.

NORTHERN THREAT

With the *Bismarck* at the bottom of the Atlantic, the Kriegsmarine withdrew *Scharnhorst*, *Gneisenau* and *Prinz Eugen* from Brest, where they had posed an alarming threat to the convoy system but were vulnerable to air attack. German heavy units were concentrated instead in Norway, from where they attempted to stop Allied convoys to Russia. But their sorties were characterised by extreme caution, since no Admiral wanted to report another defeat to an already impatient Führer. On 31 January 1942, the navy proudly informed Hitler that it was attacking one of the Arctic convoys, quoting a signal from

an over-excited U-boat captain who claimed to be observing the battle. "I see only red," he reported. So did Hitler when it emerged that the German squadron had broken off the action after a handful of escorts mounted a courageous defence, darting out of smokescreens to launch torpedoes and generally carrying on as if the whole Home Fleet was at hand.

A furious Hitler demanded the complete scrapping of the surface fleet after this fiasco. Raeder resigned. His replacement, the U-boat commander Admiral Doenitz, partially reversed the decision, but from 1943 German naval hopes rested entirely on the submarine arm. Ironically, the increased pace of surface ship construction in the late 1930s had not been extended to the submarine programme. U-boat construction actually slowed down from 1938-9 and even by mid-1940 there were only 28 operational boats.

By the time Doenitz had the sort of U-boat fleet necessary to isolate Britain, the war was already lost. British anti-submarine tactics proved increasingly effective, assisted by increased airborne surveillance, as well as better radar and sonar. Once the tremendous resources of the USA were committed to

Too late to make a difference...
Advanced U-boats

From 1943, new Allied tactics, radar, and anti-submarine aircraft made it impossible for U-boats to operate on the surface. Submarines clearly had to be optimised for submerged operations.

The Type XVII featured a hydronamically clean hull, a single propeller set in cruciform control surfaces and a Walter closed-cycle propulsion system giving a theoretical maximum submerged speed of around 25 knots.

The concept proved difficult to manage, but the later Type XXI boat was more practical, and was to be the basis for many post-war submarine designs. With

conventional machinery fitted to a hull optimised for underwater operations, the Type XXI was capable of 16 knots submerged. More than 120 were commissioned in 1944 and 1945, but none ever made a successful attack.

Sixty-two of the smaller Type XXIIIs were completed, with U-2336 making the last U-Boat attack in European waters sinking two freighters in the Firth of Forth. One torpedo was used on each, fired on the strength of passive sonar bearings from a distance of less than 500 metres. It was fortunate for the Allies that this sort of capability had come too late.

Right: The small size of the Type XXIII limited it to coastal operations. U-2326, seen here tied up alongside the pier at Dundee, was captured at the end of the war.

Below: The paint worn away from both the conning tower and stemhead of this Type XXI boat are clues to the high underwater speeds it could attain. Note the foldaway foreplanes, which reduced drag.

the battle, the U-boats faced an almost impossible task: they simply could not sink ships as fast as Allied yards built them. Above all, the ULTRA code breakers had cracked German naval codes, enabling the Allies to re-route convoys around the 'Wolf Packs'. From mid-1943, the Allies used this intelligence to reinforce convoys with dedicated escort groups and fight their way through. In May of that year they sank 56 U-boats. The Battle of the Atlantic was lost.

The Kriegsmarine's final failure was its complete inability to prevent the Normandy landings. German coastal forces had fought a savage war in the Channel and the North Sea, and managed to inflict grave losses on an amphibious rehearsal off the Dorset coast, but they could do nothing against the massive forces assembled for Operation Overlord. The U-boats were beaten too, forced to evacuate their concrete lairs along the

Right: Rear-Admiral Karl Brüning comes ashore at Felixstowe in May 1945. Within hours he will have surrendered German coastal forces to the Royal Navy.

French Atlantic coast and re-group in Germany and Norway.

The remaining units of the surface fleet, less *Scharnhorst* (sunk by the British fleet in the Arctic) and *Tirpitz* (sunk by Bomber Command Lancasters with 12,000-lb bombs), were committed to the Baltic. They provided naval gunnery support for the embattled *Ostheer* as the army fought its long rearguard

action against a vengeful Red Army. The warships sustained the isolated Army Group Courland and organised the evacuation of East Prussia.

It was a grim business as the last ships sailed from ports about to be overrun. Several large refugee-packed passenger liners were sunk by Russian submarines, the *Wilhelm Gustloff* going down with over 8,000

people on board – the greatest single maritime disaster in history, with five times as many lost as in the Titanic.

The Kriegsmarine had failed to blockade Britain into defeat, and was unable to stop the Allied invasion of Europe. But its evacuation of over two million civilians from the doomed provinces of eastern Germany was perhaps its greatest achievement.

MESSERSCHMITT Bf 109

Small, agile and very fast, the Messerschmitt Bf 109 was probably the most capable of the first generation of low-wing monoplane fighters to enter service.

THE Messerschmitt Bf 109 was the Luftwaffe's benchmark fighter throughout World War II. It was the mount of the vast majority of the German aces and scored more kills than any other Axis aircraft. It was one of the

The Bf 109, a classic combat aircraft, was Germany's most important World War II fighter.

first monoplane fighters with fully enclosed cockpit and retractable landing gear, and when delivered to the Luftwaffe in 1936 it gave the re-arming German air force the most capable fighter in the world.

Few fighters of the period bettered the Bf 109's longevity, either. It entered service in time

to be blooded in Spain, and it remained the backbone of the Luftwaffe fighter arm until the end of the war. Even after 1945 it continued to serve with several air forces and briefly went back to war in Israeli hands.

The aircraft rapidly gained a great reputation, which was carefully nurtured by Nazi

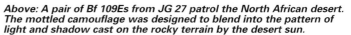

Designed at a time when most fighters carried a pair of rifle-calibre machine guns, early versions of the Bf 109 had four, which were soon supplemented by powerful 20-mm cannon.

Germany's expert propagandists, and this lived on even after the aircraft had begun to show its age, and while newer fighters on both sides were clearly its betters.

The fighter which Germany's fighter aces took in to battle bears the name of its designer, Professor Willy Emil Messerschmitt. Messerschmitt was born in Frankfurt am Main on June 26, 1898. He established an aircraft construction plant at Bamberg in 1923, and in 1926 he produced his first all-metal aircraft. Hitler thought highly of Messerschmitt, as did Colonel General Ernst Udet, the Luftwaffe's Director of Armaments from 1939-41, who gave him preferential treatment over major contracts. But Messerschmitt was detested by Field Marshal Erhard Milch who directed Luftwaffe production and development from 1941.

Messerschmitt's aircraft were built at the Bavarian Aircraft Works - *Bayerische Flugzeugwerke* AG - which is why pre-war designs bore the prefix 'Bf'. However, Messerschmitt bought out the factory and subsequent designs like the Me 262 jet fighter bore

the prefix 'Me'.

On November 11 1937 the prototype Bf l09 V13 (D-IPKY), fitted with a specially boosted DB 601A engine delivering 1,650 hp for short periods, set a international speed record for land planes of 610.536 km/h.

COMBAT-TESTED

The Spanish Civil War gave the Luftwaffe a chance to evaluate the Bf 109 under combat conditions. Condor Legion pilots based at Tablada, Seville and flying in support of Franco tested three prototypes early in 1937. They were soon followed by early production fighters which had entered service with *Jagdgeschwader* 2 'Richthofen' in the spring of 1937. The Bf 109B-1 was powered by a 635 hp Junkers Jumo 210D engine which gave a top speed of 470 km/h at 4,000 metres and was armed with three 7.92 MG 17 machine guns. Combat experience led to the improved Bf 109D and the Bf 109E, nicknamed 'Emil' by its pilots, with which Germany entered World War II.

The 'Emil' was very heavily-armed by the standards of the day, with two wing mounted 20 mm MG FF cannon and a 20 mm MG FF/M cannon in the propeller hub. Two 7.9 mm MG 17 machine guns fired through blast troughs in the upper cowling. The Bf 109E had a maximum speed of 483 km/h at sea level and 560 km/h at 4,440 m. It was the aircraft with which the Luftwaffe dominated the skies over Poland, the Low Countries and France, though it came up against much tougher opposition during the Battle of Britain when 610 Bf 109s were lost in action. Tropicalised

Right: The first production Messerschmitt Bf 109Bs entered service with the Luftwaffe in 1937. The new fighters were a huge challenge to pilots flying obsolete Heinkel He 51 biplanes.

> "Ernst Udet, the World War I fighter ace who ran the Luftwaffe technical office was visiting the factory. To him, fighters were biplanes with open cockpits. He took one look at the 109 prototype and said, 'Gentlemen, that is not a fighter.' He was not a good prophet!"

Above: A pair of Bf 109Es from JG 27 patrol the North African desert. The mottled camouflage was designed to blend into the pattern of light and shadow cast on the rocky terrain by the desert sun.

Above: Kill-markings on the tailplane of Werner Mölders's BF 109 at the end of the Battle of Britain testify to his success in combat. The Bf 109 was easily the most successful fighter of the early years of the war, and was flown by most of the Luftwaffe Experten, or aces.

Messerschmitt's rivals
Old ideas versus state-of-the-art

The first prototype of the new Messerschmitt fighter, Bf 109V1 (Werk-Nr 758) registered D-IABI, flew on May 28, 1935. It had been built to a 1934 specification for a single-seat all-metal monoplane fighter issued by the *C-Amt* (the technical department of the still-clandestine Luftwaffe). The prototype was powered by a British built 695-hp Rolls-Royce Kestrel V engine, pending the arrival of a new Daimler-Benz powerplant being designed for Germany's new generation of monoplane fighters.

Competitors included the Heinkel He 112, the Arado Ar 80, and the Focke-Wulf Fw 159

as well as the Bf 109. In a competitive fly-off organised by the Reichsluftfahrtministerium (RLM - the Reich Air Ministry) at Travemunde airfield in October 1935, only the Heinkel and Messerschmitt designs stood out, and the faster, lighter Bf 109 was judged the winner and was accepted into service as the Luftwaffe's main single-engined fighter.

Below: The Focke-Wulf Fw 159 was like an enlarged version of the Fw 156 Stosser, the Luftwaffe's first fighter, but the high-wing or parasol configuration proved to be much less agile than a biplane and much slower than low-wing monoplanes like the Heinkel and the Messerschmitt.

Above: In an attempt to save weight, Arado designed its Ar 80 with fixed landing gear. However, it was too heavy, lacked agility and with the same engine was at least 80 km/h slower than the Bf 109.

Above: Although less sophisticated aerodynamically, the Heinkel He 112 had better ground handling than the Bf 109. Performance was broadly comparable though it was a little slower. But it was more complex and expensive to produce.

Messerschmitt Bf 109E-4
I Gruppe, Jagdgeschwader 3, France 1940

Wing: The Bf 109's thin wing gave it much better high-speed performance than its German rivals. However, it left little room for bigger weapons, which came to be a problem late in the war.

Engine: Most Messerschmitt Bf 109s were powered by variants of the Daimler Benz DB 601 or its succeeding DB 605 inverted-vee piston engine. Unlike the engines of British fighters which had gravity-fed carburettors, these had direct fuel injection, and so did not cut out in a dive.

Machine guns: Two MG 17 machine guns firing through the propeller disc were housed in the cockpit cowling above the engine. These were connected via an interruptor gear to the propeller shaft, ensuring that they only fired when the propeller blades were clear.

Wing slots: Fitted in the outer part of the leading edge, these popped out automatically at low speeds to give the Bf 109 more lift and more manoeuvrability.

SPECIFICATIONS
Messerschmitt Bf 109E-4
Dimensions: length 8.64 m (28 ft 4.25 in); height 2.497 m (8 ft 2.33 in); wingspan 9.87 m (32 ft 4.5 in); wing area 16.4 sq.m (176.53 sq.ft)

Weights (typical): 1900 kg (4,190 lb) empty; 2665 kg (5,875 lb) fully loaded.

Powerplant: one Daimler-Benz DB 601Aa liquid-cooled inverted vee engine rated at 1,175 hp on take off and 1,020 hp at 4500 m (14,765 ft)

Performance: maximum speed 471 km/h (293 mph) at sea level and 560 km/h (348 mph) at 4400 m; range 660 km (410 miles); initial climb rate 1000 m/min (3,280 ft/min); time to 6000 m (19,685 ft) 7.1 min; service ceiling 10500 m(34,450 ft).

Armament: two 20-mm MG FF 20-mm cannon each with 60 rounds in wings; two 7.9-mm MG 17 machine guns over fuselage; some E-4s modified to carry four SC 50 (110 lb) bombs or one SC 250 (550 lb) bombs on an underfuselage rack.

Propeller: The three-bladed controllable-pitch propeller which was fitted to DB-601-engined Bf 109s was far more effective than the simple two-bladed props fitted to early Spitfires and Hurricanes.

versions of the Emil also accompanied Rommel's Afrika Korps to North Africa, and the type was still in service during the opening phases of the war against the Soviet Union.

CARRIER VERSION

One interesting variant was the Bf l09T-0, a modified version of the 109E-3. The 'T' stood for *Trager* or Carrier and the fighter was intended to equip the aircraft carrier *Graf Zeppelin*. Germany's pre-war naval plans called for four carriers, but the *Graf Zeppelin*, which was launched in December 1938, was the only one which came anywhere near completion. These aircraft were modified by Fieseler-Werke and had an increased wing area, spoilers on the wing upper surfaces, manually-folded outer wing panels, catapult spools and an arrester hook. The delays in the completion of the carrier resulted in the cancellation of the Bf 109T-0s which were reconverted to E-3 configuration.

The Bf 109F was sometimes

known as 'Friedrich'. It entered service in the spring of 1941 and re-established the aircraft's combat viability, which had suffered with the British introduction of the improved Supermarine Spitfire V. It was flying this superior aircraft that the Luftwaffe aces made the majority of their kills against the slower aircraft of the Red Air Force. Its performance was impressive. Capable of climbing to 5,000 m in 5 minutes and 12 seconds it had a maximum speed of 600 km/h at 6,000 m. Interestingly, the 109F had lighter armament than the Emil, with one 15 mm MG 151 cannon in the propeller hub and two 7.9 mm MG 17 machine guns in the upper cowling.

TWIN FUSELAGE

One of the most unusual experiments with the Bf 109F airframe was the Bf l09Z, in which two 109 fuselages were married by means of a common centre section and tailplane. It was originally proposed that this

Above: Luftwaffe pilots were the best trained in the world in 1939. Having a superior aircraft allied to combat-tested tactics meant that the Bf 109 was the dominant fighter in the first year of combat.

Below: A tropicalised Bf 109E-7 flown by Oberleutnant Ludwig Franzisket escorts a Ju 87 Stuka returning from a mission over Libya in April 1941. Franzisket was the adjutant of I/JG 27.

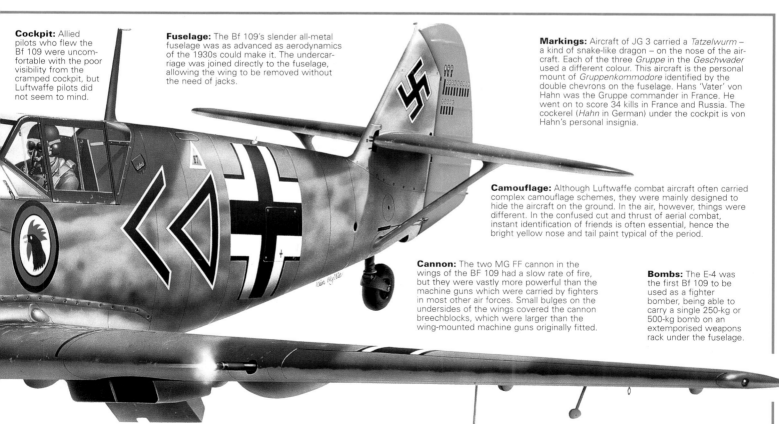

Cockpit: Allied pilots who flew the Bf 109 were uncomfortable with the poor visibility from the cramped cockpit, but Luftwaffe pilots did not seem to mind.

Fuselage: The Bf 109's slender all-metal fuselage was as advanced as aerodynamics of the 1930s could make it. The undercarriage was joined directly to the fuselage, allowing the wing to be removed without the need of jacks.

Markings: Aircraft of JG 3 carried a *Tatzelwurm* – a kind of snake-like dragon – on the nose of the aircraft. Each of the three *Gruppe* in the *Geschwader* used a different colour. This aircraft is the personal mount of *Gruppenkommodore* identified by the double chevrons on the fuselage. Hans 'Vater' von Hahn was the Gruppe commander in France. He went on to score 34 kills in France and Russia. The cockerel (*Hahn* in German) under the cockpit is von Hahn's personal insignia.

Camouflage: Although Luftwaffe combat aircraft often carried complex camouflage schemes, they were mainly designed to hide the aircraft on the ground. In the air, however, things were different. In the confused cut and thrust of aerial combat, instant identification of friends is often essential, hence the bright yellow nose and tail paint typical of the period.

Cannon: The two MG FF cannon in the wings of the BF 109 had a slow rate of fire, but they were vastly more powerful than the machine guns which were carried by fighters in most other air forces. Small bulges on the undersides of the wings covered the cannon breechblocks, which were larger than the wing-mounted machine guns originally fitted.

Bombs: The E-4 was the first Bf 109 to be used as a fighter bomber, being able to carry a single 250-kg or 500-kg bomb on an extemporised weapons rack under the fuselage.

Above: The Bf 109G introduced a new powerplant. The DB 605 was about the same size as the DB 601, but it delivered more power, and hence greater speed. However, its greater weight upset the balance of the fighter and made it harder to handle.

Above: Introduced in 1941 to combat improved marks of Spitfire, the Bf 109F had an uprated powerplant and was much more aerodynamic than the trusty 'Emil'.

machine should act a prototype for a heavy fighter bomber utilising a similar configuration of Bf l09G components. The pilot was in the port fuselage and the aircraft was armed with five 30 mm MK 108 cannon. The airframe was built but never tested.

'GUSTAV' ARRIVES

The Bf 109G, universally known as the 'Gustav', made its operational debut with Channel based *Jagdgeschwader* in May 1942 and bore the brunt of later fighting in Russia, the Mediterranean, France and in the defence of the Reich. New and improved models of allied fighters were again outclassing the 109, and with the 'G' series Messerschmitt sacrificed agility for sheer performance. The Bf l09G-2 which was powered by one 1,475 hp Daimler-Benz DB 605A twelve cylinder inverted-Vee liquid cooled engine had a maximum speed of 510 km/h at sea level and of 653 km/h at 9,000 m. Its maximum range was

850 km. The aircraft had a wing span of 9.92 m, length of 8.85 m and height of 2.50 m and a wing area of 16.1 sq m. Its empty weight was 2,253 kg and maximum weight 3,200 kg. Like the 109F, the G-2 was armed with one 20 mm MG 151/20 cannon firing through the propeller hub and two 7.9 mm MG 17 machine guns in the upper cowling.

The G-5 introduced faster-firing and more powerful MG 131s over the engine. The blisters necessitated by the larger breeches of these weapons led to the G-5 and subsequent variants of the Gustav being given the alternative nickname of '*die Beule*' or 'The Bulge'.

The G-6 became the 'standard' model of Gustav, though standard was a somewhat loose term when so many aircraft

Bf 109G-2s of JG 54 'Grunherz' on the northern sector of the Eastern Front, At this time, the summer of 1942, the 109 was still better than most Soviet fighters, but improved designs from Lavochkin and Yak were about to challenge the Germans.

109 Variants

BUILT IN HUGE NUMBERS OVER A LONG CAREER

Depending upon which records you look at, it has been estimated that between 31,000 and 33,000 Messerschmitt Bf 109s were built between 1937 and 1944. The story of the 109 parallels that of the Luftwaffe itself: after dramatic success in the early years of the war it began to show weaknesses when fighting at a disadvantage over England in 1940.

Further triumphs against a weak and unprepared enemy in the USSR in 1941 hid the fact that the basic design, while capable of considerable upgrades, was being matched and passed by fighters designed

in Britain, the USSR and the USA. Even so, it was being built in ever increasing numbers as the Allied bomber offensive took the war to the heartland of the Reich. Although in most respects outperformed by the Focke-Wulf Fw 190, the 109 had the edge in the high-altitude war forced on the Luftwaffe by high-flying USAAF bombers.

During the war the Bf 109's performance jumped from a maximum speed of 550 km/h (340 mph) in the Bf 109E-1 of 1939 to more than 724 km/h (450 mph) in the Bf 109K-4 of 1945. Climb-rate and service ceiling also improved dramatically.

But the end of the war was not the end of the line for the 109. Czechoslovakia had been home to some of the 109's assembly parts, and after the war the Letov concern continued to build the type. They used Jumo engines, and their handling can best be assessed by the nickname their pilots gave to the fighter – Mezak, or 'Mule'.

The last operational 109s were flown in Spain, where the type had made its combat debut in 1938. The last Merlin-engined versions, built by Hispano, remained on the Spanish air force inventory until the mid-1960s.

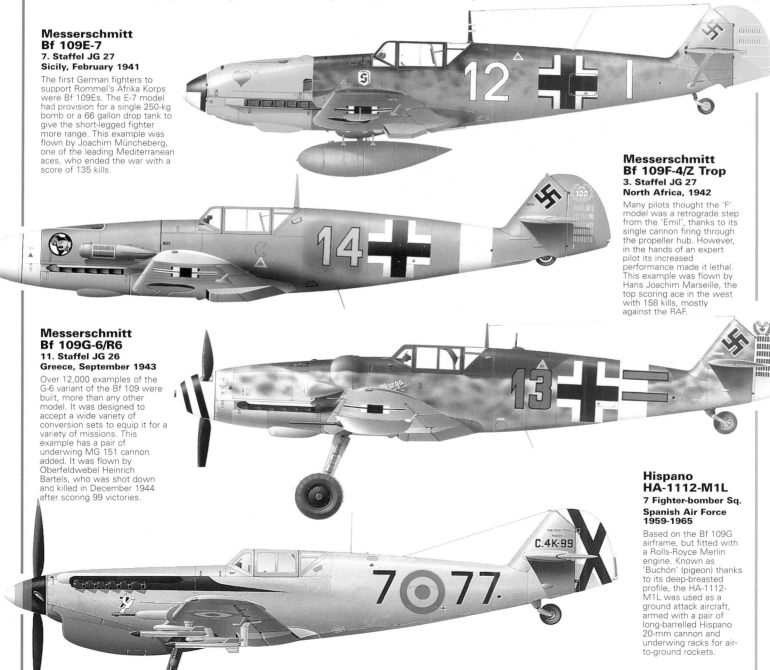

Messerschmitt Bf 109E-7
7. Staffel JG 27
Sicily, February 1941

The first German fighters to support Rommel's Afrika Korps were Bf 109Es. The E-7 model had provision for a single 250-kg bomb or a 66 gallon drop tank to give the short-legged fighter more range. This example was flown by Joachim Müncheberg, one of the leading Mediterranean aces, who ended the war with a score of 135 kills.

Messerschmitt Bf 109F-4/Z Trop
3. Staffel JG 27
North Africa, 1942

Many pilots thought the 'F' model was a retrograde step from the 'Emil', thanks to its single cannon firing through the propeller hub. However, in the hands of an expert pilot its increased performance made it lethal. This example was flown by Hans Joachim Marseille, the top scoring ace in the west with 158 kills, mostly against the RAF.

Messerschmitt Bf 109G-6/R6
11. Staffel JG 26
Greece, September 1943

Over 12,000 examples of the G-6 variant of the Bf 109 were built, more than any other model. It was designed to accept a wide variety of conversion sets to equip it for a variety of missions. This example has a pair of underwing MG 151 cannon added. It was flown by Oberfeldwebel Heinrich Bartels, who was shot down and killed in December 1944 after scoring 99 victories.

Hispano HA-1112-M1L
7 Fighter-bomber Sq.
Spanish Air Force
1959-1965

Based on the Bf 109G airframe, but fitted with a Rolls-Royce Merlin engine. Known as 'Buchón' (pigeon) thanks to its deep-breasted profile, the HA-1112-M1L was used as a ground attack aircraft, armed with a pair of long-barrelled Hispano 20-mm cannon and underwing racks for air-to-ground rockets.

Left: A Luftwaffe Experte *adds another victory to the tail of his Bf 109. The term* Experte *was used to indicate a pilot who had scored more than 10 kills.*

Above: A late-model Bf 109G taxis out for a mission in the autumn of 1944. It is fitted with a 'Galland Hood', the redesigned canopy intended to improve pilot vision.

were modified with *Rustsatze* - field conversion kits for additional or alternative underwing armament or ventral stores. The G-6 had one 20 mm MG 151/20 cannon with 150 round firing through the propeller hub and two 7.9 mm MG 17 machine guns in the upper cowling with 300 rounds per gun, plus two 20 mm MG 151 cannon mounted underwing with 120 rounds per gun.

LONG-RANGE WEAPONS

As the defensive fire power of USAAF bombers increased, the Luftwaffe looked at ways of lengthening the effective engagement range. To achieve this the Bf 109G-6/R2 carried two Army *rockets* used in the 21 cm *Nebelwerfer* 42, a towed five-barrel multiple rocket launcher. The 109 pilots would approach the formations of USAAF bombers from the rear and engage from 850 metres. Since the rocket warheads contained more than 10 kg of TNT their impact on a bomber was devastating. The drawback was that the underwing launching tubes, nicknamed *Ofenrohr* or 'stove pipes' by the pilots, were incredibly draggy. This slowed them down and made them vulnerable to escorting

Thunderbolts and Mustangs.

As the German army was forced onto the defensive, fighter pilots were increasingly required to fly ground attack missions. The 109 had been used as a fighter bomber as far back as the Battle of Britain – the Bf l09E-l/B was equipped with a Revi gunsight as a bombsight, and was fitted with racks for four 55 kg bombs or one 250 kg bomb.

However, the Bf l09G-14 was optimised for this role. It was armed with one 20 mm MG 151 and two 13 mm MG 131s. Two additional MG 151s could be fitted under the outer wing panels and a 250 kg bomb carried under the fuselage. Some aircraft were fitted with the 'Galland hood' an improved cockpit canopy which gave the pilot better visibility to the sides and rear. A developed

Left: From the G-6 onwards, Bf 109s began to sport bulges on the fuselage and wing. These covered the breeches of larger and more powerful guns.

> "Our Messerschmitts were terrible. Designed to land on grass we were using them off concrete, and tyres were always blowing. The radios didn't work - you coudn't contact your wingman!"
> **Rudy Auergarten**
> **Avia 199 pilot**
> **Israel, 1948**

Advances from Messerschmitt Experimental 109s

The Luftwaffe was continually looking at possible replacements for the 109. Messerschmitt made three serious attempts to produce new designs, the projects running alongside the continuing development and evolution of the basic 109 airframe.

In 1937 the company designed a special aircraft to make an attempt on the world air speed record. Originally called the Me 209, the German propaganda machine publicised it as the Me 109R, even though it had nothing in common with the original fighter. The design was militarised in 1939 and 1940 and again renamed the 209, but it turned out slower than the Bf 109F which was about to enter service!

First flying in 1942, the Me 309 was considered the natural successor to the 109. However, although faster than the older fighter it was less agile, and considered too difficult to fly. The Me 209 II might have been more practical, but by the time the prototype was completed in 1944, resources were being stretched to the limit to meet demand for the Bf 109G, and it never entered production.

Above: Powered by a 2,000 hp DB 627 engine and with extended wings for high-altitude operations, the Me 209H should have been capable of a speed of 740 km/h (460 mph).

Left: Messerschmitt engineers work on the Me 309 prototype. The wide-track tricycle undercarriage made the aircraft tricky to handle on the ground, with a tendency to swerve unexpectedly on the runway.

Above: After the introduction of the Bf 109G, surplus Bf 109Fs were used to research new features. This heavily retouched photograph shows the 23rd prototype after installation of an Me 309-style undercarriage.

version, the G-16, was heavily armoured, but never made it to operational squadrons.

The Bf 109K was the final production model. Similar to late model Gustavs, it had a more powerful engine and incorporated minor structural differences to save strategic resources. It was armed with one 30 mm cannon firing through the propeller hub and two 15 mm MG 151 cannon in the upper cowling. Powered by a Daimler-Benz DB 605 ASCM/DCM twelve-cylinder

inverted-Vee liquid cooled engine it had a maximum sea level speed of 608 km/h, while at 6,000 m with methanol/water boost it could deliver 727 km/h. It could climb to 10,000 m in 6 minutes and 42 seconds. The BF 109K went into action in Operation *Bodenplatte*, the series of Luftwaffe attacks launched against RAF and USAAF bases in Belgium and Holland on New Year's Day 1945.

For its achievements up to 1940 alone, the Bf 109 deserves

to go down in history as one of the world's great fighter aircraft, and if the same level of superiority over all opposition eluded the Bf 109 from the Battle of Britain onwards, this should not tarnish the fighter's reputation. In a constantly changing air war, the Bf 109 proved adaptable enough to accept new powerplants and weapons with a minimum of modification, allowing the family of variants and sub-variants to grow rapidly, with scarcely a

break in production. This versatility was the key to the aircraft's colossal success, and was due to straightforward, sensible design practice.

Variants of this classic warbird accounted for more than 60 per cent of all single-seat fighter production in Germany between 1936 and the end of the war in 1945. By that time as many as 33,000 aircraft had been built – more than any other fighter in history except for the contemporary Soviet Yaks.

The last 109-derived airframes to see combat were the Czech-built Avia S 199s used by 101 Squadron of Israel's Chel Ha'vir. Disliked by its Israeli pilots as much as it had been by the Czechs, the S 199 suffered from an alarming accident rate.

Hitler's Superguns

A 28-cm K5(E) opens fire on England from its position in the Pas de Calais. Although German railway guns could easily bridge the 35-km (21 mile) width of the English Channel, at such long range they could not engage specific targets with any great accuracy.

AFTER THE 1991 Gulf War it emerged that Saddam Hussein's 'supergun' really existed: ballistics expert Gerald Bull had helped the Iraqis assemble a gigantic cannon dug into a hillside. But it was never completed. So the world record for the biggest gun ever fired in action is still held by 'Gustav': Adolf Hitler's favourite gun. It was one of a family of monstrous cannon, intended to shatter concrete forts and bombard far distant targets – two of them fired shells deep into Kent from across the English Channel.

Incredibly, the Krupp 80 cm Kanone (Eisenbahn) was built as a private venture, not to government order. It weighed over a thousand tonnes, needed two parallel railway tracks on which to stand and took 2,000 men up to six weeks to assemble it. Its monstrous barrel was over 30 metres long. Thrust high in the air it was a horribly Freudian manifestation of Nazi superiority.

Invited to the first demonstration firing in 1940, Hitler loved it at once and called it 'Gustav' after the 70-year-old head of the Krupp family. (Gustav Krupp von Bohlen und Halbach was chairman of a group of German industrialists set up in 1933 to fund the Nazi party.)

RAIL GUN DEVELOPMENT

'Gustav' was the last and greatest of the Nazi railway guns, but the German rail gun programme had been under way since the early 1930s. The guns that eventually shelled England were experimental rather than practical weapons. The designers wanted to establish just how far a shell could be fired. In 1918 the notorious 'Paris Gun' had been used to bombard the French capital from German positions 116 km (72 miles) away. In 1938 the German army accepted the K 12 (*Kanone 12 Eisenbahn*) for service: a 210 mm (8.2 inch) gun with a maximum range of 120 km (75 miles).

The German army solved many of the technical difficulties

with the K 12, overcoming many of the problems which had affected the German gunners of 1918. It weighed nearly 300 tonnes, fired a 107.5 kg (237 lb) shell – and cost the army about RM6,000,000 (over £500,000 at 1939 values). That was a lot of money to solve yesterday's problems. Two guns were completed and brought to the Pas de Calais in 1940. While the Luftwaffe began its assault on Britain, the German army joined in, firing right across the English Channel to hit targets in Kent.

LONG-RANGE SHELLING

One shell landed in Rainham, 88 km (55 miles) from France. British experts examined the fragments and concluded that they came from a gun, not a bomb, but it was not until 1945 that the existence of K 12 was known for certain. K 12 used special shells which had ribs to engage the rifling, but the barrels only lasted for 90 rounds, such were the temperatures and pressures involved. The K 12 battery was withdrawn in 1941 and not seen again. However, shells were still exchanged across the straits from time to time. The British used World War I rail guns to fire on the Calais docks, and the German coastal batteries (like the British equipment, mostly old battleship guns) fired back, scoring a hit on at least one occasion: history's largest land-based gun duel!

The fate of K 12 remained a mystery, but in 1944 one thing was much too clear. Nothing the

British or Americans did could protect the beachhead at Anzio from a giant rail gun hidden in the hills. The soldiers dubbed it 'Anzio Annie'. To the Germans it was a K 5 (28 cm *Kanone* 5 *Eisenbahn*) or '*schlanke* Bertha' (slim Bertha), and there were in fact two of them, taking turns to emerge from a railway tunnel on the Rome-Nettuno line.

The K 5 was a brand new design, created by Krupps during the early 1930s and building on their experience from World War I. It was accepted for service by the German army in 1936, and eight were operational by 1940.

Above and below: Technologically, the 28-cm K 5(E) was one of the finest artillery pieces ever built. Unlike most railway guns it was designed from the start for the role. It was also one of the few artillery pieces of this type to see extensive service in WWII, being used from the Atlantic coast via Italy to the Eastern Front.

The Paris Gun

Shooting through the stratosphere

Above: The Paris Gun is test-fired before being deployed to the front in 1918. A German Navy project, the weapon had a range in excess of 100 kilometres but at a very slow rate of fire.

Railway guns were used by both sides during the Great War. Battleship guns were mounted on specially-built railway cars which could be moved between sectors with relative ease and used to bombard key points like headquarters or rail and road junctions far behind enemy lines.

When Hitler came to power, Britain and France still had a number of these weapons in storage, but the German army had none. Its heavy cannon, including the famous 'Paris Gun', were all lost in 1918.

The prodigious range of the 'Paris Gun' had been achieved by lobbing the shell so high it entered the stratosphere. In the thin air at 38,400 metres (126,720 feet), the shells reached their maximum velocity of over 900 metres per second. Slowed by the denser air near ground level, they struck the target at 670 metres per second. But for the shell to reach such altitude required tremendous muzzle velocity: the pressures involved were at the limits of ballistic technology in 1918.

By 1918 of course, aircraft had developed so quickly that the usual targets of the rail guns could be tackled by bombers. Late in the war,

multi-engined aircraft could deliver up to a ton of bombs over greater distances than the largest guns could reach.

But Hitler's generals had other targets in mind when they thought of reviving the railway gun: the concrete fortifications that protected the Czech frontier and the French border from Belgium to Switzerland – the Maginot line.

In 1914 the German advance into Belgium had been opposed by a number of steel and concrete strongpoints, but Krupp's 420 mm super howitzer (known as 'Big Bertha') had made short work of them.

Above: 'Big Bertha' was a Krupp heavy howitzer designed to smash fortifications. Very successful in this role, it inspired the development of even heavier guns in World War II.

Another 20 or so were built over the next couple of years and they remained in action until the end of the war. The last recorded firing took place in 1945 when a gun near Bonn fired on Maastricht.

WORKHORSE ON RAILS

Weighing just over 200 tonnes, the K 5 fired a 255 kg (562 lb) shell to a maximum range of 62 km (39 miles). Several K 5s were deployed to guard the Pas de Calais against Allied invasion. Two formed part of the formidable assembly of heavy artillery sent to the Leningrad front in 1942. Hitler refused to order an assault on the city, preferring to let the Luftwaffe bomb it and the army shell it with the heaviest ordnance in the world. The birthplace of Bolshevism would be removed from the map. K 5s pounded away at the city, which was

protected by a number of concrete and steel fortifications and also used battleship guns to retaliate.

One K 5 was involved in the initial bombardment of Stalingrad, and two were earmarked for transfer to Tunisia in late 1942, although their room for manoeuvre there would have been very limited. They were still in Italy when the Axis forces in North Africa surrendered and it was this pair that caused the Anzio beachhead so much misery. Safe from the heaviest bombardment in their deep railway tunnel, they emerged to lob their shells into the densely-packed Allied lines.

The K 5's barrel had 12 deep grooves. The shells had spines on the sidewalls which fitted in the grooves, helping them to achieve muzzle velocities of 1,128 metres per second (3,700 feet/second). To increase the

Inspired by the Paris Gun of World War I, the 21-cm K 12 (E) had an effective range of more than 100 km. However, accuracy was impossible at such ranges, and it could only be used for harassing fire.

K 5's range, a rocket-assisted shell was developed. This had a rocket motor in the forward part of the projectile with the explosive filling packed around the rocket blast pipe, heavily insulated to avoid it detonating from the heat. A time fuse initiated the rocket motor after 19 seconds' flight, by which time the projectile had reached the highest point in its normal trajectory. At this point, the rocket fired, boosting the projectile still further and increasing its maximum range to 86.5 km (54 miles). The warhead was detonated by an impact fuse inside the shell.

By the end of World War I gunners had learned how to hit a far distant target without the need for ranging shots. If a gun could be positioned accurately enough, it could engage a target correctly marked on a map. In March 1918 a German naval gun put its first round through the roof of a British headquarters far behind the front line. However, the rocket-assisted projectiles proved too inaccurate for 'blind fire' techniques. The best that could be achieved was a rectangle 200 metres wide by 3,400 m long – the shell would fall in that zone, but where within it was a matter of chance.

A second attempt to extend the range of the rail guns began at Germany's secret weapons centre at Peenemunde. In the wind tunnel there an engineer perfected a 'fin-stabilized discarding sabot' projectile – the same technology used today in the guns fitted to main battle tanks.

The Peenemunde *Pfeil Geschoss* (Arrow Shell) combined a slender arrow-shaped shell with a sabot or outer case of wider diameter fitted with four fins. The sabot functioned as a gas check inside the tube which was a smoothbore. The prototype involved a 310 mm (12.2 inch) calibre barrel firing a 120 mm (4.7 inch) calibre shell 1.9 metres (75 inches) long and weighing 136 kg (300 lb). The combination achieved an amazing muzzle velocity of 1,525 metres/second (5,000 feet/second) and sent the shell a record-breaking 151 km (94 miles). The system even got into service: two smoothbore 28-cm K 5s engaged elements of the US 3rd Army around Maastricht early in 1945.

Above: As a precaution against air attack, the K 12 (E) is moved into a railway tunnel somewhere in northern France.

Railway Guns

Ammunition: The K 5's standard ammunition was a 255.5-kg high-explosive shell fired with a muzzle velocity of 1128 m/sec. A rocket-assisted round was introduced which increased range to over 80 km, and a fin-stabilised round designed to be fired from a smooth-bore barrel was also tested at Pennemunde.

28 cm Kanone 5 (E)

Design of the 28-cm Kanone 5 (Eisenbahn) began at Krupp in 1934, with the first equipment being commissioned in 1936. Over 25 guns were manufactured and saw service all over continental Europe. The complete system weighed 218 tonnes, and had a maximum range of around 60 km.

Barrel: The K 5 (E) had a 21.5 metre barrel. Because it was slimmer than previous generation railway guns it was nicknamed *schlanke Bertha* ('slender Bertha') by its crews.

21 cm Kanone 12 (Eisenbahn)

The K 12 weighed over 300 tonnes complete with rail mount. It fired a 107-kg shell out to a theoretical maximum range of 120 km. However, wear and tear on firing was so great that each barrel had a maximum life of only 90 rounds. Two guns were completed, but contributed little to the German war effort.

Elevating mechanism: The K 12 (E)'s elevating mechanism incorporated a hydraulic jack which raised the entire gun about a metre as the barrel was brought into firing position. This was to ensure that the breech did not strike the ground on recoil, but meant that the gun had to be jacked up each time it was fired and back down again to reload.

Barrel: The long, slender 158-calibre barrel of the K 12 (i.e. the barrel was 158 times as long as its width of shell it fired) had to be externally braced to prevent the tube bending under its own weight.

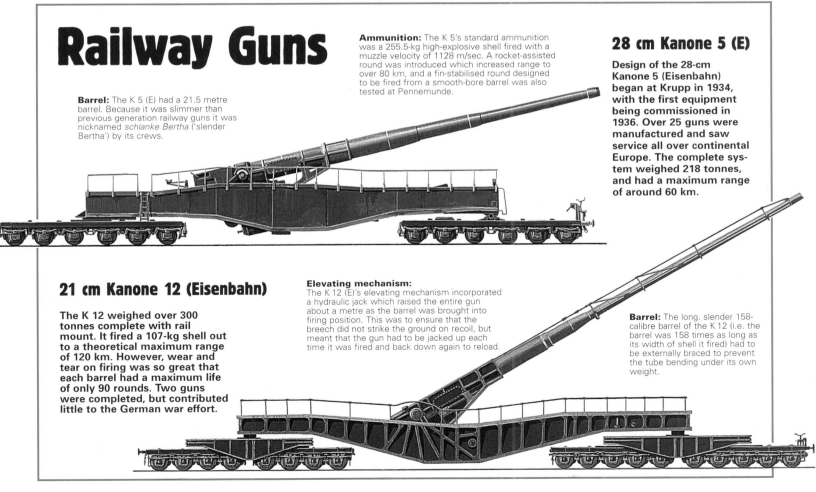

The Biggest Gun Ever Built

King of all Hitler's railway guns, the leviathan christened 'Gustav' was inspired by Hitler, who asked how big a gun would be needed to knock out the Maginot Line forts. Krupp's engineers set to work in 1937, but it took three years before the first barrel was ready to be test fired, and another two before complete weapons could be assembled. By the time it was ready in 1942, the Maginot Line was rusting far behind German lines. But there were other targets. The British fortress at Gibraltar was one, but the Spanish dictator Franco refused to join Hitler in an attack. Leningrad, under bombardment since the end of 1941, was another. Sevastopol, the Russian naval base on the Black Sea was also under siege and the commander of the German 11th army, *Generaloberst* von Manstein was in a hurry. Already supported by a formidable concentration of bombers, Manstein had amassed a siege train including the 60-cm self-propelled mortar 'Thor'. And in 25 train-loads, 'Gustav' was shipped to join him.

'Gustav' was assembled with the aid of two 110-ton cranes. It took six weeks to lay the track and put the weapon together. At last, on 5 June, 'Gustav' fired its first shots in anger. The targets were coastal batteries that protected the Russian fortress. The fall of shot was reported by a Fieseler Fi-156 Storch spotter plane. Eight rounds later, the fort was silent.

Two types of shell were employed: a 7-ton

Assembling the 80-cm K (E) was a major task. First, more than a kilometre of double track had to be built in a specially-dug railway cutting, with further service tracks on either side. Then two massive gantry cranes were built, which would be used to assemble the gun. The whole process took between three and six weeks to complete.

80-cm Kanone (E)

SPECIFICATION
80-cm Kanone (Eisenbahn)

Calibre: 80-cm (31.5-in)

Length: 42.976 m (141 ft).

Barrel length: 32.48 m (106 ft 6.7 in)

Weight: 1350 tonnes (1329 tons).

Max elevation: 65 degrees.

Ammunition: 4800-kg high-explosive or 7100-kg concrete-piercing high explosive.

Muzzle velocity: 820 m/sec (HE) or 710 m/sec (concrete-piercing)

Max range: 47000 m with 4.8-tonne round; 38000 m with 7-tonne round.

Crew: 1500 men to construct site and 500 to service weapon in action.

Structure: The gun was housed on a fairly standard box-girder structure, except for the fact that its size made it impossible to be housed on a single rail mount. This is why it was designed to be fired from a double rail track.

Bogies: The 80-cm gun was mounted on four huge rail bogies. These ran on parallel tracks in pairs, with each pair locked together to form a double unit.

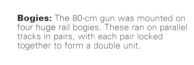

armour-piercing round designed to smash through concrete, and a five-ton high explosive round.

The next day 'Gustav' turned its terminal attention to Fort Molotov. That took seven rounds to destroy, and left time to attack an especially challenging target: the underground (and underwater) magazine dug under Sevastopol and out into Severnaya Bay. Nine rounds were fired, travelling some 25 km before plunging through 30 metres of water and the concrete roof to explode inside. 'Gustav' continued in action all week as von Manstein's siege guns

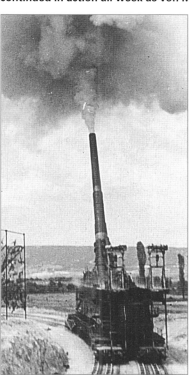

systematically pulverized every Russian position. However, the defenders still held out and had to be killed inside the labyrinth of tunnels that connected the forts. One by one they were blasted out with satchel charges or burned out with flame-throwers. On 1 July the handful of survivors surrendered.

'Gustav' was dismantled and returned to Germany. The siege train was supposed to be re-united in summer 1943 for an all-out attack on Leningrad, but this was intended as the sequel to a successful attack at Kursk. Operation *Zitadelle* failed, and it was the Russians' turn to attack. 'Gustav' does not appear to have been re-assembled. Parts of the 80 cm guns were discovered on trains in 1945, but nothing remains now but a few inert projectiles.

Above: Two powerful ammunition hoists were used on the 80-cm gun, the one on the left lifting the projectile and the other moving the propellant.

Below: A round is rammed into the barrel. It took more than 1,500 men to assemble the gun, and it required a crew of 500 in operation.

Left: The massive artillery piece fires a round at Sevastopol. In its immensely expensive career, the 80-cm gun had fired around 300 rounds, fewer than 50 of which were in combat.

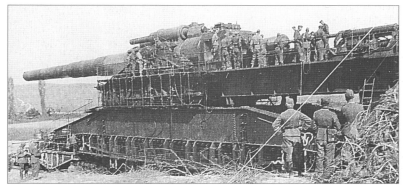

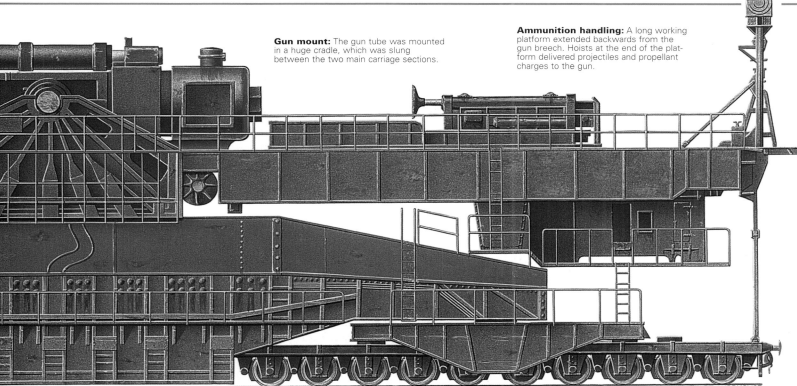

Gun mount: The gun tube was mounted in a huge cradle, which was slung between the two main carriage sections.

Ammunition handling: A long working platform extended backwards from the gun breech. Hoists at the end of the platform delivered projectiles and propellant charges to the gun.

THE ART WORKSHOP

Anti-tank Weapons

JUST AS every German tank was a Tiger for many Allied soldiers, so every anti-tank gun was an 'Eighty Eight'. One of the great artillery weapons of all time, the 8.8-cm anti-aircraft gun was certainly a tank killer of note. But it was not the only such weapon in the Wehrmacht's armoury, nor even the most numerous.

German troops used a wide variety of anti-tank weapons during the war, some captured from the enemy and others of futuristic design.

In 1939 the standard anti-tank gun with which the German Army went to war was the 3.7 cm PaK 35/36. PaK was the standard abbreviation for *PanzerabwehrKanone,* or anti-tank gun. Small, light, and relatively easy to handle, the PaK 35 was far from ideal for dealing with the larger and more powerful armoured vehicles then coming into service. Indeed, its crews ruefully called it the 'door knocker' because of

its poor performance. Attempts to enhance penetration included the use of tungsten shot and a fin-stabilised muzzle-loaded hollow charge grenade, the *Stielgranate* 41.

The PaK 35 had a maximum range with HE ammunition of 4,025 metres, and could penetrate 36 mm of armour at 30° at 500 metres with conventional ammunition or 180 mm at 300 metres with the Stielgranate 41. Over 20,000 guns were built during the war.

Aware of the deficiencies of

the PaK 35/36 the German Army demanded a larger calibre weapon. Developed from 1938, the 5 cm PaK 38 entered service late in 1940. The PaK 38 had a maximum range of 2,652 metres with HE ammunition. With tungsten shot it could pierce 55 mm of armour at 1,000 metres.

The appearance of heavily armoured Soviet T-34 and KV-1 tanks gave new urgency to anti-tank gun design, and two new 7.5 cm guns were developed, the PaK 40 being manufactured by Rheinmetall-Borsig and the PaK

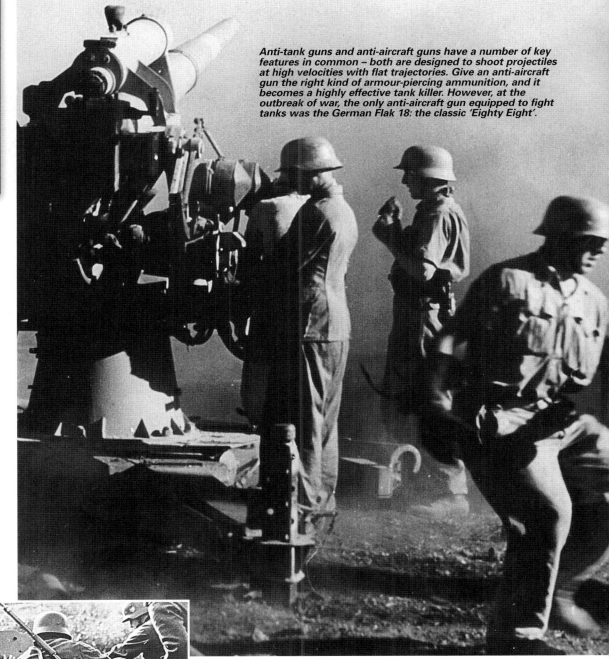

Anti-tank guns and anti-aircraft guns have a number of key features in common – both are designed to shoot projectiles at high velocities with flat trajectories. Give an anti-aircraft gun the right kind of armour-piercing ammunition, and it becomes a highly effective tank killer. However, at the outbreak of war, the only anti-aircraft gun equipped to fight tanks was the German Flak 18: the classic 'Eighty Eight'.

41 produced by Krupp entered service. Both were fairly powerful, though the PaK 40 was effectively a scaled up version of the PaK 38, and the more advanced PaK 41 was a superior weapon. The Krupp design was one of the first 'cone' or 'squeeze bore' weapons to enter service. The internal bore of the barrel tapered slightly from breech to muzzle. The pressure behind the *Pzgr Patr 41 (HK)* tungsten shot increased as it travelled down the barrel, and it emerged with a muzzle velocity of 1,125 m/s.

The shell consisted of a light ballistic cap, behind which was a tungsten carbide shot. The shot was enclosed in an outer case

The standard German anti-tank gun at the outbreak of war was the 3.7-cm Pak 35. Designed in the 1920s, it was a light and handy weapon, though in 1940 its crews found that it could not deal with the thick armour of British and French infantry tanks.

with flanges at the centre and base. The flanges were compressed as the shell passed along the barrel.

The penetrative power of the advanced new weapon was remarkable; the PaK 41 could punch through 145 mm of armour at a range of 1,000 metres. Fortunately for the Allies there was a shortage of tungsten in Germany. Another problem was barrel wear: the high pressures meant that the gun tube

had to be replaced every 500 rounds. Eventually only 150 PaK 41s were built.

The Germans experimented with two more tapered bore guns during the war. The little sPz B 41 which entered service in 1942 was regarded by the German Army as a heavy anti-tank rifle rather than a gun. It fired a 2.8 cm shot through a barrel which tapered from 28 mm at the breech to 20 mm at the muzzle which produced an awesome

57

The fearsome 'Eighty-Eight'

SENT TO protect German forces fighting in Spain, early 'Eighty Eights' were pressed into service in the ground role. The Flak 18 proved devastatingly effective against the light armoured vehicles of the period. As a result, armour-piercing ammunition became a standard item in the inventory of all German Flak batteries.

Right: Although dedicated anti-tank versions existed, the Flak version was used against tanks up to the end of the War.

This was to prove useful in the early years of World War II, since the 8.8-cm anti-air-craft gun was the only weapon that could easily stop heavily armoured tanks like the British Matilda, the French Char B and and the Soviet KV-1. The Flak 18 was followed into service by the improved Flak 36, 37 and 41, the latter largely a new design.

Useful though the anti-aircraft guns were, they were far from per-fect in the anti-tank role since they were bulky, were difficult to cam-ouflage, and were very slow to get into action. The Eighty Eight could be fired from its wheeled transport carriage in an emergency, but for maximum accuracy it had to be lowered onto a firing platform, which was a time-consuming process.

The first purely anti-tank version entered service late in 1943. The PaK 43/41 used the barrel and breech of the FlaK 41, much modified for anti-tank work, and fired an entirely new range of ammunition.

These anti-tank 'Eighty-Eights' were mounted on the carriage of a 10.5 cm light field howitzer with the wheels from a 15 cm medium/heavy howitzer. At nearly five tonnes it was a brute to handle – its crews called it the *Scheunentor* or 'Barn door' – but it had a much lower profile than the Flak versions. It kept all of the power of the earlier guns. It was used on both the Eastern and Western fronts.

The 8.8 cm PaK 43 which entered service at about the same time was less mobile than the PaK 43/41, being mounted on a modified version of the Flak carriage, and it still needed to be dismounted from its wheels for maximum accuracy. However, once this had been done the gun presented a very low profile – when dug in it was only 1.5 metres high. In combat it proved to be one of the best anti-armour weapons of the war, capable of destroying any Allied tank at ranges of at least 2 kilometres.

Above: First used against tanks during the Spanish Civil War, the 8.8-cm Flak gun was one of the weapons most feared by British and American troops in North Africa and Italy.

muzzle velocity of 1,402 m/s and a maximum range of 1,000 metres . The airborne version, the sPzB 41 *le Feldlafette* 41, weighed only 118 kg in action, but along with the standard version it could penetrate 50 mm of armour at 30° at 500 metres.

The 4.2 cm PaK 41 looked at first glance like the PaK 35/36 with a longer barrel. The bore in fact tapered from 4.2 cm down to 2.8 cm. It had a maximum range of 1,000 metres and could penetrate 70 mm of armour at 30° at 500 metres and 50 mm at 1,000 metres. It was not widely used, but is known to have been issued to some parachute divisions in 1942-43.

In 1944 Rheinmetall developed the 8 cm PaW 600, a muzzle loaded weapon which fired a fin-stabilised 2.7 kg hollow-charge projectile. This was a very advanced concept for the time, but though it could penetrate 140 mm of armour at 30° at 750 metres, it could not engage an enemy much beyond that range.

Given its impact on the battlefield, the family of 8.8-cm guns deserves pride of place in any study of German anti-tank weapons. Known as the 'Eighty Eight' to its opponents and the *Acht-Acht* to its crews, the original 8.8 cm Flak 18 was an anti-aircraft gun which had been designed in 1931 in Sweden. A team of engineers from Krupp worked secretly with Bofors to get around the provisions of the Treaty of Versailles.

FAMILY OF KILLERS

The 'Eighty-Eight' served as the basis for a whole series of tank guns and anti-tank guns as well as in its original role as an anti-aircraft weapon.

However, as the war progressed even these superb weapons were being faced with challenging new targets. Powerful Soviet tanks like the Josef Stalin (IS) 1 and 2 had larger, hard hitting guns and much thicker armour than the T-34. A bigger gun was needed to counter them and in 1943 Krupp and Rheinmetall began work on a dual-purpose anti-tank/field gun of 12.8 cm calibre.

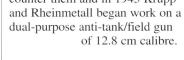

The PaK 44 saw only limited service before the war ended. Fifty one examples were produced, mounted on an improvised carriage taken from a French 155-mm gun. Firing Pzgr 43 shot the PaK 44 had a muzzle velocity of 1,000 m/s and could penetrate 230 mm of armour angled at 30° at a range of 1,000 metres.

Driven by desperate need, by the end of the war German

engineers were pushing the boundaries of artillery design. They developed automatic loaders for 7.5 cm and 8.8 cm guns, and experimented with infrared sights to allow them to be used at night. Ammunition developments included the use of

SPECIFICATION
Flak 18/41
Early versions had an MV
(muzzle velocity) of 795 m/s
(metres a second) with armour
piercing (AP) ammunition, and
a maximum horizontal range
of 14,813 metres. The Flak 41
pushed the muzzle velocity up
to 1,000 m/s and could reach
out to 19,730 metres.

Left: The key to the success of the Eighty-Eight was the very high velocity of its shells. It could damage most Allied tanks even when firing high explosive rounds, and with armour-piercing shot it was lethal. Curiously, the Germans were the only nation which used heavy dual-purpose weapons: most Allied armies had comparable anti-aircraft guns, but these were never used to engage ground targets.

Apart from an added muzzle brake, The barrel of the PaK 43 was the same as the Flak gun from which it was derived, but it was fitted with a much simplified breech mechanism.

SPECIFICATION
PaK 43
Firing Pzgr 40/43 tungsten AP shot the PaK 43 had an increased muzzle velocity of 1,130 m/s, allowing a maximum range with High Explosive (HE) ammunition of 17,500 metres. With AP ammunition it could penetrate 182 mm of armour at 30° at 500 metres and 136 mm at 2,000 metres.

8.8-cm PaK 43/41

Weighing in at around five tonnes, the PaK 43/41 was a brute for its crews to handle, well-deserving its nickname of 'Barn Door'. However, once in place, it was an immensely powerful weapon able to dominate a battlefield.

For ease of production, the PaK 43 gun tube was fitted to the carriage of the 10.5-cm leFH 18 light field howitzer, with wheels from the 15-cm sFH 18 medium/heavy howitzer.

Above: Toulon, 1944, and French resistance fighters examine a 7.5-cm PaK 40 they have just captured. The PaK 40 was one of the most effective anti-tank guns of the war, and was used on all fronts after its introduction to service late in 1941.

Right: Ideally, anti-tank guns should have a low tactical profile, making them harder to spot by opposing forces. They worked most effectively from ambush, with large numbers of guns surrounding a killing ground into which the enemy is lured.

steel and plastic for shell cases, to save brass.

Through their campaigns in Europe and Russia the German Army had captured vast numbers of guns and vehicles and these were pressed into use as the war swung against them. Among this booty were Soviet M 1936 or M 1939 76.2 mm field guns, nick named 'Ratsch Boom' by the Germans for their distinctive sound when they fired.

SKODA GUNS

The Germans also used the Czech manufactured 47 mm Skoda anti-tank gun which they had acquired with the annexation of 1939. It was designated the 4.7 cm PaK 36 (t). It weighed 400 kg in action and fired 1.45 kg AP shot at an muzzle velocity of 900 m/s and could penetrate 51 mm of armour at 500 metres.

Another piece which was 'acquired' from Austria and captured from the Poles and Dutch was the Austrian 47 mm Bohler AT gun. In German service it was known as the 4.7 cm PaK (Bohler) and was issued to mountain divisions.

INFANTRY WEAPONS

German infantry entered the war with two 7.92 mm anti-tank rifles, the PzB 38 and PzB 39, however along with the 20 mm PzB 41 they were not effective against the thicker armour of modern tanks. There was even a small shaped charge projectile which could be fired from the Walther 27 mm flare pistol, though it was described as "very much a last ditch, inaccurate and ineffective weapon".

In 1942 however they received the Panzerfaust or 'armoured fist'

This one shot, hollow charge rocket propelled anti-tank weapon was designed by Dr Heinrich Langweiller at Hugo Schneider AG. Langweiller improved the design, which initially had an effective range of only 30 metres. By the end of the war, the Panzerfaust 100 could hit tanks at 100 metres. The shaped charge warhead of the Panzerfaust 30 could penetrate 140 mm of armour angled at 30°. Later versions, with 15-cm diameter warheads, could penetrate 200 mm at a range of

80 metres. For many Soviet and Allied tank crews the greatest fear was the determined Panzerfaust-armed German infantryman lurking in the ruins or vegetation close to a track or road. The Germans recognised this type of cool courage with special tank destruction badges.

PANZERSCHRECK

In 1942 in North Africa the Germans captured American 'bazooka' 60-mm shoulder fired anti-tank rocket weapons. Some efficient retro-engineering

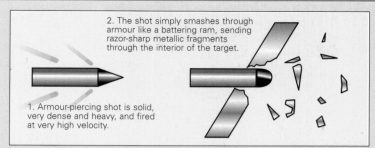

2. The shot simply smashes through armour like a battering ram, sending razor-sharp metallic fragments through the interior of the target.

1. Armour-piercing shot is solid, very dense and heavy, and fired at very high velocity.

Smashing through: In concept, armour-piercing shot is exactly the same as the very first cannon balls: solid lumps of metal using kinetic energy to smash through a target. The faster and denser the projectile, the more effect it has.

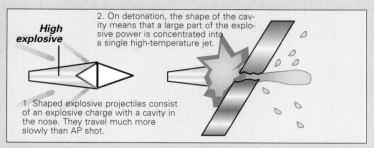

2. On detonation, the shape of the cavity means that a large part of the explosive power is concentrated into a single high-temperature jet.

High explosive

1. Shaped explosive projectiles consist of an explosive charge with a cavity in the nose. They travel much more slowly than AP shot.

Burning through : The shaped-charge effect relies on creating a jet of molten metal which burns through a target's armour into the interior. Penetration increases dramatically with a wider projectile carrying more explosive behind a bigger cavity.

Piercing Metal

THE EFFECTIVENESS of anti-tank guns depends on the velocity at which they can fire projectiles. Before the war, standard armour-piercing shot was a solid chunk of very hard steel which used kinetic energy to punch through armour plate.

The faster shot could be fired, the better, and the heavier the shot the more enemy armour it could penetrate. During World War II, new harder and denser materials began to increase penetrating power. The most effective rounds utilised tungsten.

As the war progressed German industry was increasingly constrained by shortages of wolfram, the ore from which tungsten is extracted. Old-style steel shot was not as dense or as effective, so the military engineers began to look at alternatives.

The most promising was the hollow or shaped charge projectile. This used the Munro principle, in which an explosive covering a hollow metal cone was detonated. The collapsing cone produced a jet of extremely hot gas and molten metal which burned through armour. Unlike more conventional rounds, hollow charge projectiles worked most effectively without spinning, and as a result they were mostly used in slower moving rocket propelled weapons.

The most common shaped-charge weapon in German service was the hand-held Panzerfaust.

produced the 8.8 cm *Raketen Panzerbuchse* 54. This had an effective range of 120 metres firing a fin stabilised rocket. It delivered a 0.66-kg shaped charge warhead which could penetrate 100 mm of armour. The German propaganda machine called the weapon the *Panzerschreck*, the 'armoured nightmare' or 'armoured battle-axe'. The soldiers who used it, as soldiers will, gave it the descriptive and more mundane name of *Ofenrohr* or 'stovepipe'. Though the launching tube was 1.64 metres long, it weighed only 9.18 kg and consequently was ideal for tank hunters.

CLOSE-RANGE

However, even if the weapon was effective and well designed, it needed a gunner or crew with steady nerves to wait until a tank was within effective range before they opened fire.

On 13 February, 1943 a 20-year old Dutchman single-handedly knocked out 13 Soviet tanks with his French-made PaK 97/38 during an attack in the Lake Ilmen area. Gerardus Mooyman, a volunteer with the *Waffen-SS Freiwilligen- Legion Niederland,* became the first non-German to be awarded the coveted Knight's Cross of the Iron Cross.

By his own admission however, Gerardus was a rather unenthusiastic soldier and was sulking in a bunker when the Soviet forces attacked. A German officer attached to the Dutch Legion practically dragged him out by his ear and the angry young Dutchman vented his fury on the advancing Soviet armour.

Right: Light, low to the ground and easily handled, the 5-cm PaK 38 was able to knock out Soviet T-34 tanks when firing tungsten-cored shot. However, it was complex and expensive gun to produce, and succeeding designs were much simplified and made less use of light alloys.

Leibstandarte SS Adolf Hitler

Few military formations have earned a reputation for ruthless efficiency and brutality to compare with that of *Leibstandarte SS Adolf Hitler*.

IN ITS SHORT but violent existence, between March 1933 and May 1945, the *Leibstandarte* grew from a bodyguard of 120 men protecting the Führer to an outsized armoured division more than 20,000 strong, equipped with the most modern weapons that German industry could produce. In battle, it was led by some of the toughest and most controversial figures in German military history – men like *SS-Oberführer* Kurt 'Panzer' Meyer, *SS-Obersturmbannführer* Joachim 'Jochen' Peiper and *SS-Obersturmbannführer* Max Wunsche. Undoubtedly superb leaders, they allied their undoubted skills as soldiers with a ruthless determination and the ability to commit atrocities without flinching.

The man who did most to shape the character of *Leibstandarte* was its first commanding officer, Josef 'Sepp' Dietrich. In German, 'dietrich' is slang for a skeleton key, so to honour their commander the division adopted a shield with a key as its insignia.

The soldiers and officers of the *Leibstandarte* initially wore the distinctive black uniform of the *Allgemeine SS*, complete with *Totenkopf* or Death's Head cap badge. The first armed SS guard unit was the *SS-Stabswache Berlin*, later renamed the *Wachtbataillon Berlin*.

This became the *Leibstandarte SS Adolf Hitler* (SS Bodyguard Regiment Adolf Hitler) in September 1933. Two months later, on the tenth anniversary of the Munich Putsch, its members took an oath of personal allegiance to Adolf Hitler.

In the early days, the main purpose of the *Leibstandarte* was ceremonial – standing like black statues outside the main buildings in Berlin or executing crisp drill movements as honour guards for visiting VIPs. But its capacity for violent action was never far from the surface. In June 1934 Dietrich and his men – using weapons and transport supplied by the Army – were used by the Nazi party in 'the Night of the Long Knives', the bloody purge which eliminated senior *Sturmabteilung* leaders and other political enemies.

ARMED SS

When it was decided to set up a private Nazi army, the *Leibstandarte* provided the core of the new 'armed SS'. In December 1934 it was expanded to regimental size and began to move away from its political bodyguard function to a more conventional military role. It participated in the bloodless occupation of the Rhineland in March 1936, and a motorised battalion under Sepp Dietrich took part in the invasion of Austria in March 1938.

When war broke out in September 1939, the *Leibstandarte* was organised as a motorised infantry regiment. By

Above: The SS was looked on with suspicion by the Army, but as soon as the fighting prowess of units like the Leibstandarte became clear they were welcomed by Wehrmacht commanders.

Right: Jochen Peiper, one of the most celebrated (or infamous) of all Leibstandarte officers.

this time, the armed or Waffen-SS was wearing field grey uniform like the army. However, unlike army units its soldiers were also equipped with a range of well-designed camouflaged smocks and helmet covers – which were later to become complete camouflage uniforms.

The *Leibstandarte* was distinguished from other Waffen-SS formations by cuff titles worn on the left sleeve of uniform jackets. The *Leibstandarte* cuff title consisted of a strip of black ribbon with a woven silver border and facsimile of the signature 'Adolf Hitler'. In day-to-day usage, the full title *Leibstandarte SS Adolf Hitler* was usually contracted to 'LSSAH' or 'LAH'.

On 1 September 1939, LAH

"My Honour is Loyalty"

ALTHOUGH NOTED FOR their fighting spirit, above all else SS men were ideological warriors. Their motto was *Mein Ehre heisst Treue* – 'My Honour is Loyalty'. That loyalty was beyond question, and the prime recipient of their absolute belief was the man to whom they swore a personal oath of allegiance – Adolf Hitler. The Leibstandarte stayed loyal to their Führer to the end, only wavering when he abandoned them in the last days of the war.

Ideology played a major part in SS training. Each man had to attend several lectures every week during which they were indoctrinated into the SS creed. Central to that creed was that the SS was a brotherhood dedicated to creating a new Aryan world, the vanguard of the master race whose destiny it was to rule that world. They were also exposed to Heinrich Himmler's pseudo-Teutonic mythology, but there is some evidence to suggest that few of the fighting SS actually paid more than lip service to the Reichführer's fantasies.

They were trained to be hard – though often that hardness was accompanied by a willingness to commit atrocities. Even so, their belief in the cause meant that Waffen SS units generally fought with suicidal courage and a disdain for death.

Left: The ideal SS warrior was tall and blond, fighting with total conviction for Hitler and the Third Reich. By the end of the war, however, that conviction was diluted as men were conscripted direct into the SS.

had expanded to regimental strength. During the invasion of Poland it was part of General von Reichenau's 10th Army. When the war expanded westwards, LAH linked up with German paratroopers in the Dutch city of Rotterdam. After Holland it was deployed to France and was one of the regiments which drove across northern France to the sea at Boulogne. LAH was expanded to brigade strength in August 1940 and at this time its members were told by their Führer "It will be an honour for you, who bear my name, to lead every German attack".

INTO THE BALKANS

In the spring of 1941 the LAH were transferred from their barracks in Berlin to Sofia the capital of Bulgaria, which was then a German ally. On 6 April 1941 it crossed the border as one of the lead elements in the invasion of southern Yugoslavia. Via Albania, it pushed on into Greece. Moving down the west coast LAH commandeered two caiques (Greek fishing boats) and organised a ferry across the Gulf of Corinth. LAH swung east, linking up with paratroopers of the 2nd *Fallschirmjäger* Regiment who had secured the

Corinth Canal. During the Greek campaign the *Leibstandarte* won a reputation for being hard but fair – a reputation which was to change dramatically on the Eastern Front. Following a victory parade in Athens the unit returned to barracks in Czechoslovakia.

By the opening of Operation Barbarossa in June 1941, LAH was a division in name, but not in strength. Between July and November 1941 it fought non-stop from the Polish border to Kherson near the Black Sea and then along the Sea of Azov to capture Rostov on the Don. However, the Soviet winter counteroffensive pushed LAH out of the city and back over the river Mius, all but destroying the division in the process.

Its performance in the fierce fighting on the Eastern Front won the *Leibstandarte* considerable respect from the army for its combat ability, but the hardness of its men was also reflected in the increasing number of atrocities they committed.

Below: Men of the **Leibstandarte** *move towards battle before the Battle of Kursk. The SS fought ferociously in the bitter war on the Eastern Front, showing no mercy to its Russian foes.*

Hitler's Praetorians

From its creation the SS looked on itself as the standard bearer of National Socialism. The *Leibstandarte* saw itself as an elite within an elite, Hitler's personal Aryan warriors, ready to obey the Führer without question.

Before the war, the SS was an exclusively volunteer force, and its physical entry standards were high (though the educational standards of the average SS man was surprisingly low).

The *Leibstandarte* was especially particular: Sepp Dietrich wanted men not boys, and would not accept anybody younger than 23 years of age. The minimum height was 180-cm (five feet eleven inches) and recruits had to be in perfect health: a single tooth filling was grounds for rejection. The prospective *Leibstandarte* member also had to prove his Aryan heritage.

Training was along regular army lines, though the SS emphasised fitness even more than the Wehrmacht, and sports played a greater part in the SS man's life. Aggression was highly prized, and exercises emphasised speed and ferocity of attack.

In addition to the normal SS training, the *Leibstandarte* also had to master ceremonial drill – so much so that other units gave them the nickname of 'asphalt warriors'.

Above: Leibstandarte *on parade, circa 1933. The officer on the left is Theodor 'Teddy' Wisch, who was one of the founder members of the unit and who was to become Dietrich's successor as commander in 1943. He was seriously wounded during the 1944 battle for Normandy.*

Below: An SS band on parade. The Leibstandarte's ceremonial function led many to discount its fighting ability – but not for long after any shooting started.

Above: Hitler inspects the Leibstandarte's barracks at Lichterfelde. The function of SS men like these was to provide the Führer with a force which would obey his orders without question.

LEIBSTANDARTE LEADER

Left: Sepp Dietrich confers with Field Marshal Gerd von Runstedt in Normandy. The two men could not have been more unalike, and the aristocratic Prussian General Staff officer had little respect for the military abilities of the former street fighter.

Sepp Dietrich was born in Bavaria in 1892. He was an apprentice butcher before serving as a sergeant in the Imperial German army in World War I. He joined the police after the war, at the same time enlisting in the *Oberland Freikorps.* He saw action in the 1921 campaign to repel the Polish invasion of Silesia. Dietrich joined the SA in 1923 – just in time to take part in the Munich putsch, for which he

was dismissed from the police. After drifting from job to job, he became a full member of the Nazi party in 1928. For a time he was Hitler's driver, which earned him the nickname *Chauffeureska* from his patron.

Dietrich joined the newly formed SS, winning election to the Reichstag in 1930 and being promoted *SS-Brigadeführer* in 1931. In March 1933 he was given command of the

SS-Stabswache Berlin. This became the *Leibstandarte* in September 1933 and two months later on the tenth anniversary of the Munich Putsch the LSSAH took an oath of personal allegiance to Adolf Hitler.

Hitler once described Dietrich as being a mixture of cunning, ruthlessness and hardness – a word much used in National Socialist propaganda. He was certainly very tough, and instilled

a unique fighting spirit into the LSSAH. He was popular with the men he commanded because he cared for their welfare. However, he was not as highly regarded by the professional Army officers with whom he served as the LSSAH expanded.

Partly this was because he never lost his NCO manner, but mostly it was because he lacked the intellectual capacity for the ranks to which he was elevated. Dietrich was to end the war as *SS-Oberstgruppenführer und Generaloberst der Waffen-SS* in command of an armoured army.

SS-Obergruppenführer und General der Waffen-SS Paul Hausser, who had served with distinction as an officer in the German Army in World War I, said of Dietrich that he "would make a fair Sergeant Major, a better Sergeant and a first-class Corporal". *Generalfeldmarschal* Gerd von Rundstedt described him as "decent, but stupid". A US Army officer who interrogated him after the war said that Dietrich reminded him of "a rather battered bartender".

Vengeance was a major motive: over three days in April 1942 the *Leibstandarte* killed 4,000 Soviet POWs in retaliation for the murder of six of their own.

The mauled LAH was withdrawn to France in June 1942. There it was partly re-equipped with armour and designated a *Panzergrenadier* or armoured infantry division. In this new role it returned to Russia in January 1943 as part of the XXXVIII Panzer Corps under Field Marshal von Manstein. In February 1943, after the fall of Stalingrad, the LAH played a critical part in the battle for Kharkov. Following the battle – Germany's last major victory on the Eastern Front – Josef Goebbels recorded in his diary that Hitler "was exceptionally

happy about the way the *Leibstandarte* was led by Sepp Dietrich. This man has personally performed real feats of heroism".

Dietrich was promoted to command a corps, and between July 1943 and August 1944 LAH was commanded by *SS-Brigadeführer und Generalmajor der Waffen-SS* Theodor 'Teddy' Wisch. Wisch took over just in time for the ill fated German counteroffensive at Kursk, Operation Citadel.

KURSK

Leibstandarte was part of the southern pincer attempting to pinch off the Kursk salient. It by-passed Byelgorod and reached Teterevino before being forced to withdraw. In the intense fighting the division knocked out about

500 Soviet tanks.

The Soviet forces moved from the defensive at Kursk to a huge rolling summer and winter offensive. The LAH played a significant part in the relief of the Cherkassy pocket, where 50,000 Germans, including men of the Waffen-SS Division *Das Reich*, had been trapped by the Soviet advance. About 35,000 survivors were able to break out and link up with advanced guards of the *Leibstandarte*.

By the beginning of 1944 the division was a shadow of the well-armed, full-strength force that had spearheaded Operation Citadel. It was withdrawn to Western Europe to rest and refit, becoming a fully-fledged Panzer division in the process.

In the summer of 1944 the

1st SS Panzer Division *Leibstandarte* was based near Bruges in Belgium. Following the D-Day landings in Normandy it was ordered to northwest France to form part of the 1st SS Panzer Corps.

NORMANDY MAULING

The LAH suffered badly from Allied fighter and ground attack aircraft, as well as from naval gunfire and continuous action against overwhelming British, Canadian and American forces. By the close of the Battle of Normandy it had been reduced to less than 30 serviceable armoured vehicles. Among the casualties was the seriously wounded Teddy Wisch. From August 1944 to February 1945 command of LAH passed to

SS-Oberführer Wilhelm Mohnke.

The defeat in Normandy did not mean that the fighting days of the LAH were over. Between 16 December and 1 January, 1945 it played a key part in Operation Autumn Fog – the Ardennes Offensive against the US Army. By now the Waffen SS had grown to nearly a million men, enough to provide an entire armoured army for the campaign.

SS PANZER ARMY

The most powerful unit in the Sixth SS Panzer Army. was the 1st SS Panzer Division, which had just re-equipped with massive King Tiger tanks. Spearheading the attack was an LAH *Kampfgruppe* or 'Battle Group' commanded by *SS-Obersturmbannführer* Jochen Peiper. The 5,000 men of *Kampfgruppe* Peiper pushed forward nearly 60 kilometres. It was during this thrust that the *Leibstandarte* was held responsible for the murder of 71 American prisoners of war at the Malmedy cross roads.

Steady Allied pressure halted and finally broke the German attack. The remnants of LAH were withdrawn to Bonn to refit. The Ardennes Offensive had cost the Germans nearly 100,000 dead and the Americans 76,000.

The final battle for the *Leibstandarte* came in January 1945 as the Russians opened their winter offensive into Hungary. It was no longer the elite formation of the early 1940s and included among its reluctant recruits men from factories, the Kriegsmarine and the Luftwaffe. From February 1945 to the end of the war LAH was commanded by *SS-Brigadeführer und Generalmajor der Waffen-SS* Otto Kumm.

LAST BATTLES

After a fruitless attempt to recapture the Hungarian oil fields, the Germans withdrew into Austria but were ordered to hold Vienna. When Hitler heard of the withdrawals he flew into a rage. Remote from the battlefield in his bunker in Berlin, he

ordered that the men of SS Divisions *Leibstandarte Adolf Hitler*, *Das Reich*, *Totenkopf* and *Hohenstaufen* should remove their cuff titles and that all promotions and decorations, authorised on Hitler's birthday on 20 April, were to be cancelled.

Sepp Dietrich's reaction was typical and robust. When the commander of the 6th SS Panzer Army received the signal he remarked, "There's your reward for all you've done these past five years". After considering putting all the honours into a chamber pot and sending them to Hitler, he simply ignored the order.

Following the news of Hitler's death, Dietrich ensured that most of the Waffen-SS divisions in the east were able to break contact with the advancing Russians and surrender to the Americans at Steyr in upper Austria.

But the war was not over for the men of the *Leibstandarte*. They might have considered themselves the elite of the German armed forces, but to the Allies, they were all members of the SS. They faced years of captivity in POW cages after the International Military Tribunal at Nuremberg determined that the SS was an illegal organisation. Many of its leading lights were tried and sentenced as war criminals, though few served their full terms.

Above: Members of Kampfgruppe *Peiper move through the snowy Ardennes as the spearhead of the great German winter offensive of 1944. The murder of 71 helpless American PoWs was to add another stain to the Division's already blotted copybook.*

Below: The demand for more and more troops saw the SS forming a fighting division from the Hitler Youth. The 12th SS Panzer Division Hitlerjugend *was formed around a core of* Leibstandarte *professionals, and the 16 and 17 year olds saw the LSSAH as their parent division.*

Right: The SS soldier of 1944 was a prototype of the modern infantryman, wearing an effective camouflage uniform and carrying the world's first practical assault rifle, the StG 44 or Sturmgewehr.

The Heinkel 111 was the mainstay of the German bomber force for most of the war, even though by 1942 its performance and crew protection had become decidedly second rate. But it was reliable, and was available in large numbers. Known to its crews as the spaten or 'spade', the He 111 was largely restricted to transport missions by the end of 1944.

LUFTWAFFE

The Luftwaffe's rise in the 1930s was meteoric. Its fall from grace and ultimate annihilation during WWII was just as dramatic.

AFTER IMPERIAL Germany's defeat in World War I, the victorious Allies decreed that the Imperial Air Service be disbanded and the aircraft dismantled and destroyed. It had been a formidable force, though as with most other air forces of the time, it had been a part of the army. It was not until the Nazis came to power that it became the Luftwaffe, a separate arm.

The inter-war period saw air power theorists and enthusiasts promote the effectiveness of bombers and fighters in an atmosphere which made aircraft both glamorous and omnipotent. Although the Luftwaffe was not formally established until March 1935, Germany had managed to develop medium-range bombers and transports and train pilots from as early as 1926.

Key to early developments was the state airline Deutsche Luft Hansa (changed in 1934 to Lufthansa). Headed by World War I veteran Erhard Milch, the civil airline operated the versatile Ju 52 as well as sleek Heinkel airliners that could be re-engineered as bombers.

To provide pilots for the new airline the Weimar Government sponsored the German Union of Sport Flying which by this time had 50,000 members. The organisation gave boys and young men the chance to fly gliders and light aircraft and therefore provided an excellent pool of experienced or semi-trained pilots.

Although plans for the new German air force had been made under the Weimar republic, it was the Nazis who eventually threw off the shackles of the Versailles

Treaty. World War I fighter ace Hermann Goering was minister of Aviation in the new regime. At that time second only to Hitler in the Nazi hierarchy, Goering was in a position to further the new air force. A clandestine organisation was set up in 1933, and the Luftwaffe came into the open in 1935 with full German rearmament.

BOMBERS SHELVED

In 1936 the Luftwaffe lost its first Chief of Staff in an air accident. General Walther Wever was an advocate of long-range strategic bombers, which would allow Germany to attack industrial targets deep inside enemy territory. With his death, this critical weapon was neglected as aircraft designers and manufacturers concentrated on medium bombers and dive bombers, suitable for close support operations with the army.

By the time Germany sent military support to Franco in the Spanish Civil War, the Luftwaffe was well established. The war was a valuable proving ground for new aircraft designs, and also gave the pilots in the Kondor Legion the opportunity to test tactics and polish combat flying skills. The Heinkel He 111, Dornier Do 17, Junkers Ju 52, Ju 86 and Ju 87 and the Messerschmitt Bf 109 and Bf 110 were flown in action in Spain by pilots who were rotated through the war zone. The Kondor Legion demonstrated the effectiveness of air power, when in July 1936 shuttles of Ju 52s flew 7,350 Nationalist troops with their artillery and equipment from Morocco to Spain.

The Luftwaffe played little part in the 'Flower Wars' in Austria and the Sudetenland. But

Above: The Focke-Wulf 190 was one of the outstanding fighters of WWII. It made its dramatic debut in the West in July 1941, and by war's end 20,000 had been produced. Pictured here is the ground-attack version serving on the Eastern front in mid-1943.

Left: The Henschel 123 undertook the first ground support mission of WWII on the first day of the Polish invasion. Production had already ceased, but the biplane continued to operate with great success in the East until the last went out of commission in 1944.

Air Fleet Organisation

IN SEPTEMBER 1939 the *Luftwaffe* was organised into four *Luftflotten* (air fleets) but as the war progressed three more were added including *Luftflotte Reich* which was formed for the defence of Germany. Each *Luftflotte* had a strength of between 200 and 1,250 aircraft, grouped in a number of *Fliegerkorps* (flying corps). The next command level down was the *Fliegerdivision* but this was often made directly subordinate to the *Luftflotte*.

Both corps and division contained a number of *Geschwader* that equated roughly to an RAF Group or a USAF Wing. These were designated by type KG – *Kampfgeschwader* (bomber), JG – *Jagdgeschwader* (fighter), NJG – *Nachtjagdgeschwader* (night fighter), StG – *Stukageschwader* (dive bomber), ZG – *Zerstörergeschwader* (destroyer or heavy fighter) and LG – *Lehrgeschwader* (operational training). Later in the war the *Stukageschwader* were largely superseded by *Schlachtgeschwader* (ground attack, abbreviated SG or Sch.G). A *Geschwader* was normally divided into three *Gruppen,* which in turn were composed of three to four *Staffeln* (squadrons) of 9-12 aircraft.

At the outbreak of war the *Luftwaffe* comprised 302 *Staffeln* with 2,370 operational crews and 2,564 combat aircraft.

The structure of the *Luftwaffe* was an obvious asset in *Blitzkrieg* warfare, but posed its own problems. The most damaging being that there was no bomber or fighter command. This meant that aircraft were dispersed at times when strategic considerations demanded their concentration, as in Russia or the defence of the *Reich*.

Luftflotte		
Fliegerkorps		assigned to each Luftflotte according to operational requirements
Geschwader (90-120)		varying number assigned to each Fliegerkorps as required
Gruppe I (40)	Gruppe II (40)	Gruppe III (40)
Staffel (12)	Staffel (12)	Staffel (12)
Schwarm (4)	Schwarm (4)	Schwarm (4)

Above: The Luftwaffe chain of command. Figures should be taken as a guide only: numbers were dependant upon resources and the strategic reasons for deployment. Additionally, bomber staffels were usually formed from three-ship Kette rather than four-ship schwarme.

Right: One of the most important men in the early development of the Luftwaffe was former Lufthansa director and deputy air minister Erhard Milch, who also served as a Luftflotte commander early in the war.

when the shooting started in September 1939 it was a different matter. German aircraft enjoyed considerable success in the first years of the war. Very efficient close support tactics enabled panzer formations to call up Ju 87 Stuka dive bombers as flying artillery. The Stukas could blast aside opposition as well as spreading fear among enemy troops and civilians. German fighters were as good as any in the world, and German aircrews were better trained and tactically superior to their opponents. Though the air campaign against Britain was not a success, the campaigns in France, the Balkans and the initial months of the war in Russia, where 2,700 aircraft were deployed, seemed a vindication of the use of tactical air power. Flying against inexperienced Russian pilots in obsolescent aircraft Luftwaffe pilots racked up huge scores.

In addition to combat and transport aircraft, the Luftwaffe had responsibility for air defence and airborne forces.

In 1939 two-thirds of the Luftwaffe's strength – about 800,000 men – was assigned to the Flak arm, and by 1944 this had risen to 1,250,000. Flak is an abbreviation of *Fliegerabwehrkanonen* or anti-aircraft artillery, and it was used in two main ways. Fixed Flak batteries were used to protect the German homeland and major Luftwaffe bases, while mobile units provided armies in the field with anti-aircraft cover (and on frequent occasions with fire support against ground targets). Heavy weapons used ranged from the massive 12.8-cm Flak 40, through the 10.5-cm Flak 38 to the numerous 8.8-cm Flak 18, 37 and 41. Fast-firing light and medium weapons in 2-cm and 3.7-cm calibre were used to engage low-flying targets and to protect mobile forces.

FLAK ATTACK

At the height of the Reich's defences a complex belt of radar, searchlights and flak batteries ran from the east of Paris to southern Denmark, while day and night fighters – the latter equipped with

Above: An 88-mm flak battery in action in November 1939. The guns were organised into batteries which 'boxed' areas of the sky with rapid, intensive fire. Numerically, the flak arm was the most important in the Luftwaffe, with around a million men serving the weapons.

Close support of the Wehrmacht

IN PRE-WAR Germany aircraft tactics were in an experimental stage as in many other countries. Some flirted with the idea of strategic bombing, but experience in the Spanish Civil War persuaded the Nazis of the value of the Air Force force as a strategic arm of the Army alone. Indeed the man in head of Luftwaffe planning and procurement, Ernst Udet became obsessed by the role of the air force as mobile artillery to the exclusion of all else. He wanted every bomber to have a dive-bombing capacity.

The air force had an essential role in the Blitzkrieg tactics of the opening years of the war.

An initial assault by the Luftwaffe was to be against the enemy air force, including its supporting aircraft and aero engine factories and ground installations, in order to gain air superiority from the outset. This achieved, the Army could then commence its ground attack unharried by enemy aircraft action. Next, vital enemy centres now unprotected by air cover were to be assailed by maximum bombing forces, so hindering counter attacks and facilitating greater ground troop penetration.

These tactics in large part were responsible for the spectacular victories in East and West up until 1941. The Allies learnt from these successes and employed the tactics themselves in the invasion of Normandy and during the great soviet advances from 1943 onwards.

Top: Few fighters have looked more aggressively purposeful than the Fw 190. The heavily armed G-series shown here, was developed as an extended range fighter bomber. It proved extremely successful. The F-series close-support variant was similar but more heavily armoured.

Above: The Wehrmacht's classic instrument of close support – taking the place of field artillery – was the Junkers Ju 87 Stuka dive bomber. Although frighteningly vulnerable to fighters it earned terrifying reputation in Poland, the Balkans and the Eastern Front. It was the tank buster of choice for Hans Rudel with 519 Soviet kills.

Left: The massive Soviet tank threat on the Eastern Front saw the development of dedicated ground-attack aircraft like the Henschel Hs 129. It could be fitted with a 75-mm PaK anti-tank gun. This drastically reduced its already pedestrian performance and agility, although it could hit hard. One shot on target could knock out the largest tank.

LUFTWAFFE GROUND FORCES

THE *FALLSCHIRMJÄGER* were created at Goering's instigation in 1936 and within two years the world's first airborne division, *Fliegerdivision 7*, was operational.

Germany was unique among the combatants in World War II in having its airborne forces under air force command – all other nations assigned the bulk of their parachute and glider troops as part of their armies.

Paratroops saw action in Norway and in the 1940 campaigns in Holland and Belgium. Perhaps their most notable feat was the extraordinary coupe de main operation against the fortress of Eben Emael.

Early airborne operations tended to be on a small scale. They first dropped en masse in the world's pioneering airborne assault, the capture of Crete in May 1941. The successful operation saw the decimation of the paratroopers – 4,000 were killed, 2,000 wounded and 220 aircraft were destroyed. Hitler declared that "the day of the paratrooper is over" and with these words he condemned this elite force to a ground role serving as light infantry. The opportunity was therefore missed to use the paratroopers in operations against Malta or Cyprus.

The Luftwaffe's other elite ground fighting unit was the Hermann Goering Panzer Division. Originally formed as a police unit in 1933, it was transferred to the Luftwaffe as the Hermann Goering Regiment in 1935. It played a small part in the battles in Poland, Norway and France before growing to brigade size on the Eastern front. All but wiped out in Tunisia in 1943, it was reconstituted as the Panzer Division Hermann Goering. Transferring to Poland in 1944, it was reorganised as an armoured corps in October that year.

If the paratroopers and the Hermann Goering division were the elite of the Luftwaffe ground forces, the 21 field divisions raised from surplus Luftwaffe personnel late in the war were at the other end of the quality scale. These reluctant soldiers were ill equipped and poorly led and suffered badly in fighting on the Eastern Front.

Right: The Germans were the pioneers of parachute and glider-borne fighting formations. Their successes in 1940-41 were not lost on the allies, who developed their own paratroop units as a high priority. They wore high-laced rubber soled boots and zippered jump smocks. They were issued from 1942 with the FG 42, an advanced, high-powered assault rifle capable of fully-automatic fire.

The Messerschmitt 321, the Gigant, was the largest glider ever employed on operations. It had a 55-m wingspan and could carry up to 200 troops. Most of the 200 airframes built were converted to Me 323 transport planes with the addition of six engines. A flight of 14 Me 323's was slaughtered by Allied fighters whilst attempting to resupply Tunisia in 1943.

airborne radar – were vectored onto the British and American bomber squadrons.

As the demand for able-bodied men increased during the war, the Luftwaffe relied increasingly on members of the *Hitlerjugend*. Boys aged between 16 and 18 were used to man guns and searchlights. By 1945 children as young as 14 had been pressed into service.

FEMALE EMANCIPATION

The Luftwaffe employed more women than the Army, Navy or Waffen-SS. The other services had some women working as nurses and in communications, but the air force had about 130,000 women in uniform at peak strength. Most women worked in communications, early warning and administration, but in 1943 they took on a combat role. It was then, with the rising demand for fighting men on the Eastern Front, that the Luftwaffe mobilised *Flakwaffenhelferinnen* (anti-aircraft arm assistants). By the end of the war a significant proportion of German AA gun batteries were manned by women.

The Nazis had always been proponents of the principle of 'divide and rule'. Although the *Führerprinzip* called for power to be concentrated in the hands of one senior officer or leader, beneath that rarefied height multiple separate chains of command were the norm, and backbiting, rivalry and distrust were common. The *Reichsmarschall* added to the problems for the Luftwaffe by appointing personal friends from his wartime days. They relished the chance to create a new air force, but were often less effective as staff officers or logisticians.

UDET UNDONE

Goering had two main areas of responsibility. Besides being Commander-in-Chief of the Luftwaffe, he was also Reich aviation minister and through the *Reichsluftfahrtministerium* – RLM or Reich Aviation Ministry – controlled air matters using two staffs. The first was headed by the secretary of state for air, Erhard Milch. In addition to being inspector-general of the Luftwaffe, Milch dealt with all aviation matters other than operations. The second was under Luftwaffe Chief of Staff Hans Jeschonnek who headed the operations, intelligence, quartermaster's organisation, training and signals branches. However, he only had direct access to Goering on operational matters. Jeschonnek, who committed suicide following the failure of the Luftwaffe to supply the surrounded 6th Army at Stalingrad, had numerous administrative burdens. He had no control over personnel, who were appointed directly by Goering, nor did he have control over supply and procurement.

Above: The Jack of all trades – the Junkers Ju 88. No other German aircraft was adapted for as many roles. Final close-support versions were armed with flame throwers and recoilless rocket projectors.

Left: Reich propaganda had Goering's air crews singing lustily at the onset of the Battle of Britain. But in three months his bombers were to be driven from the daylight skies.

Below: Nicknamed 'The Flying Pencil', the Dornier Do 17 was the fastest bomber in the world before the war. However, by 1939 it was obsolete and had been replaced by the more powerful Do 17Z.

Bomben auf Engelland

Lied aus dem Film der Luftwaffe „Feuertaufe" von Hans Bertram
Worte: Wilhelm Stoeppler   Musik: Norbert Schultze

1.

Wir fühlen in Horsten und Höhen des Adlers verwegenes Glück,
Wir steigen zum Tor der Sonne empor, wir lassen die Erde zurück!

Kehrreim:

Kamerad! Kamerad! Alle Mädels müssen warten!
Kamerad! Kamerad! Der Befehl ist da, wir starten!
Kamerad! Kamerad! Die Losung ist bekannt:
Ran an den Feind! Ran an den Feind! Bomben auf Engelland!
:/: Hört ihr die Motoren singen: Ran an den Feind!
Hört ihr's in den Ohren klingen: Ran an den Feind!
Bomben! Bomben! Bomben auf Engelland! :/:

This was the responsibility of Ernst Udet, a daring pilot and former stunt flyer who committed suicide in 1941.

Udet was head of the Luftwaffe's technical office, and exercised a great deal of influence on German aircraft design. At Udet's door must be laid the failure of the German aviation industry to develop jet aircraft until it was too late for them to have more than a local tactical impact. With Udet's death, Milch took over supply and procurement – this did not make the RLM run smoothly because there was considerable animosity between Milch and Jeschonnek.

Like so much in the Third Reich, the Luftwaffe was only put onto an efficient footing when the war had effectively been lost. As the war swung against Germany, Goering withdrew from direct command of operations into a sybaritic world of drugs and high living. In mid-1944 a Luftwaffe High Command was established, Milch's post was abolished and aircraft production was transferred to Albert Speer's armaments ministry, under whose capable hands it soared.

TOO LITTLE TOO LATE

But much of the production was of old designs. The Heinkel He 111, Junkers Ju 52, Ju 87, Junkers Ju 88, Messerschmitt Bf 109 and the Bf 110 had all entered service before the war.

Above: One of the greatest fighters ever built, the Messerschmitt Bf 109 sits in the combat aircraft hall of fame alongside its great opponent the Spitfire. The Bf 109E-4 shown here fought in the Battle of Britain and enjoyed huge success in the North African campaign. Its strengths were its small size, speed and manoeuvrability. Later in the war the dominant version was the 'G' series, constituting the bulk of the 35,000 Bf 109s produced between 1935 and 1945.

Below: The Me 262 could have been a war winner. It represented a quantum leap in aircraft design, though too few were delivered to frontline units to ever challenge the Allied command of the air over Europe. Stunning though its performance was, the 262 suffered from its unreliable axial engines and casualties due to engine failure, fires or break-up were heavy. The 30-mm cannon were also prone to jamming and the landing gear to collapse.

have been radically different. Fortunately for the Allies, Hitler's insistence that the 262 be used as a 'Blitz bomber' meant that it was not until late in 1944 that sufficient fighters were available for air defence operations, and by this time the Allies were closing on Germany from all directions.

By the end of its single decade of existence, Hitler's Luftwaffe advanced from wood and fabric biplanes to operating futuristic Me 262 jet and Me 163 rocket-powered interceptors armed with R4M air-to-air missiles. In 1944 the Luftwaffe deployed the world's first operational 'cruise missile' – the Fieseler Fi 103 Flying Bomb. Universally known as the V-1 this pilotless aircraft had a maximum speed of 645 km/h (400 mph) and range of 240 km (150 miles).

CRASH LANDING

But such technological advances were too little, too late. Five years of war had taken a fearful toll on the experienced pilots who had started the war. Unquestionably the Luftwaffe had many brave aircrew, but by 1945 the odds were stacked brutally against their survival. Training had suffered, Allied pilots and aircraft were more capable and far more numerous, and fuel was non-existent. Above all, a corrupt and inefficient leadership beset by cronyism and poor technical and strategic judgement had betrayed the Luftwaffe. But pilots still took off against the enemy, fighting to the last over the crumbling remnants of the Reich.

Only the Focke-Wulf Fw 190 of the major types had become operational since 1939. Improved engines and equipment had enhanced their performance considerably, but most were being outclassed by newer Allied designs.

It could have been very different. Heinkel had built a working jet-powered aircraft as early as 1938. The twin-engined Heinkel He 280 flew on 2 April 1941, reaching a maximum speed of 820 km/h (510 mph). The superior Me 262 flew in

1943. Powered by two Junkers Jumo 004B turbojets, it had a maximum speed of 868 km/h (539 mph) – more than 150 km/h faster than any Allied fighter. Had it entered service in any numbers, the character of the air war in Europe would

Air Knights of the Reich

THE LUFTWAFFE HAD some 2,500 aces – pilots with five kills or more. In the Western theatre where targets were the hardest to come by the top Allied flyer was accredited with 40 kills, against eight Germans scoring in excess of 100. This is partly explained by the fact that Luftwaffe pilots fought continuously for years, unlike their opponents who were generally withdrawn from combat after 30 or 40 missions.

Walter Nowotny 1920-44

Walter Nowotny became the first fighter pilot to score 250 kills, achieving the feat in 442 missions. In February 1944 he was transferred from the Eastern front to command a pilot training school. He was then given command of the world's first jet fighter unit. On 8 November 1944 he launched his Messerschmitt 262 against an escorted bomber formation. The jets cut out in combat and Nowotny's parachute failed properly to deploy. He was given a state funeral in Vienna.

Heinz Schnaufer 1922-50

With 126 victories, Schnaufer is the world's top-scoring night-fighter ace. Known as the 'Night Ghost', he flew Messerschmitt Bf 110s, and his *Geschwader* accounted for over 700 Allied bombers. His fighter with its 'kills' displayed was put on show in Hyde Park after the war. Schnaufer died in a car accident near Biarritz.

Erich 'Bubi' Hartmann 1922-93

The most successful fighter pilot in history, with 352 victories in 1,425 missions. Remarkably, he amassed the bulk of his victories in the last two years of the war. He was shot down 16 times, bailed out twice but was never wounded. After the war the 'Black Devil of the Ukraine' suffered ten years of harsh treatment as a prisoner in the USSR. On release he rejoined the Luftwaffe, becoming commander of West Germany's first jet fighter wing.

Joachim Marseille 1920-42

The Luftwaffe's most talented ace achieved all but seven of his 158 victories in North Africa. He was awarded the diamonds to his *Ritterkreuz* after shooting down 17 British aircraft in a single day. On 30 September 1942, while returning from a Stuka escort mission, the engine of his Bf 109G-2 caught fire. Marseille, blinded by smoke, nursed the aircraft back over friendly territory. He then jettisoned the canopy, half-rolled his machine and bailed out. Knocked unconscious by the tail-plane, he never deployed his parachute.

Adolf Galland 1911-94

Galland cut his teeth in Spain, flying 280 missions with the Condor Legion. He transferred from ground support work to fighters, and was the top scoring ace in the Battle of Britain with 57 victories. He became General of the Fighter Arm on the death of Werner Mölders in 1941. He had 96 victories at this time and continued to fly fighter missions against orders. He was known for his penchant for good brandy, fine cigars and the women attracted by his fame. After being sacked by Hitler as a scapegoat as Germany failed to defend the airspace over the Reich, he was given command of a jet fighter squadron. Their belated success proved that Galland had been right to advocate them all along.

Werner Mölders 1913-41

Having joined the Luftwaffe in 1935, Mölders went on to become the top scoring ace in the Condor Legion with 14 kills. He was also the first fighter pilot to reach the psychologically significant figure of 100 victories in World War II. An outstanding leader as well as a superb pilot, Mölders was instrumental in developing modern fighter tactics, which gave the Luftwaffe a distinct advantage over the RAF during the Battle of Britain. In 1941 he was the first man to be awarded Diamonds to add to the Oak Leaves and Swords of the Knight's Cross. Appointed Inspector of Fighters in 1941, he was killed as a passenger in a plane crash en route to the funeral of General Ernst Udet.

The light cruiser Nürnberg passes through the Kiel canal. Under the terms of the Treaty of Versailles, Germany was allowed to have six such vessels in service, but by the time this one was laid down in 1934, plans were well in hand for a vastly expanded navy.

CRUISERS & DESTROYERS

The German navy's capital ships drew most of the attention – but it was the cruisers and destroyers which did most of the surface fleet's work.

UNDER THE TERMS of the 1935 Anglo-German Naval Agreement, the British government accepted a massive increase in the German navy and relaxed previous restrictions on German submarine building, imposed after World War I. Two heavy cruisers were announced as part of the programme: the first of a five-strong class that was supposed to conform with the Washington Treaty. This stipulated a maximum displacement of 10000 tonnes and a maximum calibre for the main armament of 203 mm (8 in). In fact, the Kriegsmarine cheated; the first two *Hipper* and *Blücher* displaced 13900 tonnes, enabling them to carry more armour than their British or American equivalents. They were followed by a third unit, *Prinz Eugen* which had an upgraded powerplant, then two more, taking the famous battlecruiser names from World War I, *Seydlitz* and *Lützow*. The last pair were sold, incomplete, to the Soviet Union in 1939 as a sweetener to the Nazi-Soviet pact. They were not completed before the German invasion of 1941.

CONFUSION TO THE FOE

With 'Atlantic bows' and a clinker screen on the funnel top, these heavy cruisers had almost identical profiles to the two Bismarck-class battleships. Indeed, when *Bismarck* and *Prinz Eugen* encountered Hood and *Prince of Wales* in the Denmark Strait, the British mistook the cruiser for the battleship at the beginning of the action.

Blücher had already been lost: carrying hundreds of troops in April 1940 she led a charge up Oslo fjord, but was torpedoed and sunk by a Norwegian coastal defence battery.

Hipper spent much of 1940 at sea, ranging far into the Atlantic to attack Allied convoys and sinking a dozen vessels totalling 66000 gross tonnes. However, the heavy cruisers proved to be fuel-hungry sprinters, not suited to long-distance commerce raiding and *Hipper* spent the next two years in Norway, venturing to sea occasionally to menace the Arctic convoys. She was paid off after the Barents sea debacle on 31 December 1942: superior German surface forces failing to destroy a convoy defended with consummate skill by its small British escort.

ESCAPING THE BRITISH

Prinz Eugen anchored in Brest after the disastrous Bismarck sortie and escaped back to Germany in the 'Channel Dash' with Scharnhorst and Gneisenau. Employed in the Baltic thereafter, she assisted in the evacuation of East Prussia in 1945 and provided naval gunfire support for several beleaguered garrisons as the Soviet army swept along the German coast. Ceded to the USA after the war, she was expended as a target at Bikini Atoll where her radioactive hulk remains to this day.

GERMAN PLANS

Hitler went to war before the German naval construction programme had got into its stride. The Kriegsmarine had only five light cruisers available, not counting the Emden, completed in 1925 and used for training. The three 'K' class of 1929-30 shipped nine 152-mm (6-in) guns, but departed from convention in having two of the three turrets aft (and offset too, to simplify ammunition handling arrangements). As a class, these cruisers suffered from excess

weight, a feature they would share with German destroyer designs of the same period. The fourth unit, *Leipzig*, had a single, trunked funnel in place of the earlier ships' two, which gave the AAA batteries better arcs and saved some topweight. An extra metre in the beam increased her stability. All were designed with commerce raiding in mind and had a diesel for cruising as well as steam turbines. The final ship, *Nürnberg* had a slightly larger hull as the vessels continued to have a stability problem.

The light cruisers played little part in the war after the Norwegian campaign in which *Konigsberg* had the unfortunate distinction of becoming the first warship to be sunk in action by carrier aircraft (FAA Skuas, flying from Scotland). *Karlsruhe* was scuttled after being torpedoed by the British submarine *Truant*. *Leipzig* had the indignity of being wrecked in collision with the cruiser *Prinz Eugen* in October 1944.

INTERWAR DESTROYERS

The first destroyers built by Germany since 1918 were the Maass class, a group of 16 laid down during 1934-35. Their standard displacement of 2200 tonnes dwarfed that of most contemporaries and their armament included five 127-mm (5-in) guns: enough to challenge older cruisers. Weight was saved by the use of welded construction and aluminium was used in the superstructure. However, their high-pressure steam machinery caused endless difficulties. The navy recognised that the Maass class attempted too much on a limited displacement, and the next sub-class of German destroyers, the six 'Von Roeder' types, were three metres longer and half a metre broader, although their armament and machinery were identical.

Such was the pace of German naval construction that it outstripped the capacity of German yards, and some of these destroyers took four years to complete. The Kriegsmarine's

Above: The most numerous type of large German warship were the light escort destroyers or Torpedoboote. *These vessels were used much more intensively than their larger brethren, serving mostly in the cut-throat fighting off the French coast.*

Below: Prinz Eugen *enters Brest after separating from the doomed Bismarck. Prinz Eugen* was one of three 'Hipper' class heavy cruisers to see action. Nominally built to treaty limits of 10000 tonnes, the 'Hippers' actually displaced as much as 19000 tonnes.

Destroyer Escorts

Above: With their single funnel and 105-mm gun at the stern, Type 35/37 Torpedo boats were fairly easy to distinguish from their predecessors and successors. This is one of the first eight boats, launched in 1939.

Below: T23 was the second of the Type 39 boats to enter service. Larger than the Type 37, it was a genuine small destroyer with four 105-mm guns. T23 survived the war, and was taken by the Royal Navy. Passed to the French in 1946, it was decommissioned ten years later.

IN BOTH WORLD WARS, the German navy operated large numbers of 'Torpedo Boats' – in effect small destroyers. Without the need to operate with the fleet, these torpedo boats were smaller and cheaper to build than conventional destroyers, but could carry a respectable gun armament as well as torpedoes and mines.

Torpedo boats were the first new-build vessels permitted to the Weimar Republic after World War I. Displacing up to 1300 tonnes, the first dozen vessels entered service between 1926 and 1929. Based on World War I destroyer designs, they proved successful in service. However, During World War II their versatility meant that they were most often used in the close-range war in the North Sea, the English Channel and the Bay of Biscay, and all 12 were lost.

These ships were followed in the 1930s by 21 numbered ships of the 'Type 35' and 'Type 37' classes. Smaller, with single funnels and a reduced armament, they were not an improvement on their predecessors. However, they were used as escorts, submarine chasers, and offshore minelayers with some degree of success. About half were lost during the war, most being bombed while in harbour.

The 15 vessels of the 'Type 39' class launched between 1941 and 1944 returned to the two-funnel layout and heavier gun armament of the original design. Used primarily as destroyer escorts, they suffered heavily in the bitter fighting in the Bay of Biscay, at least five being sunk in action. Four of the class were destroyed by Soviet mines during operations in the Baltic late in 1944.

22 destroyers were the core of the force that invaded Norway in the face of a far superior Allied surface fleet. However, the boldness of the original operation was not matched once the troops were ashore. Ten German destroyers were sunk during the two battles of Narvik in April 1940: the boldness of the British paying dividends; the vacillation by the German commander (later lost with the *Scharnhorst*) setting a pattern for future surface actions between the Kriegsmarine and Royal Navy.

DISASTER AT NARVIK

The annihilation of the German destroyers in Norway was celebrated as a heroic stand against superior odds. A new 'Narvik flotilla' was formed in late-1940 from the next class of destroyers, laid down in 1937-38. Many of the survivors of the Narvik battle were transferred to the new boats which reverted to the old German practice of using numbers, not names for destroyers and smaller warships.

What became known as the 'Narvik' class packed a terrific punch for a destroyer: four 150-mm (5.9-in) guns with the forward pair in a turret and the

aft pair in single mountings. Production of the turrets was too slow, so some were completed with a single 150-mm gun forward, replaced by the twin mounting when possible. Too big for destroyers and too small for light cruisers, the Z23-34 types were required to have high endurance, high speed and heavy armament. In heavy seas their forward turret proved wet and unreliable: once again the Germans had shoe-horned too much into the design. The next two units, Z35 and Z36 reverted to five 127-mm guns, but Z37-39 had five 150-mm guns. The shells weighed some 45 kg (100 lbs) but still had to be loaded by hand. The forward turrets were disproportionately heavy and the boats yawed badly in heavy seas, a situation worsened in the Arctic by the inevitable icing.

TORPEDO BOATS

The name 'destroyer' derived from 'torpedo boat destroyer', a class of small vessels built in the first decade of the 20th Century to protect battleships from torpedo boats. Over time, they evolved into multi-purpose platforms, carrying both guns

'Möwe'-class torpedo boats form line ahead during pre-war exercises. Based on Imperial German Navy designs, they were classed as destroyers when completed in the late 1920s. However, they were reclassified as torpedo boats in 1934, when the Kriegsmarine's first true fleet destroyers were laid down.

Coastal War

LARGE WARSHIPS and U-boats grabbed most of the Kriegsmarine's headlines during the war, but it was the destroyers and coastal craft which did most of the German navy's close-quarters fighting.

Larger fleet destroyers were used extensively in northern waters. They escorted capital ships and heavy cruisers in forays against the arctic convoy routes, but they also mounted attacks in their own right. This was dangerous, however: at least five ships were sunk in surface actions with British cruisers and destroyers, and another six were destroyed or damaged beyond repair by mines.

Smaller craft lacked the endurance for such missions. Their primary functions were coastal convoy escort, attacking Allied coastal trade, inshore submarine hunting and minelaying. Areas of operation included the Baltic, the North Sea coasts of Denmark, Germany and Holland, the English Channel, the Brittany coast of France and the Bay of Biscay.

These were far and away the most dangerous waters of the European conflict. They were well within the range of land-based air power. The RAF and the Soviet air force accounted for at least 15 boats, some being attacked at sea while others were wrecked in harbour.

Mines were also a threat: at least seven T-boats were lost, including three on a single day in the Baltic in 1944. One was sunk by the Royal Navy submarine *Swordfish,* and four came out on the wrong end of attacks by coastal torpedo boats. Another four were sunk by British cruisers and destroyers, three in one action in the Bay of Biscay on the night of 28 December 1943.

But it was not all one-sided: one of the most effective attacks of the war was carried out on 22 October 1943 by the experienced crews of five 'Elbing'-class torpedo boats.

Escorting a blockade runner off the Brittany coast, the five boats launched 24 torpedoes against the British light cruiser HMS *Charybdis* leading six destroyers. The cruiser and one 'Hunt'-class destroyer were sunk, and the German boats escaped without being hit.

Above left: Speed and stealth were the keys to survival in the coastal war. Early operations by day were dangerous, a danger which increased as Allied maritime air power grew.

Below: A flotilla of Torpedo boats head out into the North Sea. The quadruple 20-mm cannon mount from which the photo is taken indicates that it is relatively late in the war: though surface ships, submarines and mines took their toll of German destroyers, it was the aircraft which proved the biggest threat.

Above: A torpedo is launched from a Kriegsmarine destroyer in northern waters. Many of the larger destroyers were based in Norwegian fjords for much of the war, where they were used to escort capital ships and heavy cruisers in rare forays against Allied arctic convoys taking supplies to Russia.

EVOLUTION OF GERMAN DESTROYERS

THE GERMAN HIGH command never appreciated the potential of its surface fleet, and during the war Kriegsmarines' destroyers were inefficiently deployed.

Recommencing destroyer construction in the early 1930s after a 15-year break, the Germans produced the 'Maass' type. A very conventional ship, it was well armed, of adequate size and could outperform the contemporary British destroyer.

However, like the British destroyers it appeared a little nondescript. The British didn't care, just as long as they had enough hulls to do the job, but the Germans looked for more dash, feeling the need to respond to French practice.

Between the wars the French exerted great influence through the magnificent series of big destroyers they built. The French empire was not as extensive as the British, so they did not need as many vessels, and they could afford to build fewer, larger ships on their allocated total displacement figure.

While the big Frenchmen were extremely fast and heavily armed, they had some stability problems. But they really looked the part, and encouraged both

the Italians and Germans to build in a like image. The resulting Axis designs being large and overgunned were poor seaboats, suffering not only from excessive topweight but unreliable armament and, worse, unreliable machinery.

The latter resulted from a beguiling principle that German designers adopted: using high pressure steam turbines would mean more power from less space.

In practice it resulted in endless technical difficulties. The Americans did not crack some of the problems until the 1960s. The unreliability of their engines forced German designers to develop plans for destroyers with combined steam and diesel propulsion and, finally, diesel propulsion alone. The lack of priority accorded to surface ship production – correctly, for submarines were far more cost-effective – prevented these ships ever getting beyond the prototype stage.

While, later in the war, all Axis destroyers had their AA armament enhanced to a greater or lesser degree, they proved equally poor AA platforms and just as vulnerable as Allied ships to air attack.

SPECIFICATION 'Hipper' class cruisers
Displacement: 13900 tonnes (standard), 18600 tonnes (full load)
Armament: eight x 203-mm (8-in); 12 x 105-mm (4.1-in) dual-purpose; 12 x 37-mm AA; 8 x 533-mm (21-in) torpedo tubes; 2 x aircraft; capacity for 160 mines
Power: 100,000 shaft horse power (shp) steam plant
Maximum speed: 32.5 knots
Dimensions: 210 x 21.8 x 7.9 m
Armour: sides 80 mm, deck 60 mm, turrets 160 mm
Crew: 1,600
Class: *Admiral Hipper, Blücher, Prinz Eugen, Lützow, Seydlitz*

SPECIFICATION 'Köln' class light cruisers
Displacement: 6980 tonnes (standard), 8380 tonnes (full load)
Armament: nine x 152-mm (6-in); 8 x 88-mm, 8 x 37-mm AA; 12 x 533-mm (21-in) torpedo tubes; 2 x aircraft
Power: 66,000 shp steam turbines, 12,400 bhp diesels
Maximum speed: 32 knots
Dimensions: 181 x 16.4 x 6.4 m
Armour: decks 25 mm, sides 50 mm, turrets 60 mm
Crew: 896
Class: *Köln, Karlsruhe, Konigsberg, Leipzig, Nürnberg*

SPECIFICATION 'Type 35' Torpedo boat
Displacement: 844 tonnes (standard), 1088 tonnes (full load)
Armament: one x 105-mm (4.1-in) gun; 8 x 20-mm AA; 6 x 533-mm (21-in) torpedo tubes; 30 mines
Power: 31,000 shp
Maximum speed: 35.5 knots
Dimensions: 84 x 8.6 x 2.9 m
Crew: 119

Similar in size and appearance to torpedo boats, the 'F' class escorts were far less satisfactory. An experimental design to test high-pressure steam boilers, they were poor seaboats and their advanced propulsion systems gave endless trouble. They were primarily used as tenders.

Above: Few of the Kriegsmarine's destroyers made it through the war unscathed. This is one of the war-built destroyers captured at Kiel in 1945. Several were taken over by the French navy, serving into the middle of the 1950s.

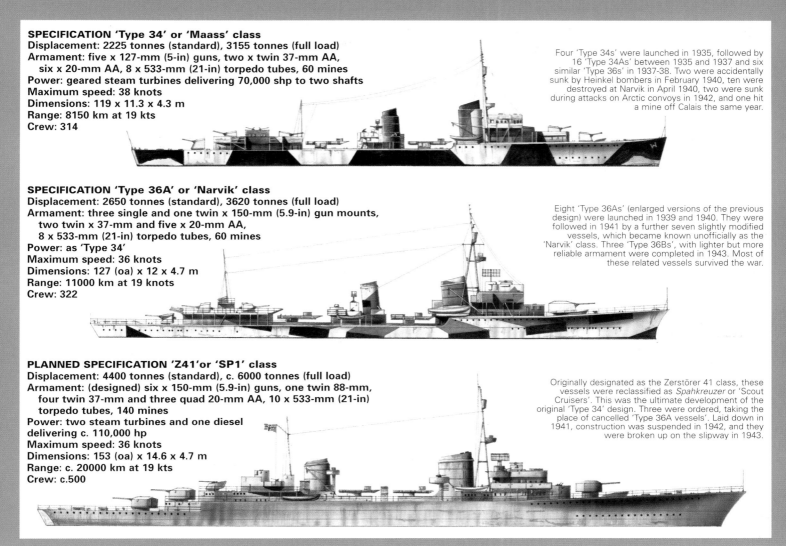

SPECIFICATION 'Type 34' or 'Maass' class
Displacement: 2225 tonnes (standard), 3155 tonnes (full load)
Armament: five x 127-mm (5-in) guns, two x twin 37-mm AA,
  six x 20-mm AA, 8 x 533-mm (21-in) torpedo tubes, 60 mines
Power: geared steam turbines delivering 70,000 shp to two shafts
Maximum speed: 38 knots
Dimensions: 119 x 11.3 x 4.3 m
Range: 8150 km at 19 kts
Crew: 314

Four 'Type 34s' were launched in 1935, followed by 16 'Type 34As' between 1935 and 1937 and six similar 'Type 36s' in 1937-38. Two were accidentally sunk by Heinkel bombers in February 1940, ten were destroyed at Narvik in April 1940, two were sunk during attacks on Arctic convoys in 1942, and one hit a mine off Calais the same year.

SPECIFICATION 'Type 36A' or 'Narvik' class
Displacement: 2650 tonnes (standard), 3620 tonnes (full load)
Armament: three single and one twin x 150-mm (5.9-in) gun mounts,
  two twin x 37-mm and five x 20-mm AA,
  8 x 533-mm (21-in) torpedo tubes, 60 mines
Power: as 'Type 34'
Maximum speed: 36 knots
Dimensions: 127 (oa) x 12 x 4.7 m
Range: 11000 km at 19 knots
Crew: 322

Eight 'Type 36As' (enlarged versions of the previous design) were launched in 1939 and 1940. They were followed in 1941 by a further seven slightly modified vessels, which became known unofficially as the 'Narvik' class. Three 'Type 36Bs', with lighter but more reliable armament were completed in 1943. Most of these related vessels survived the war.

PLANNED SPECIFICATION 'Z41'or 'SP1' class
Displacement: 4400 tonnes (standard), c. 6000 tonnes (full load)
Armament: (designed) six x 150-mm (5.9-in) guns, one twin 88-mm,
  four twin 37-mm and three quad 20-mm AA, 10 x 533-mm (21-in)
  torpedo tubes, 140 mines
Power: two steam turbines and one diesel
delivering c. 110,000 hp
Maximum speed: 36 knots
Dimensions: 153 (oa) x 14.6 x 4.7 m
Range: c. 20000 km at 19 kts
Crew: c.500

Originally designated as the Zerstörer 41 class, these vessels were reclassified as *Spahkreuzer* or 'Scout Cruisers'. This was the ultimate development of the original 'Type 34' design. Three were ordered, taking the place of cancelled 'Type 36A vessels'. Laid down in 1941, construction was suspended in 1942, and they were broken up on the slipway in 1943.

and torpedoes and the Royal Navy had all but abandoned the torpedo-boat type before 1914. The Imperial German Navy persisted with both types during World War I and, unusually, built a new generation of torpedo boats during the late-1930s. Intended for coastal operations, especially in the Baltic, they doubled as minelayers.

GROWING IN SIZE

The first class, T1-8 were of only 844 tonnes standard displacement, but towards the end of the war the T61 type had grown to 1930 tonnes. All were driven by steam turbines to achieve impressive top speeds. Their primary armament remained the torpedo, carried in two triple banks of tubes. A single 105-mm (4.1-in) gun

was carried aft and, as the war progressed, they carried increasing numbers of 20-mm anti-aircraft guns. Some had bowchaser guns retrofitted. They never saw any battleships to torpedo but had busy wars in the Baltic, the Channel and off the French Atlantic coast where they escorted blockade runners in and out of port until 1944.

Most surviving torpedo boats were handed over to the Allies after the war. Britain and the USA handed their share of the spoils to the French, to provide a nucleus for their post-war navy.

Right: Mottled and daubed by camouflage paint, twin 105-mm anti-aircraft guns of a German pocket battleship frame a pair of escorting destroyers as they head out to sea in an attempt to intercept an Allied convoy.

EARLY PANZERS

Panzers race through the French countryside as the Wehrmacht uses its mobility to outflank and cut off its enemies. The lightweight Panzer II (right) and the Czech-built Panzer 38(T) (left) were not as powerful as their opponents, but it was the way that they were used which led the Germany army to victory.

Early German panzers were well constructed and mobile, but not particularly powerful. Yet they managed to spread the terror of Blitzkrieg all over Europe.

VICTORY THROUGH superior technology has been a key theme of warfare in the 20th Century. The latest example was the 1991 Gulf War in which a third-world power tried to take on the US Army at armoured warfare – and came second. However, the early days of Hitler's panzers are a salutary reminder that technology alone is no guarantee of victory. In 1940 the best tanks in the world were built and operated by France and the Soviet Union. French tanks were better armoured than their German opponents and carried heavier guns. The Soviets not only fielded better tanks than the

panzer divisions, they had five times as many of them. Yet the French tank force was crushed in a few weeks; only a few hundred of the Red Army's 20,000 tanks survived the initial German onslaught in 1941.

SECRET TANKS

The Versailles Treaty banned Germany from possessing tanks, but a secret training programme was initiated, ironically in Russia. In the late-1920s the *Reichswehr* sent a succession of officers to train with the Red Army, while German engineers kept current with tank designs worldwide. The first post-1918 German tanks were ordered before Hitler came to power.

Design submissions were invited in 1932 and prototypes were delivered in December 1933. In July 1934 the *Panzerkampfwagen (MG) I Ausführung A* entered production, the Nazi regime seeing no need to conceal their defiance of the hated treaty. Hitler formally abrogated the treaty in March 1935, by which time the *panzerwaffe* had ordered the tanks with which it would begin World War II. One type was destined to soldier on until the bitter end in 1945.

In World War I Germany had been on the receiving end of tank assaults that had torn through its frontline defences. The army high command had dismissed tanks as a novelty without a future, so the

German offensive of 1918 was supported by captured British tanks and only 20 or so A7Vs, the sole German-built tank of World War I. The A7V required 18 crew and was the size and shape of a double-decker bus, with similar standards of cross-country mobility. Most were captured by the British when they toppled over.

The *Reichswehr* had studied the technological and tactical controversies that followed 1918. Turning away from 'land battleships', the first tank it ordered was a small, two-man affair, armed with a pair of machine-guns in a turret. It was no more than a mechanically superior version of the most widely built tank of World War I, the Renault FT-17. The *Reichswehr* intended it for training. Hitler used it to invade Poland and France.

INTERIM ARMOUR

The *Pzkpfw. I* was not a complicated vehicle to manufacture, but its chosen successors, 20-tonne tanks carrying a 37-mm anti-tank gun or short 75-mm infantry support gun, would take several years to perfect and enter series production. The German army therefore ordered an interim vehicle in 1934, under the designation 'industrial tractor 100'. The first three versions were built in small numbers, fewer than a hundred vehicles combined, but the fourth, known as the *Pzkpfw. II Ausf C.*, was destined to become one of the standard battle tanks of the

panzer divisions formed in 1935. At that time the German army was planning for a war against Poland, with a possible Franco-German war in the mid-1940s. It never intended to go into battle with such lightly armed combat vehicles.

The Panzer II had a three-man crew and was armed with a 20-mm cannon with co-axial machine-gun. Whereas the Panzer I's machine-guns were fired from 25-round strips, the Panzer II's was belt-fed, better able to deliver sustained fire. Together with the 2,000 or so *Pzkpw. Is* constructed by 1939, the Panzer II served to train tank crews and fill out the first panzer divisions. The first three panzer units were established in 1935, the fourth and fifth in 1938.

CARDBOARD CUTOUTS

General Heinz Guderian's first exercises with 'armoured' units had involved pedal-driven 'tanks' that the opposing infantrymen liked to stab with a bayonet when the umpire ruled they were over-run. Now it became a more serious business. Although some combat lessons were learned from Spain, where around 100 Panzer Is and a few Panzer IIs served with the Condor Legion, large scale exercises in Germany revealed more about the strengths and weaknesses of the panzer

Above: Germany's first mass-produced tank, the tiny Panzer I, gave the Wehrmacht experience in operating armoured formations. Although intended as a training tank, more than 1,500 were used operationally in Poland, and 500 were still in front line service during the invasion of France.

Below: The Panzer II, introduced in 1935, was a much more effective fighting machine, although it too was pretty much obsolete by the outbreak of war. However that did not stop the Wehrmacht using it in large numbers in all of its campaigns up to the invasion of Russia in 1941.

Secret Experiments

ARMOURED VEHICLES were among the many military products forbidden to Germany by the Treaty of Versailles. The Reichswehr knew they were important – after all, German troops had been on the receiving end of the first British tank attacks. To get round the ban, the first German tank designs were called tractors. For testing the Germans had come to an agreement with the Soviet Union, and in the late 1920s a secret tank facility was set up at Kama, near Kazan, about 800 kilometres east of Moscow. Early light tanks showed some promise, but the medium and heavy tank prototypes, usually built of mild steel rather than armour plate, were more problematical. But they did give German vehicle designers valuable experience.

Even before Hitler came to power, the Reichswehr had settled on a family of standard armoured vehicles which it would require to fight the next war. These included the Panzer I training tank, the Panzer II light training and reconnaissance tank, the Panzer III medium tank, and the Panzer IV support tank. To these should have been added the NbFz Panzer V and VI heavy tanks, but they were found to be unnecessary for the new kind of mobile warfare then being evolved.

Right: Reichswehr soldiers prepare to create a 'tank' for exercises in the late 1920s. Forbidden true armoured vehicles by the treaty of Versailles, the German army learned its first lessons in armoured operations by using dummy tanks strapped on to car bodies.

Below: The Reichswehr ordered the development of new multi-gun medium tanks in 1932. Both Rheinmetall and Krupp submitted designs, designated NbFz V and VI (NbFz standing for Neubaufahrzeug, or newly-built vehicle). Each carried two main guns, a 37-mm and a short 75-mm. In the Krupp turret they were mounted side by side: in the Rheinmetall turret the 37-mm was mounted above the bigger gun. Independent machine-gun turrets completed the armament. They proved costly and impractical, and in tests in 1935 and 1936 showed they offered no advantage over the forthcoming Panzer III and Panzer IV.

Right: The first heavy tanks were ordered in 1925. The Daimler-Benz Grosstractor had a 75-mm gun and three MGs. It was designed by Ferdinand Porsche. Two mild steel prototypes were built and secretly tested.

Left: The five prototype NbFz tanks saw action in Norway. This is one of the Rheinmetall tanks, being fitted with a Krupp turret in the Krupp factory in 1939. Panzer IIIs are being assembled in the background.

Below: Although smaller and lighter than the experimental tanks, the Panzer III was to prove far more useful on the battlefield.

force. By September 1939 the panzer divisions had rehearsed long marches, refined their logistic organisation and developed the vital combined arms tactics that were to serve them so well. Some tank forces – the British were the worst offenders – fostered an exclusivity inimical to co-operation with other arms. The Germans understood that armour could only achieve its full potential by fighting in harmony with infantry, artillery, anti-tank gun batteries and aircraft.

Three design criteria dominate tank design: firepower, mobility and protection. Some designs balance all three elements, others favour one or two at the expense of the third. Although the German army was to end the war with some of the heaviest tanks in service, fuel-guzzling behemoths with monstrous guns, its main battle tanks in 1939 were relatively nimble, respectably armed and reasonably well-armoured.

BATTLE TANK

Both the Panzer III and IV were kept below 24 tonnes, a weight limit imposed by the army's bridging equipment. Each tank battalion was to consist of three companies of Panzer IIIs, five-man tanks armed with a 37-mm anti-tank gun; a fourth company would have Panzer IVs, slightly larger tanks with a short-barrelled 75-mm howitzer. The Panzer IVs were to provide close support for the infantry, their larger calibre main armament firing a high-explosive shell big enough to destroy an enemy strongpoint. The 37-mm gun of the Panzer IIIs could fire an HE round, but it carried very little explosive and lacked the punch of the 75. Its primary round was a solid 'bullet', fired at high velocity to penetrate the armour of enemy tanks. Once inside a target vehicle, it would ricochet around inside with the same effect as the metal blades of a food mixer.

War broke out before the panzer divisions could be fitted out with Panzer IIIs and IVs. For

the invasion of Poland, the army's seven panzer and four light divisions mustered just 98 Panzer IIIs and 211 Panzer IVs between them; 1,445 Panzer Is and 1,223 Panzer IIs provided the overwhelming bulk of the German tank fleet. The Polish army's tank force was minuscule, but Panzer Is and IIs were vulnerable to anti-tank rifles and close-range machine-gun fire could jam their turrets. The real danger came from anti-tank guns or field artillery using direct fire. The 4th Panzer division lost 60

Above: The Panzer IV, armed with a short-barrelled 75-mm gun, was designed to provide fire support for formations of lighter German tanks. In production from the late 1930s, the Panzer IV was able to accept more powerful guns and heavier armour, and remained a potent fighting vehicle right up to the end of the war.

85

Panzers were designed for European conditions, but during World War II proved capable of handling extreme climates. This Panzer III of Rommel's Afrika Korps is making its way through the scorching heat and pervasive sand of the Libyan desert.

Below: A Panzer III in Russia. German tanks were a little too complex for running in sustained sub-zero temperatures, and it took far more effort for the Wehrmacht to keep them operational than it took the Soviets with their crudely-built but simple machinery.

tanks in one day, trying to break into Warsaw. Nearly 700 German tanks were out of action after a campaign that lasted less than a month. Enemy fire accounted for many, but mechanical breakdowns were unavoidable among the fleet of Panzer Is which were approaching the end of their useful mileage.

CZECH TANKS

The 1st and 3rd Light divisions were largely equipped with Czech, not German tanks. The annexation of Czechoslovakia in 1938 produced a major windfall for the *panzerwaffe*: the Skoda armaments factories, former arsenal of the Hapsburg Empire and now the manufacturer of excellent tanks, field guns and armour-plating for British battleships. Both weighing under 10 tonnes, the Czech tanks were superior in some respects to the German designs. The LT35, known as the *Panzerkampfwagen 35(t)* in German service was a three-man vehicle armed with a 37-mm gun; the LT38 was a slightly larger four-man vehicle, similarly armed but better protected. The latter would remain in production until 1942, by which time its day had passed and German tank production had at last gathered pace.

The 6th, 7th and 8th Panzer

divisions were fitted out with Czech tanks for the invasion of France in May 1940. German factories had provided 349 Panzer IIIs and 278 Panzer IVs, but the majority of the tank companies were still operating the earlier vehicles: there were 955 Panzer IIs and 523 Panzer Is. How would they fare against the French fleet, equipped with an excellent medium tank, the Somua and a core of almost invulnerable heavy tanks?

FRENCH OPPONENTS

For a week, the answer seemed to be: badly. The 3rd and 4th Panzer divisions ran into two French mechanised divisions in Belgium on 12-13 May, losing 100 tanks against well-handled Somuas with their powerful 47-mm guns and thick armour. But it did not matter. The majority of the French tank battalions were parcelled out among infantry armies, rather than concentrated in the German manner. Most were in the wrong place. Five German panzer divisions raced down forest tracks to emerge from the 'impassable' Ardennes forest and force their way over the Meuse. The French front collapsed, local counter-attacks were beaten off, and the panzer troops had all-but claimed their biggest scalp to date.

ARMOUR COMPARISONS

Char B1
Right: Derived from World War I tank designs, the 31-tonne Char B was regarded with respect by the Wehrmacht's Panzer troops. Slow and heavily armoured, it carried a 47-mm gun in the turret and a 75-mm gun in the front hull. Even though the latter had little traverse, it was powerful enough to destroy any German tank. But the Char B was a complex beast which was unreliabile in combat. The 400 in service in 1940 were used in penny-packet quantities to support local strongpoints rather than being gathered into a single strike force which could have inflicted serious damage on the advancing Panzer divisions.

Pzkpfw II
Left: Although never considered more than an interim tank type awaiting the arrival of the Panzer III and the Panzer IV, the lightweight Panzer II provided the bulk of German armoured strength in both the Polish and the French campaigns. In a stand up fight it was no match for opposition – it carried a 20mm gun and its armour was less than half as thick as on the heavy British and French tanks – but its speed more than compensated for these shortcomings. With a road speed of more than 50 km/h it could outmanoeuvre the lumbering Allied units with ease.

Pzkpfw III
Right: Intended to equip about 60 percent of the Panzer division planned by pre-war German armoured theorists, the Panzer III medium tank was originally armed with a 37-mm cannon, but was later up-gunned to carry a 50-mm weapon. Not as fast as the Panzer II, it could nevertheless outperform the heavy British infantry tanks, while its heavier gun and armour meant that it could outfight lighter Allied vehicles. Although fewer than 200 had been completed by the outbreak of war, nearly 6,000 Panzer IIIs had been manufactured by the time production of tank variants ceased in 1943.

Infantry Tank Mk I Matilda
Left: Although not much larger than the Panzer III, the Matilda had armour up to 78mm in thickness which was all but invulnerable to German tank and anti-tank guns – with the exception of the 88-mm Flak gun. Designed to support infantry on foot, the Matilda was slow compared to the German tanks. It also carried a less than effective 2-pounder (40-mm) gun. In spite of this, it provided the mainstay of British tank forces in 1940 and 1941

KV-1
Right: The early stages of the German invasion of Russia were a triumph for the Wehrmacht. However, amid the victories there were some ominous signs that the Red Army was far from being as backward as had been thought. In addition to the superb T-34 medium tank, Soviet armoured units were equipped with the powerful Klimenti Voroshilov or KV-1 heavy tank. Introduced to service in 1940 and weighing in at more than 43 tonnes, the KV-1 had a 76.2-mm gun and armour up to 100mm thick. It was more than a match for any German tank, though like the French heavy tanks it was not used in large enough concentrations to have any major effect on the early stages of the battle.

PISTOLS AND SMGs

Above: Two Panzergrenadiers armed with MP40 sub-machine guns take cover in a shell hole on the Russian Front. Although sub-machine guns were not much more accurate than pistols, their ability to deliver easily-controlled automatic fire was very useful at short range.

Even though the handgun was of little use in combat, during World War II, more and more soldiers used pistols as personal weapons.

AN EASY ANSWER to the often-posed question "What use is a pistol in combat?" is – "not much." The pistol has a very limited range. At best – in the hands of a trained marksman – it has little more than nuisance value beyond about 20 metres. In the interests of controllability the pistol also fires slow, low-powered rounds, capable of terrific impact at short ranges, but rarely as lethal as a high-velocity projectile from a rifle. Furthermore, they are not particularly cheap to make.

Given this catalogue of disadvantages, it is surprising that soldiers continue to carry

pistols, yet carry them they do. The simplest reason is that there is often no alternative. For some soldiers it is impractical to carry any form of weapon larger than a pistol. These include tank and vehicle crews, airmen and men carrying heavy equipment such as radio sets or machine-gun mounts. They have no hands free to carry a personal weapon, and very little space about the person or place of operations to stow anything larger than a pistol.

GOOD FOR MORALE

Carrying a pistol is good for morale, for two reasons. Any sort of weapon gives the user considerable authority over those who are not armed, like civilians.

A pistol becomes an important symbol when dealing with an unarmed or demoralised enemy, such as prisoners of war. But carrying a weapon also gives self confidence to the carrier.

Pistols do have a genuine defensive role. Soldiers in rear areas are just as likely to come under attack from partisans or Commando raiders as their front-line counterparts. German personnel working in the occupied territories during World War II were under constant threat of attack; every servicemen had to be armed for virtually his entire waking existence. Pistols were an easy way to do this. Pistols are also status symbols – which is why so many staff officers far from the battle area went about armed, as a reminder that they were still fighting men.

The most famous pistol carried by German forces during World War II, and the one battlefield trophy that every Allied soldier wanted, was the Luger. Known in German Army service as the *pistole 08* from its year of adoption, it was named after designer Georg Luger. Dating back to the beginning of the century, the standard pistol had an eight shot box magazine and fired a 9-mm Parabellum round with a maximum effective range of 70 metres. The toggle-joint mechanism was complex, but made the weapon easier to fire and therefore more accurate.

Tough and fairly reliable, it was only replaced in production for the German army because of cost: it was too demanding in resources, took too long to produce and required too many matched spare parts. Nevertheless, it was not until 1942 that production ceased, and it remained in service to the end of the war.

SERVICE PISTOL

The 9 mm Walther P 38 was designed to replace the P 08. The expansion of the Wehrmacht in the 1930s called for a rugged service pistol that was quick and easy to produce. The P38 was, and still is, an excellent service pistol. It could be stripped easily, and had a number of safety devices, including a positive safety catch that prevented accidental firing even when cocked. A pin indicator, which could be felt in the dark, showed the user if a round was loaded.

Production was undertaken not only in Germany but also in Belgium and Czechoslovakia and the unit cost to the German treasury was reduced to RM 32.

The Walther *Polizei Pistole* (PP) introduced in 1929 was originally produced for police use, but was adopted in large numbers by the military. A smaller version, the PPK (for *kurz*, or short) was introduced for concealed carry by detectives and other plainclothes security forces. PPs were used by uniformed police all through the war, and the PPK was the weapon of choice for Gestapo, Kripo and SD officers. Large numbers of both types were used by Luftwaffe aircrew, and the Walther was also used by senior officers as a personal weapon.

When the Germans overran Belgium in 1940 they captured the long established small arms factory of Fabrique Nationale at Liège. Consequently they obtained the excellent 9 mm *Pistole Automatique Browning modèle à Grande Puissance*, or Browning High Power. First entering service in 1935, its major attraction was the magazine that accommodated 13 rounds in two staggered rows.

At the time, the Waffen SS were supplied by the Army, and were often last to obtain new weapons. However, they were quick to see the utility of the High Power, and adopted it as a standard side arm, giving them a weapon at least as good as and in some ways better than its German equivalents.

Brownings were also used by British and Canadian forces during World War II, but those manufactured under German control can be identified by the markings 'Pist. 640(b)' stamped on the slide.

SUB-MACHINE GUNS

If the pistol was only of limited use as a combat weapon, the same cannot be said for its big brother, the sub-machine gun, known to the Germans as the *maschinen pistole* or MP.

Sub-machine guns evolved during World War I. In the confined, close quarter fighting of the trenches, troops needed a special kind of weapon: a compact gun, capable of automatic fire like a machine-gun, but that would be less of a handful in a trench than a bayonetted rifle. There were a number of designs, but the German Bergmann MP 18 was the first really practical weapon to reach the troops.

Above: Although it was expensive to make, and in spite of the fact that it had been in service since the beginning of the century, the Pistole 08 or Luger was a tough, reliable hand gun used by German troops on all fronts.

Below: The Luger was one of the first modern self-loading pistols. It gained a considerable reputation in its long service life, not least amongst the Allies, for whom it was one of the most keely sought-after battlefield trophies.

German Military Pistols

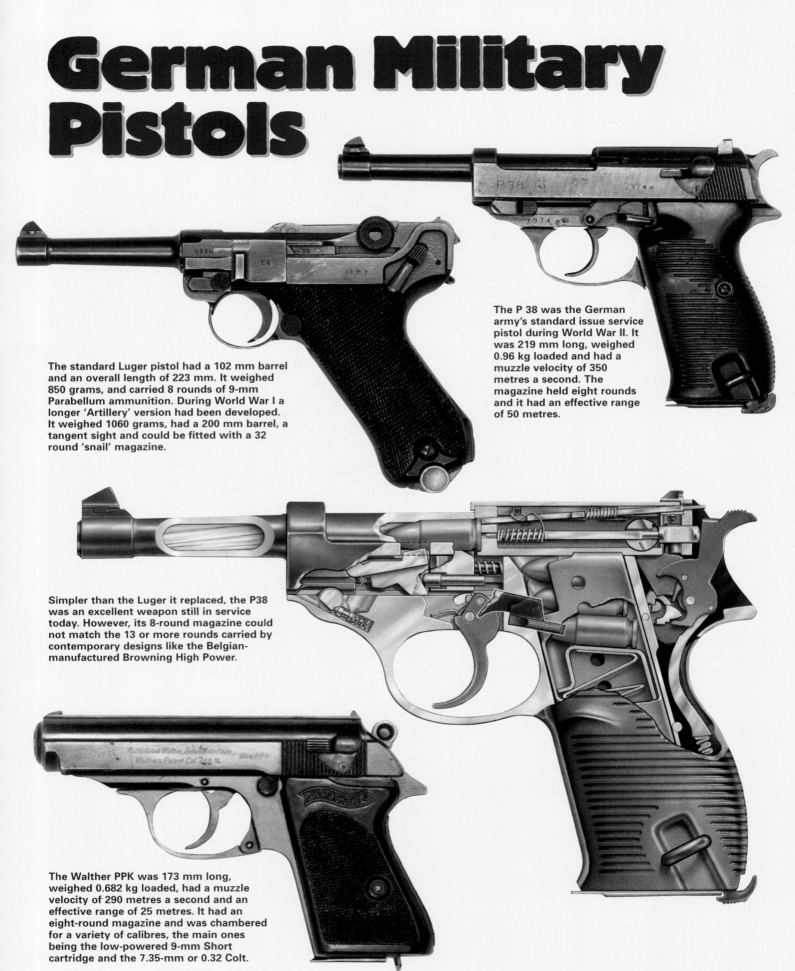

The standard Luger pistol had a 102 mm barrel and an overall length of 223 mm. It weighed 850 grams, and carried 8 rounds of 9-mm Parabellum ammunition. During World War I a longer 'Artillery' version had been developed. It weighed 1060 grams, had a 200 mm barrel, a tangent sight and could be fitted with a 32 round 'snail' magazine.

The P 38 was the German army's standard issue service pistol during World War II. It was 219 mm long, weighed 0.96 kg loaded and had a muzzle velocity of 350 metres a second. The magazine held eight rounds and it had an effective range of 50 metres.

Simpler than the Luger it replaced, the P38 was an excellent weapon still in service today. However, its 8-round magazine could not match the 13 or more rounds carried by contemporary designs like the Belgian-manufactured Browning High Power.

The Walther PPK was 173 mm long, weighed 0.682 kg loaded, had a muzzle velocity of 290 metres a second and an effective range of 25 metres. It had an eight-round magazine and was chambered for a variety of calibres, the main ones being the low-powered 9-mm Short cartridge and the 7.35-mm or 0.32 Colt.

Even today, more than 80 years after the end of that war, the MP18 displays the classic features of the sub-machine gun. It fired a pistol cartridge using a simple 'blowback' mechanism. The low power ammunition meant that it was relatively easy to control even when firing in fully automatic mode – lightweight hand-held weapons are almost impossible to control firing bursts of full-power ammo.

INTER-WAR DESIGN

After the war stocks of the MP18 were taken over by the French Army who substituted a 20 or 32 round box magazine that loaded from the left for the Luger-type snail-drum magazine originally fitted. This feed mechanism was adopted when production resumed in Germany in 1928. It was used by the Waffen-SS and police units.

The 9 mm MP34/35 designed by the Bergmann brothers in Denmark was very similar in appearance to the MP28. In 1934 production started in Germany and the bulk of the stock made by Junker und Ruh AG at Karlsruhe went to the Waffen-SS. Up until the outbreak of war, the sub-machine gun remained a specialist weapon, used primarily by security troops. With the start of hostilities, however, it was found to be uniquely suitable for a number of missions, and demand for such weapons soared. That demand was met by a revolutionary new weapon, the MP 38.

MASS-PRODUCTION

Mechanically very little different from other machine pistols of the period, the MP 38 replaced the fine wooden furniture and intricate machine-tooled parts of earlier weapons with simple metal stampings, die-cast parts and plastic fittings. It was the first sub-machine gun to have a folding metal butt, reducing the weapon's length from 833 mm to 630 mm and made it ideal for paratroops and vehicle crews. It had a lug called a 'resting bar' below the muzzle so that it could

be fired on automatic through weapon ports or over the side of vehicles with no danger of the vibration causing it to slip back inside.

Designed by Berthod Giepel and Heinrich Vollmer of the *Erfurter Werkezeug und Maschinenfabrik (Ermawerke)*, the MP38 is best known as the Schmeisser – though noted gun designer Hugo Schmeisser had nothing to do with its design. The sharp sound of the MP38/40 firing, compared to the slow beat of the US Thompson M1928 'Tommy Gun' earned it the descriptive if inelegant nickname of the 'Burp Gun'.

FLAWED DESIGN

The MP 38 went into production and in the campaign in Poland in 1939 it soon emerged that the weapon had a dangerous fault. When the SMG was cocked the bolt could easily be knocked forward, accidentally causing it to fire. An improvised solution was a leather collar that fitted over the barrel with a strap that held the cocking handle. At the factory a simple safety catch was produced which consisted of a folding latch on the cocking handle which could be engaged in a notch on the receiver when forward thus preventing any bolt movement. Weapons with this modification were designated the MP 38/40.

The drive to cut production costs and speed manufacture led to the MP 40. In the new weapon machining was reduced to a minimum and steel pressings and welds used wherever possible. Sub-contractors manufactured many of the components and weapons were assembled in Germany by Erma, Haenl and Steyr as well as plants in the occupied countries. The manufacturers can be identified by the code stamped on the rear receiver cap; 'ayf' or '27' indicates Erma, 'bbnz' or '660' for Steyr and 'fxo' for Haenel.

It was an acceptable weapon to the German soldier, and it was popular with Allied soldiers who used captured weapons. But it

Above: Anti-Communist French volunteers served with the Wehrmacht on the Eastern Front. Originally part of the army, most of those who survived had been transferred to the Waffen SS by the end of the war.

Below: German troops in Norway are armed with MP28s. Developed from the pioneering MP18, the MP28 had a bayonet mount and long-range sights, but like all sub-machine guns it was essentially a short-range weapon.

German troops were very impressed with the Soviet PPSh-41 sub-machine gun. Although crudely finished, the important parts were tough and well made, and it was very reliable – which is more than could be said for the MP40 under the harsh conditions of the Eastern Front. Captured examples were nicknamed 'Balalaikas'

Below: The sub-machine gun in its element. The last thing a soldier wants when fighting in built-up areas is a rifle: the longer the weapon, the more unwieldy it is in close combat. The light, handy MP40 was ideal for fighting from house to house and room to room.

was far from perfect: fighting in Russia MP 40-armed soldiers found themselves outgunned by Soviets carrying the PPSh41, which had a 71-round drum magazine.

SOVIET WEAPONS

In addition to its increased firepower, the Soviet weapon was simpler and more robust in field conditions. To address the firepower problem, Erma introduced the MP40/1 late in 1943. This consisted of a special housing which took two 30 round magazines fitted side by side. When one was expended the soldier simply slid the loaded magazine into position. While this effectively produced a 60 round weapon, it also increased the weight to 5.4 kg. The MP 40 was also produced with a solid wooden stock. Designated MP41, it was used by paramilitary and police units.

By the end of the war, over one million MP 40s had been manufactured. It is reported that Communist Partisans used an MP40 to kill the Italian fascist leader Benito Mussolini when

they captured him in 1945. After the war it was used by the French and remained in service with the Norwegian Army for AFV crews into the 1980s.

At the close of the war, with Germany under pressure from the East and the West, the need for cheap, easy to manufacture weapons became critical. The answer was the MP 3008. It was a weapon that was very familiar to British troops, since it was a reverse engineered Sten Mk 1 SMG. The major difference was that the magazine housing faced vertically downwards. The MP 3008 weighed 2.95 kg, while the Sten was 3.235 kg. The German 'Sten' had a muzzle velocity of 381 metres a second and a cyclic rate of 500 rounds per minute. Some 10,000 versions of the MP3008 were produced and the model saw action against the advancing Allies.

The Erma EMP44 was an even cruder weapon, fabricated from sheet steel and pipework. An ingenious design, that used the 30 round MP40 magazine, it was not put into mass production.

MASCHINENPISTOLE 40

NO HOLLYWOOD WAR MOVIE would be complete without the MP40, usually called (erroneously) the 'Schmeisser'. One of the first weapons designed to be used from a vehicle, it weighed just over 4 kg, and was 833 mm long with stock extended, reducing to 630 mm with stock folded.

The pistol grip and trigger combination drew on the US Thompson M1928 for inspiration – earlier SMGs retained a carbine style wooden stock.

The MP40 fired 9 mm Parabellum ammunition, developed around the turn of the century for the first self-loading pistols. A good compromise between power and ease of handling, the 9 mm round had a muzzle velocity of 381 metres a second from the MP40, and was fired at a cyclic rate of 500 rounds per minute. If the weapon had a weakness, it was in the 32-round magazine: friction in the single column of rounds could lead to jamming, and the long projection downwards made the weapon difficult to fire from behind cover. The 251 mm barrel meant that the MP40 was reasonably accurate at combat ranges. The gun's front sights were of the hooded post type, with a V-notch flip up bar type rear sights set for 100 and 200 metres.

Noted ace Adolf Galland became General der Jagdflieger in 1942. After flying an early version of the Me 262, he knew Jets were the way forward, but could never persuade Hitler to release enough as fighters. Hitler saw them as bombers.

The jet was the wonder weapon that could potentially have won the war for Hitler. But its importance was not realised until it was too late to make a difference.

Had enough of the thousand or more Me 262s that were built been used as fighters, they would have wreaked havoc among American daylight bombers. And a night fighter version would have been able to catch the RAF's otherwise unstoppable Mosquitos. Fortunately for the Allies, this did not happen.

JETS

GENERAL LIEUTENANT Adolf Galland was notoriously outspoken, even for a fighter 'ace' with nearly 100 kills to his credit by April 1943. It was he who famously asked Hermann Goering for a squadron of Spitfires in a bitter exchange during the Battle of Britain. In his capacity as General der Jagdflieger, he had test-flown the Messerschmitt Me 262 jet fighter and it had impressed him enormously. Faster than any Allied aircraft – even able to catch the hitherto elusive de Havilland Mosquitos – and packing four 30-mm cannon, the Me 262 could transform the war in the air. The Me 262 was rushed into production that summer, Galland insisting that at least a quarter of German fighter output should be Me 262s. It was an impossible demand.

AT A DISADVANTAGE

The Luftwaffe had started the war with aircraft of equal or superior performance to any in the world. The British and Americans had since reaped the benefit of development programmes begun just before hostilities broke out, introducing a range of heavy bombers and new, more powerful fighters like the P-51 and P-47. With the exception of the Focke Wulf Fw 190, most new aircraft produced for the Luftwaffe were failures. The Heinkel He 177 bomber was prone to fires; the Henschel Hs 129 ground-attack aircraft was unreliable; while the Messerschmitt Me 210 fighter-bomber consumed vast quantities of labour and strategic materials (making a fortune for the company) before it was written off as a fiasco.

The German aviation industry was not short of talent, but the technical brilliance of its design teams was negated by leaden bureaucracy, corruption and the personal rivalries of Nazi leaders. Pre-war plans for heavy bombers were scuppered by Ernst Udet, who also opposed the

Above: The Messerschmitt P.1101 was still a prototype at the war's end – hence the painted armament – but it could have been the world's first operational swept-wing fighter. The US Air Force took the project back home where it was developed into the Bell X-5 and flew in June 1951.

Right: The Heinkel He 178 took to the air under its own power on 27 August 1939, the first flight of an air-breathing jet aircraft. Despite the initial scepticism of Milch and Udet several manufacturers began to develop frames for the jet engines which were being designed at Heinkel and Junkers.

development of jet engines. Nevertheless, by 1941 both Heinkel and Messerschmitt test-flew prototype jets within weeks of the British Gloster E.28/39 taking to the air.

The Messerschmitt had a conventional piston engine in its nose because its intended jet engines were incomplete (and the one it did carry failed, nearly causing it to crash on its first flight). This was the cutting edge of 1940s technology and neither the Allies nor the Germans would perfect reliable jet engines before the end of the war. However, with the Reich itself under sustained attack – US bomber fleets by day, and RAF Bomber Command at night – this immature technology represented a desperate hope. Galland was

correct in one sense: several hundred Me 262s could inflict sufficient losses to stop the American daylight bombing campaign. What remained to be seen was whether such a revolutionary aircraft could be put directly into production before the problems with its powerplant were overcome; if German industry could build the aircraft in quantity before the Allies flattened the factories; and whether the Luftwaffe could train enough pilots to fly them.

FACTORY BOMBED

The second question was answered first: on 17 August 1943 the US 8th Air Force bombed Regensburg, destroying

the intended production line. Manufacture was transferred to a new site in Bavaria, adding to the delays already caused by shortages of skilled labour, strategic materials and the remorseless deterioration of the railway network. Between summer 1943 and April 1945 Messerschmitt built some 1,300 Me 262s of which fewer than 1,000 were delivered to the Luftwaffe. Over the same period, combined Allied fighter production exceeded 2,000 aircraft per month.

Engine reliability plagued the Me 262 throughout its brief operational career. The Jumo 004 engine required an overhaul after ten hours and its total life was no more than 25 hours. The exhaust cone sometimes dropped off, causing the engine to flame out and the aircraft to skid sideways into a fatal spin. It tended to snake at high speed, hampering accurate shooting, which was already hard enough thanks to rapid closing speeds and the low velocity of its cannon.

SUPERFAST FIGHTER

Yet in capable hands, provided the engines ran smoothly, the Me 262 was a formidable adversary. Its phenomenal speed advantage could be used to make slashing attacks on bomber formations, hurtling away faster than the escorts could react. A single hit from a 30-mm cannon shell was often enough to destroy a four-engined bomber, or at least cripple it, causing it to fall out of formation where less capable German fighters could finish it off. By spring 1945 the Me 262 would carry packs of R4M unguided air-to-air rockets: firing deadly volleys into the bomber squadrons from beyond the effective range of their defensive machine-guns.

During 1944 the Luftwaffe lost pilots faster than it could replace them. Daily battles over Germany eroded the overall quality of its aircrew until squadrons included a high proportion of green pilots with a hard core of *experten* – veteran 'aces' with scores sometimes running to three figures and a nagging suspicion that their luck was running out.

EXPERTEN OF JV 44

Many early Me 262 fliers were re-trained bomber pilots whose inexperience in fighter tactics often prevented them getting the best out of their machines. Only in the last weeks of the war was a truly expert formation, JV44, created. Led by Galland and filled out with 'aces', it ran up a 5:1 kill ratio in some of the final air battles, but it was too little and too late.

The first Allied jet to enter service, the Gloster Meteor, was retained in England to deal with

Above: Willi Messerschmitt and Alexander Lippisch between them built the fastest aircraft of WW2. The Me 163 Komet's performance was literally explosive – its temperamental rocket engine was dangerous and unpredictable. Although some 300 aircraft were produced, only nine kills were accredited to the Komet. Its high speed was a liability, as target closing speeds were too fast to properly bear the guns on to the bombers. It was an aircraft of last resort.

Below: Not as fast as the Komet but much more practical, the Messerschmitt Me 262 was also plagued by engine trouble. The Jumo 004 axial turbojets did not like being accelerated hard, and they had a service life of only 25 hours. Nevertheless, the jet engines gave the 262 a speed advantage of at least 100 mph (150km/h) over the best Allied fighters, and it was considerably more advanced than the first Allied jets, the Gloster Meteor and the Bell P-59.

the V1 flying bombs and was not deployed to Europe until the last months of the war. The world would have to wait until the Korean War for a jet vs jet dogfight. Allied piston-engined aircraft might not be able to intercept the Me 262 at will, but they enjoyed such crushing numerical advantage that the jets were never able to inflict significant losses on the bomber fleets. The Allies were able to spare ground-attack aircraft to bomb the Me 262 bases – seldom knocking them out, but inflicting further attrition and reducing readiness. They soon discovered that the Me 262 was vulnerable when returning to its base, and many jets were lost trying to recover their own airfields at very low level (dubbed 'knight's cross height' by the pilots).

The Luftwaffe had to deploy squadrons of Fw 190s to protect the jet bases as well as additional flak battalions.

ROCKET FIGHTER

The other main type of Nazi jet could only be intercepted as it landed: it was the fastest aircraft to see action during World War II. The Messerschmitt Me 163 Komet was actually a rocket, capable of nearly 600 mph and able to reach 30,000 ft in less than three minutes! This extraordinary aircraft earned a grim reputation for killing more of its own pilots than the enemy. First flown in 1941, it was a tail-less glider with a rocket motor: the idea was to use the incredible acceleration of the rocket to gain altitude, cut the engine and glide at high speed through an enemy formation – it only had enough fuel for six minutes' flight at full throttle. The process could be repeated several times before gliding home to land. At least, that was the theory. In reality, the Me 163 closed with its target in the twinkling of an eye, faster than most pilots could aim their guns properly. Switching off the motor for high-speed glide attacks demanded great skill and courage: the engine could not be reignited for two minutes,

Above: In the crisis months late in 1944, the German Air Ministry ordered the mass production of a simple, lightweight jet interceptor. The He 162 People's Fighter was to be built at the incredible rate of 135 aircraft per day, and was to be flown by Hitler Youth glider pilots! Vast production plants were set up at Rostock-Marienehe and in the underground slave factory at Nordhausen Mittelwerke.

Right: To save weight, the Arado 234 was launched from a trolley and landed on a skid. Entering service late in 1944, this advanced reconnaissance aircraft and high-speed bomber's most famous mission, an attack on the bridge at Remagen, was in March 1945.

leaving the pilot with few options if Allied fighters closed in. Most Me 163 fliers restricted themselves to a single high-speed pass from astern, before attempting the hardest part of the mission: getting down alive.

VULNERABLE ON LAND

The Me 163 glided beautifully, but was alarmingly vulnerable to roving P-51s as it made its final approach. The aircraft's skid landing gear did little to absorb the impact. Hard landings were commonplace and serious spinal injuries resulted. Worse still, the rocket fuel was corrosive, highly toxic and explosive: many

Me 163s blew up as they landed. Others exploded on take-off; some in fuel accidents, some by bouncing into the ground as the Komet porpoised down the runway, others due to sabotage. Slave labourers not only built key components, they carried out some final assembly work: the Me 163 today preserved in Washington's Air and Space museum was captured in 1945 before anyone tried to fly it. Examination revealed a piece of steel placed where the violent acceleration on take-off would

cause it to rupture the fuel tank, causing it to explode; scratched in the metal (in French) is the legend 'I am not happy in my work'.

The Luftwaffe was the only air force to operate a jet bomber during World War II. Developed in 1940 and submitted to the air ministry in 1941, the single-seat Arado Ar 234 Blitz was powered by twin turbojets. The pilot sat in the nose, a plexiglass affair that ensured he would be 'very close to any accident', as British test pilot Eric Brown observed when

he evaluated the aircraft. The project was seriously delayed by Junkers which promised engines by the end of 1941, but did not deliver any until early 1943, eighteen months after the airframe was completed. Luftwaffe reconnaissance flights over England were few and far between from late-1943, as the preparations for D-Day gathered pace. The advent of the Arado, so fast that no piston-driven fighter could catch it, could have significantly altered the German intelligence picture on the eve of the Allied landings. But, thanks to the protracted delay in flight testing, the first operational Arados were not in action until a month after D-Day. By autumn 1944 German aerial reconnaissance flights over Britain and the Italian front had resumed, but the information was of little more than academic interest. The Arado 234B-2 was a bomber variant, able to carry 1500 kg (3,300 lb) of bombs. Flown by *Kampfgeschwader 76*, they attacked the Remagen bridge in 1945, escorted by Me 262s – the first all-jet air raid in history.

PEOPLE'S FIGHTER

The last jet to enter service with the Luftwaffe did not see action until the last days of the war. After the surrender, Allied soldiers discovered hundreds of them in underground factories, ready for action. In September 1944 Karl-Otto Saur issued a requirement for a lightweight (no more than two tonnes) jet that would be easy to fly and could be mass-produced by largely unskilled labour. Two proposals were received, and although the rival Blohm und Voss design was better on paper, the Heinkel P.1073 Spatz (Sparrow) was ordered. Designated the He 162, it was test-flown, put into production and delivered to frontline squadrons in six months. The first operational aircraft to be fitted with an ejection seat, it combined a modern-looking cockpit with bubble canopy with a single turbojet bolted on top of the fuselage. The wings, fins and nose were made of wood. The first unit to receive the He 162 was I/JG 1, which handed over its Fw 190s on 6 February 1945 and began conversion training. Not that training figured largely in Saur's original concept: by Spring 1945 Nazi leaders were expecting to take Hitler Youth members straight from glider classes into combat with the He 162. In the event, fewer than 100 He 162s entered service.

A STEP TOO FAR

A second, wilder project for a semi-disposable rocket interceptor was only stopped by the advance of Allied ground forces. The Bachem Ba 349 Natter took off vertically and carried 24 unguided air-to-air rockets in its nose. Having fired its salvo into the Allied bomber formations, the pilot would then bail out, the rear section of his aircraft also returning to earth by parachute. Ten Natters were ready at Kirchheim, but were destroyed on the ground when Allied tanks approached the airfield. There were 200 of these bizarre weapons on order, mostly for the SS, but it is highly unlikely that Himmler's men would have managed an aerial *gotterdämmerung* with such a dangerous, even suicidal craft.

Top left: 28 February 1945 – the Bachem Natter is prepared for its first piloted vertical launch. A desperation measure, the Natter was little more than a piloted surface-to-air missile. It was very dangerous: Lothar Siebert, the pilot on the first test, was killed.

Middle left: The Junkers Ju 287 was the most futuristic of WW2 jets. Its forward-swept wings were aerodynamically very efficient, but they required an extremely strong main spar, and available materials were not strong enough to withstand the stresses produced in flight.

Bottom left: The Me 262 had superb handling in flight, but its engines were prone to flame out when throttled forwards or back. Pilots concentrating on landing were easily 'bounced' and most Allied jet kills were scored as the 262s approached the end of their missions.

LATE NAZI JETS: GENIUS OR LUNACY?

Right: The Heinkel 162 suffered from the terminal malaise of 1945 Germany – lack of fuel, poor materials, inexperienced workmen and pilots, and hasty design and development. Attempts to overcome these problems were halted by the Allied advance. But extensive post-war testing revealed the ingenuity of a design which, though not easy to fly, would have proved effective in experienced hands.

Left: The twin-jet tailless Horton Ho IX fighter-bomber. Two prototypes of this design were built before the end of the war. It was a highly advanced design, utilising the experience of the Horton brothers who developed flying-wing gliders. The second model flew at Oranienburg establishing a speed of 497mph. It was however destroyed whilst attempting a landing on one engine. None of the 20 pre-production models on order at the end of the war were completed.

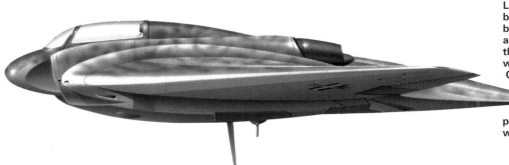

Above: When work on the Heinkel He 178 was discontinued in the Autumn of 1939, effort was concentrated on a more advanced twin-engined design powered by a pair of new Heinkel turbo-jets. After several flights towed behind two Me 110s the Heinkel He 280 – the world's first jet warplane and the world's first twin-jet – made its first powered flight on 2 April 1941. However, the aircraft was plagued with development problems and was abandoned in favour of the Messerschmitt 262.

Below: In March 1944 Hitler sanctioned the use of piloted missiles to attack high-priority targets.The Fiesler Fi 103R was essentially a piloted V-1 flying bomb. It was intended that after launch from a mother plane the pilot would aim his craft at the target and then bale out. Some early test flights were made by Hanna Reitsch. One hundred and seventy five were produced intended for use by the 'Leonidas' Staffel. The plan was abandoned in October 1944.

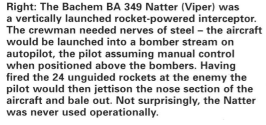

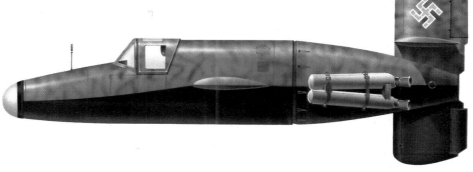

Right: The Bachem BA 349 Natter (Viper) was a vertically launched rocket-powered interceptor. The crewman needed nerves of steel – the aircraft would be launched into a bomber stream on autopilot, the pilot assuming manual control when positioned above the bombers. Having fired the 24 unguided rockets at the enemy the pilot would then jettison the nose section of the aircraft and bale out. Not surprisingly, the Natter was never used operationally.

FALLSCHIRMJÄGER
HUNTERS FROM THE SKIES

The Luftwaffe was unique among the combatants in World War II in having airborne forces under its command. Other nations recruited and trained paratroops and glider pilots as part of the army.

Above: With their efficient uniforms, cut-down helmets (designed to avoid snagging parachute rigging) and automatic weapons, Germany's elite Fallschirmjäger have some claim to being the first truly modern infantrymen.

Right: Adolf Hitler poses with some of the assault team which captured the Belgian fortress of Eben Emael in 1940. Many felt that special operations like this – a small, hand-picked force swooping down out of the night – was where paratroopers would shine, but the Luftwaffe had much grander plans.

MODERN AIRBORNE troops were first proposed by American general Billy Mitchell, who suggested dropping several battalions of infantry during World War I. The idea was forgotten with the 1918 armistice. It was not until 1927 that Italy experimented with the idea and by 1930 Italy had at least two trained parachute battalions.

The Soviets also saw the value of parachute troops, and started experimenting with the idea in 1928. By 1930, techniques were advanced enough to allow a small group of airborne infiltrators to 'capture' a corps headquarters during an exercise. By the mid 1930s, the Red Army was mounting massed parachute drops of 1,500 troopers.

Germany, however, was the most enthusiastic advocate of the paratroop concept, since it seemed tailor-made for the *blitzkrieg* tactics being evolved by the Wehrmacht.

ORIGINS

The *Fallschirmjäger* were created at Goering's instigation in 1936 and within two years a complete division, *Fliegerdivision* 7 commanded by *Generalmajor* Kurt Student, was operational. Student, a World War I fighter ace, had been initially reluctant to get involved with airborne forces, but nevertheless managed to forge a highly effctive unit from the materials he was given.

Parachute training was initially undertaken at Stendal, about 100 kilometres west of Berlin. Training schools were later set up at other locations in Germany, and at Dreux near Paris. A sixteen-day course ended with six training jumps.

In a world in which soldiers were dressed in serge and wore leather soled hobnailed boots, the *Fallschirmjäger* with their special helmets, padded gauntlets, rubber soled jump boots and zippered gabardine smocks were soldiers of the future, troops suitable for the new Germany.

At the beginning of the war 4,500 paratroops were ready for action, backed up by the 12,000 men of the air-transportable 22nd Infantry Division. Although there were plans to use airborne forces in Czechoslovakia and Austria in 1938-39 and for the Polish campaign in 1939, paratroops did not see action until 9 April 1940. They were used in the assault on Denmark and in Norway in the battle for Narvik when they were landed to support mountain troops.

INVASION OF HOLLAND

Their first major operation was the May 1940 campaign in Holland. Paratroopers from *Generalleutnant* Student's 7th Air Division made a series of battalion strength jumps. *Fallschirmjäger* Regiment 1 (FJR 1) seized the two bridges at Moerdijk, and bridges at Dordecht and Waalhaven. This gave German forces a fast route across rivers and flooded land into the core of the Dutch defences.

Spearheaded by a battalion of FJR 2, the troops of the 65th and 47th Infantry Regiments of the 22nd Air Landing Division under *Generalleutnant* Graf Sponeck were tasked with the capture of the Dutch government and the Hague and the airfields at Delft and Ypenburg. The airlanding forces came under sustained anti-aircraft fire and were widely scattered along the coast. However, they enjoyed more success at Rotterdam airport where they were supported by the 3rd Battalion of FJR 1 and backed up by troops diverted from The Hague and Valkenburg.

EBEN EMAEL

At the same time in Belgium, the paratroops launched an extraordinary operation against the fortress of Eben-Emael.

The massive concrete fortification covered key bridges across the Albert Canal at Canne, Vroenhoven and Veldwezelt. At dawn on 10 May, ten gliders carrying 55 assault engineers of the Koch Assault Detachment from FJR 1, commanded by

Above: The Luftwaffe learned from Italian and Soviet experience of the 1920s and 1930s when setting up their own parachute force, but quickly surpassed their mentors. Not the least of their advantages was the possession of a stable and reliable drop platform, the Junkers Ju 52.

Below: German Fallschirmjäger drop onto a glacier in northern Norway. They have been deployed to support mountain troops fighting the British and French at Narvik. Air mobility gave the Germans the first example of what would now be called a rapid deployment force.

Above: The invasion of Crete was the first major airborne assault in history. Over 8,000 men were delivered by parachute and glider in the face of fierce resistance. Over 200 aircraft were shot down: most of the losses were Junkers Ju 52s.

Below: The Fallschirmjäger had performed well in Greece, so their losses in Crete came as a severe shock. Total German losses in the assult were more than 4,000 killed or missing with a further 2,500 wounded. Hitler forbade any further assaults.

Leutnant Rudolf Witzig, landed within the fortress perimeter. Using shaped charges they attacked the armoured casemates housing the 120-mm and 75-mm artillery. For six killed and 20 wounded they held the fortress for 24 hours before being relieved by the 61st Infantry Division.

The glider-borne combat engineers had effectively neutralised the 700 strong Belgian Army garrison and so opened the route for German ground forces to push into France and Belgium. Glider born troops and paratroops also seized the bridges across the Albert Canal.

INVASION OF GREECE

The next major parachute operations came a year later in Greece. On 25 April 1941 the reinforced FJR 2 under *Oberst* Sturm was tasked with the capture of the bridge across the deep Corinth Canal that separated the southern Peloponnese from the rest of Greece. A mixed force of gliders and paratroops captured the bridge before it could be demolished.

The German airborne forces suffered only eight killed but they were to be cheated of their objective when a stray shell or bullet triggered the demolition charges attached to the bridge and dropped it deep into the canal. But this was only the prologue. The main act came the following month.

CRETE

In May 1941, 13,000 paratroops of the 7th Air Division under *Generalleutnant* Kurt Student and 9,000 men of the 5th Mountain Division under -*Generalmajor* Julius Ringel, under the overall command of *Generaloberst* Alexander Lohr, were committed to the capture of the island of Crete. They were supported by 500 fighters and bombers, 500 transports and 80 gliders.

The island was held by 28,000 British and Commonwealth troops, reinforced by Greek battalions and Cretan irregulars who brought the total strength up to

Above: Fallschirmjäger *march through Tunis on 4 February 1943.* VII Fliegerdivision *had been withdrawn from Russia in July 1942 for a possible assault on Malta, but all available paratroopers were rushed to North Africa at the end of the year, after the Allied invasion of Algeria.*

Right: With the establishment of a second airborne division, VII Fliegerdivision *was renamed* I Fliegerdivision. *It was flown to southern Italy after the invasion of Sicily, and was quickly deployed to the island in a futile attempt to stem the Allied tide.*

42,500. Though the Allied forces were very poorly equipped and many had been recently evacuated from mainland Greece they had a major advantage over their adversaries. ULTRA decrypts had given their commander, Major General Bernard Freyburg a complete breakdown of the German plans. ULTRA intelligence had earlier allowed the British to withdraw successfully from Greece.

The attack, code named Operation *Merkur* (Mercury), divided the island into four drop zones, from Maleme in the west through Canea, Retimo and Heraklion in the east. Lack of transport aircraft meant that the island was attacked in two waves: in the morning and in the afternoon of 20 May. The first wave, Group West under *Generalmajor* Eugen Meindl landed in the Maleme/ Canea drop zone. In the afternoon, Group Centre under *Generalmajor* Süssmann landed at Retimo. Group East under *Generalleutnant* Julius Ringel would be spearheaded by paratroops of FJR 1 and a battalion of FJR 2, who would seize the airfield at Heraklion to allow the 5th Mountain Division to be landed by Ju 52s.

STIFF OPPOSITION

The response of the Imperial and Greek forces to the German attacks was violent and effective. Those men who had landed at Retimo and Herakleion suffered heavily and were effectively bottled up. Only at Maleme airfield did the paratroops manage to find cover and set up a viable base in the dried up riverbed of the river Tavronitis.

The key feature, a hill known as Point 107 which dominated the airfield, was held by the New Zealand 22nd Battalion. Under pressure and without reliable communications they pulled back and this gave the Germans their opening. With an airfield in their possession they poured in reinforcements.

The island fell to the Germans, but the airborne forces suffered very heavy losses – 4,000 were killed, 2,000 wounded and 220 aircraft were destroyed. Among the losses was a seaborne convoy of Greek fishing vessels carrying heavy equipment, which was intercepted at night by the Royal Navy and destroyed.

Hitler declared that "the day of the paratrooper is over" and with these words he condemned this force to a ground role, when it could have been better used against Malta or Cyprus.

PARAS ON THE GROUND

As elite ground forces the *Fallschirmjäger* fought in North Africa and on the Eastern Front. They defended Sicily and Italy – notably at Monte Cassino, and fought in Normandy, Holland and in the final defence of Eastern Europe. In North Africa, Sicily, Normandy and Holland the German paratroops found themselves fighting British and American paratroops who had landed to secure beachheads or bridges. Hitler paid tribute to the *Fallschirmjäger* during the fight for Monte Cassino saying they were harder than the Waffen-SS.

On the night of 13-14 July 1943, as part of Operation Husky, the Allied invasion of Sicily, the British 1st Air-Landing Brigade was tasked with the capture of the Simeto Bridge north of the town of Primasole. The British troops, landing by glider, were widely scattered but managed to hold the bridge until they were forced to withdraw. The troops who forced them out were men of FJR 3, and the Machine Gun and Engineer Battalions of FJR 4. They had flown from bases in southern France, via Italy to Sicily and jumped at Catania airport on 12 July as part of a rapid reinforcement for the island.

MUSSOLINI RESCUE

On 12 September 1943 paratroops of the 1st Company of the *Fallschirmjäger Lehrbataillon* (training battalion) commanded by *Leutnant* von Berlepsch, and a small group of Waffen-SS men commanded by *Obersturmbannführer* Otto Skorzeny were carried in 12 DFS 230 gliders to rescue the Italian leader Benito Mussolini. Following his arrest by the Italian authorities the former Italian leader had been held in a remote hotel on the Gran Sasso plateau near Rome. Since the hotel could only be reached by a funicular railway, airborne assault was the

Above: The Fallschirmjäger *expanded rapidly in 1943 and 1944, as another four divisions were formed. However, only I and II were real paratroopers. I Division served in Italy for the rest of the war, and was to form an important part of the German defences at Cassino.*

Above right: The paratroopers were an elite fighting force, and as such they were often thrown into battle at the most desperate point. As a result, they suffered heavy losses in killed, wounded and captured. These Fallschirmjäger *have been captured by New Zealanders, getting some measure of revenge for Commonwealth losses in Crete.*

Below: Wounded Fallschirmjäger *rest before returning to the line. By the last years of the war, most units were made up from redundant Luftwaffe personnel drawn from air, communications and flak units.*

only viable option. Eight of the gliders reached the rocky landing zone and Mussolini was rescued. Though Paratroops had seized the funicular railway, Skorzeny and the Duce made their exit in a hazardous flight in a Fieseler Storch observation aircraft.

AEGEAN ACTION

On 12 November 1943 a force of 500 paratroops of the 1st Battalion of FJR 2 were used in the Aegean when they spearheaded a sea and air assault on the island of Leros, garrisoned by British and Italian troops. They were dropped onto a bone dry DZ strewn with boulders and bisected by gullies. The slow flying Ju 52s took heavy ground fire and the paratroopers had suffered 40 per cent casualties before they had even jumped. On the drop zone, broken limbs accounted for a further 20 per cent. However once on the ground the British reported them to be tough opponents. The paratroops were reinforced with subsequent drops of men and equipment during the campaign, which resulted in an unexpected British defeat.

SS PARATROOPERS

Two airborne assaults took place in 1944 that were not conducted by men of the parachute arm of the Luftwaffe. On 25 May men of the 500th *SS-Fallschirmjäger* Battalion used gliders and parachutes to attack the headquarters of Tito the Yugoslav Partisan leader. Codenamed *Rösselsprung* the surprise attack

in the Drvar valley was almost successful, but the Waffen-SS paratroops suffered heavy casualties. It was reported that the unit was made up from a mix of volunteers and men taken from penal units and was therefore deemed to be dispensable.

The battalion was reformed as 600th *SS-Fallschirmjäger* battalion and in July twenty gliders with parachute troops attacked the mountain stronghold of the French Maquis in the Vercors region. They inflicted heavy casualties on the French, but also committed numerous atrocities.

LAST DROP

On the night of 15 December 1944, as part of the German offensive in the Ardennes, a reinforced battalion of 1,200 men from FJR 6 parachuted behind American lines near Malmédy. They were led by the veteran *Oberst* Freiherr von der Heydte, who was suffering from a broken arm and so jumped using a Russian parachute with a triangular canopy – one of the most stable parachutes then in use. The battalion was dropped by inexperienced pilots and scattered and though it caused some concern made little contribution to the main offensive. Von der Heydte, with no communications with the main German ground forces was obliged to surrender.

Fallschirmjäger continued to be used as ground troops until the close of the war, but the Ardennes was their last airborne attack.

PARATROOP PLATFORMS

Junkers Ju 52

Right and below: The workhorse of the *Fallschirmjäger* for operations and training was the tough and reliable aircraft the Ju 52 affectionately known as "Iron Annie", *Judula* or Tante Ju "Auntie Junkers". The Ju 52 was a slab sided, three motored aircraft with a striking corrugated metal fuselage and wings. It had a crew of two or three and could carry 12 parachutists or 17 men, though in emergencies it was often overloaded. The Ju 52 was powered by three 830 hp BMW engines had a top speed of 165 mph (265 kph) a ceiling of 18,000 feet (5500 meters) and range of 800 miles (1287 kilometres). About 3,000 were produced between 1939 and 1945.

DFS 230

Left and above: The DFS 230 glider carried ten soldiers or a useful load of 1,288 kg. It landed on a skid having taken off on a jettisonable wheel undercarriage. It had a wingspan of 21.98 metres, length of 11.24 metres and a height of 2.90 metres. The DFS 230C employed rockets underneath the fuselage to act as a brake. The gliders were later used to re-supply surrounded pockets on the Eastern Front. Approximately 1,510 DFS 230 were built during the war.

Gotha Go 242

Below: The Gotha Go 242 was introduced in 1942 to replace the DFS 230. It had a crew of two and could carry 3,600 kg of cargo or 23 troops. It had a wingspan of 24.50 metres, length of 15.80 metres and height of 4.26 metres. The Go 242C was fitted with floats for a projected assault on the Royal Navy base at Scapa Flow in Scotland.

Messerschmitt Me 321

Right: Airborne success in 1940 came in spite of the lack of any means of delivering heavy equipment by air. The *Reichsluftfahrtministerium* asked Messerschmitt and Junkers to design huge transport gliders capable of carrying light armour. The Messerschmitt 321 entered service in the middle of 1941, but *Fallschirmjäger* losses in the battle for Crete meant that from that time on they were used as elite ground troops. As a result, the huge gliders were not needed, so most were converted into powered transports.

COASTAL RAIDERS

It was the *Kriegsmarine's* capital ships which stole the headlines, but much of the valuable war work was done by hundreds of small escort vessels, attack craft and coastal raiders.

THE GERMAN motor torpedo boats called *S-Boote* or *Schnellboote* (Fast Boats) were known by their crews as *Eilboot* or 'boat in a hurry.' The British called them E-Boats, which legend has it stood for 'Enemy' boat.

Several classes of *S-Boote* were built before and during the war. Although diesel-drive was specified from the outset the original boat *S1* constructed at the Lürssen yard was powered by three 800-hp Daimler-Benz petrol engines whilst Daimler-Benz and MAN developed a suitable diesel unit. Originally of 32.4m in length the type had to be stretched to 34.7m to cope with an increase in speed. This length remained consistant to the war's end. The later *S-Boote* carried their two torpedo tubes forward of the wheelhouse, giving space for two skid-mounted reloads abaft of them.

Later innovations were to raise the forecastle, so enclosing the tubes, leaving a forward gunpit between them. The raising of the craft's freeboard also gave it an enviable dryness.

Later craft displaced between 100-105 tonnes with a complement which increased from about 28 at the beginning of the war to 32-34 men by 1944.

The boats had hammock space for half the crew. The rest slept on or under tables in the wireless room or by the torpedo tubes. A very small galley allowed them to prepare hot meals and coffee. Space was so cramped that the crew normally lived ashore and stayed aboard only for operations and maintenance.

The craft had a distinctive rudder configuration that produced the so-called *Lürssen* effect. It consisted of two small rudders fitted aft of the wing propellers that could be rotated outboard 30 degrees without

moving the main centreline rudder. This altered the flow of water aft and resulted in greater acceleration and propeller efficiency, and by 1945 such innovations had pushed speed to a maximum of 42 knots.

UPGUNNED CRAFT

Armament varied. For most of the war it consisted of one or two 2-cm Flak (anti-aircraft) guns and two 21-inch torpedo tubes. From 1944, as Allied air power increased and rocket-and cannon-armed aircraft regularly strafed German convoys, the defensive weapons fit was upgraded. Late-war boats typically carried one 4-cm and three 2-cm Flak or one 3.7-cm and five 2-cm Flak guns. Larger types could also carry six or eight mines in place of reload torpedoes.

The driving force behind the establishment of *S-Boote* as a separate command was *Kapitän* Rudolf Petersen. Taking

command of the 2nd *S-Boote* Flotilla in August 1938, he led it through the first campaigns of the war. Under his command from 1939-41 it fought in Norway, the North Sea and the Baltic. In April 1942, after seven months ashore as a staff officer he was given the position of commander of *S-Boote*. His headquarters where in Scheveningen, Holland, from where he ran operations in the Channel, North Sea, Baltic, Black Sea and Mediterranean.

In Berlin the effectiveness of *S-Boote* was acknowledged on 30 May 1941 when a *Schnellboot-Kriegsabzeichen* or S-Boat War Badge was instituted. The badge, designed by Wilhelm Ernst Peekhaus, showed a short high-silhouette *S-Boote* cutting through the water. It was surrounded by gold oak leaves and surmounted by a gold national emblem (eagle and swastika). Prior to the issue of the badge *S-Boote* crews received

Above: The R-Boote *were originally 60 ton craft armed with a couple of 20mm cannon plus depth charges or mines as appropriate. From R17 on they grew to S-Boot size, and mounted an increasing armament of up to one 37mm gun and six 20mm mounts. This was necessary on the vital Norwegian iron ore route.*

Right: S-Boote of 1. Flotilla, flying the Kriegsmarine ensign before the swastika was incorporated into the new flag of 1934. This unit had mixed powerplants, the standard diesels only being introduced with S6. The other five boats had petrol engines.

the Destroyers War Badge.

Criteria for the award of the badge were 12 sorties against enemy vessels or installations, outstanding leadership, a particularly successful mission or to be wounded during the course of an action. A new badge designed jointly by Peekhaus and Captain Petersen was instituted in January 1943 showing a longer, newer *S-Boote* and an enlarged national emblem.

A special version of the first pattern *S-Boote* badge was awarded to eight outstanding commanders. These men had already received the Knight's Cross to the Iron Cross with Oakleaves but continued to perform bravely in combat. The award consisted of a silver badge with gold plate and nine small diamonds in the arms of the swastika. The award of the *Schnellboot-Kriegsabzeichen mit*

Brillanten was the prerogative of *Grossadmiral* Erich Raeder, the head of the Navy and not the Führer. They were presented at an informal luncheon.

E-BOAT ALLEY

During the war the Allies played down the effectiveness of *S-Boote*. The popular press regularly carried stories of *S-Boote* being sunk or driven off by the Royal Navy.

The *S-Boote* were, however, respected by coastal forces in the Channel since they were fast, well armed and more capable of surviving battle damage than Royal Navy Torpedo Boats.

CONVOY WAR

The first truly effective campaign launched by the *S-Boote* was against the convoys carrying coal to the mainly coastally-sited British coal-fired electricity generating stations. Even before the fall of Dunkirk *S-Boote* were deploying from Dutch ports covering the 160 km to the English coast in under three hours. Such was the menace that they posed to Allied shipping that the stretch of coast from the straits of Dover northwards toward the Thames Estuary was known as 'E-Boat Alley'. Publicly, the government played down the problem, but soon embarked on a programme of motor gun-boats to beat the enemy at its own game.

S-Boote were small enough to be transported by rail or to operate on the larger European rivers, so they joined the Italian forces in the Mediterranean and also saw action in the Black Sea.

The greatest test for the *S-Boote* was the Allied invasion of Normandy in June 1944. There were five flotillas of *S-Boote* (totalling 37 craft in varying states of readiness) based along the coast opposite southern England in 1944 under Petersen's command.

The units involved were the 8th *Schnellboote* Flotilla at Ijmuiden, Holland, the 2nd at Ostend, Belgium, the 4th at Boulogne, France, with the 5th and 9th at Cherbourg, France. The 9th was commanded by the aristocrat *Fregattenkapitän* Gotz Baron von Mirbach.

SURPRISE ATTACK

However, before D-Day the *S-Boote* had caused the invasion fleet serious losses. On 26 April 1944 the US Army 4th Infantry Division undertook an exercise codenamed Tiger. Landing craft would transport troops and

Top: R and S-Boote *could carry up to eight mines in place of additional torpedoes. The Germans laid and maintained extensive minefields around their coastal waters, especially in the English Channel and the Baltic. In terms of tonnage sunk, mines were far more effective than fast torpedo boat attacks.*

Above: S142*, built in 1943, mounted a 40mm AA gun aft and a 20mm gun in the forward position. Displacing over 100 tons,* S142 *was among the largest* E-Boote *built, but suffered in terms of reduced speed.*

Left: *An* R-Boote *flotilla operating in the Baltic. This type was the mainstay of the highly sucessful German and Finnish naval operations in the area. The high point came in 1943. In that year not one Soviet ship or submarine penetrated the anti-submarine net erected from Helsinki to Tallinn.*

vehicles to the sandy beaches at Slapton Sands, Devon in preparation for their landings at UTAH beach in Normandy. During the night of 27-28 April an inadequately escorted convoy of eight US Navy Landing Ships, Tank (LST) was attacked by nine *S-Boote* from the 5th and 9th *Schnellboote* Flotilla operating from Cherbourg.

HEAVY LOSSES

The Germans sank LSTs *507* and *531* and severely damaged LST *289*, which limped into Dartmouth harbour after the exercise. The Germans returned safely having suffered no losses, but 441 US soldiers and 197 sailors perished in the attack – more than were to die at UTAH beach on D-Day – and the loss of the tank landing craft imposed constraints on Allied planners.

For the successful action *Kapitän* Petersen was awarded Oakleaves to his Knight's Cross. The attack on the Tiger convoy was not made public until after D-Day, since it would have provided the Germans with an indication that the invasion of Europe was in the offing. This secrecy resulted in a myth of a 'cover up' over Tiger.

On the night of 5-6 June 1944, when the first airborne landings were reported, the *S-Boote* put to sea at 3 am but made no contacts.

INVASION

On the night of 6-7 June all available *S-Boote* were deployed, but the 5th Flotilla lost *S139* and *S140* to mines. The *S-Boote*

sortied almost every night, weather permitting. In the face of the massed Allied firepower they enjoyed limited success. German press reports of their actions were couched in dramatic language, which gave a false impression of their effectiveness.

Even so they were a threat. Among the *S-Boote* successes in June 1944 were the torpedoeing of the battleship HMS *Nelson* and the destroyer USS *Meredith*, which was later sunk. Other warships damaged included the frigate HMS *Halstead* and LST *538*. S-Boats sank the landing craft LCT *875*, *105*, *376* and *314*, and the freighters SS *Dungrange* (621 Gross Registered Tons – GRT), SS *Ashanti* (534 GRT), and SS *Brackenfield* (657 GRT), all of which were carrying fuel and ammunition. The tugboats *Partridge* and *Sesame* fell victim to the *S-Boote* as, rather prosaically, did an element of the Mulberry artificial harbour under tow.

During the same month, *S-Boote* sank two of their opposite numbers – the gun boat MGB *17* and the torpedo boat MTB *448*. The *S-Boote* also dropped 68 mines and on the night of 22-23 June, *S130*, *S145* and *S168* transported artillery ammunition and 24 officers from Saint-Malo to Cherbourg,

Above: S-Boote saw service in East and West. They were in action against the Red Fleet in the Black Sea, where they helped frustrate Soviet attempts to resupply Sevastopol, and later in the Sea of Azov, where they supported the Wehrmacht's drive into the Caucasus.

which had been cut off by the advancing US forces.

The greatest damage to the *S-Boote* force came not from surface action, but from the air. During an RAF air raid on Le Havre on 14 June, three larger torpedo boats and 14 *S-Boote* were destroyed. Earlier, on 11 June, *S136* was sunk in action, and on 13 June fighter bombers intercepted and sank *S178*, *S179* and *S189*. On 23 June *S190* was also sunk.

On 26 June eight boats from the 6th *Schnellboote* Flotilla arrived from the Baltic. The reinforcements were based at Ijmuiden on the Dutch coast. By the end of June there were 23 *S-Boote* in the West, of which

only 15 were battle ready.

The *S-Boote* were now equipped with new, more effective T-5 *Zaunkönig* acoustic homing torpedo. These could also be fitted with *Flächen-absuchende Torpedos* – surface search or FAT – controls, which enabled the weapon to follow an indirect, random-seeming path to the target.

The supply of torpedoes could not keep up with their use and the shortage was compounded when in a suspected act of sabotage early on the morning of 6 July the torpedo assembly and maintenance shop at Le Havre blew up. Forty-one assembled weapons were destroyed.

Below: Always quieter than British equivalents, the S-Boote's low profile made them hard to detect without radar. Although they had a lower maximum speed than some of their opponents they were generally more seaworthy.

Above left: The end came on 13 May 1945. At Felixstowe German S-Boote became the first surface craft to surrender. On board one of the Kriegsmarine's vessels was Rear Admiral Karl Bruning (far left) who had been in charge of S-Boot operations and who signed the instrument of surrender.

Above: Craft constructed after S66 featured an armoured conning tower as a defence against the increasingly powerful gun armament carried by English boats.

Left: S-Boote in their lair. They issued forth from their concrete pens to attack the regular coastal convoys off the English coast. Bombing the pens was often attempted but this seldom destroyed them. Finally, it was air superiority and improved gun-boats with radar which defeated the S-Boot.

As the Allies became established on the Normandy beach-head, the military situation further deteriorated, although the S-boats continued to enjoy some limited success. In July they torpedoed the frigate HMS *Trollope,* causing such severe damage that she was written off as a constructive loss.

At the close of the month, *S91, S97* and *S114* of the 6th *Schnellboote* Flotilla were operating away from the beach-head. At 1.22 am on 31 July they intercepted a convoy east of Eastbourne. Firing six FATs, they sank thefreighter SS *Samwake* (7,219 GRT) and torpedoed four more ships totalling 26,699 gross registered tonnes.

The introduction of the new long-range T-3D torpedoes in August did not improve the success of the *S-Boote*. In engagements between 4 and 15 August they launched 84 T-3Ds but hit only the old British cruiser HMS *Frobisher*, the minesweeper HMS *Vestal*, the freighter SS *Iddesleigh* (5,205 tonnes) and the tender *Albatross*.

The *S-Boote* arm continued to fight on, like their colleagues in the submarine service. But by the end of 1944 the game was up. In their attacks against the English coastal convoys as many *S-Boote* as colliers were being lost.

RAUMBOOTE

Raumen is the Geman verb 'to clear'– hence the *Raumboote* or *R-Boote* type of coastal minesweeper. These craft were of such a useful size that they also served as minelayers and, suitably rearmed, as convoy escorts. In this guise they were involved in frequent clashes with British craft. Like the *S-boote,* they were built of wood on metal framing. The first 16 boats constructed in the early 1930s displaced only 60 tons and were 26m long. Propulsion was by twin screw diesels, producing a modest speed of 17 knots. From *R17* onwards however, their dimensions were similar to the *S-boote* though with extra draught. Even with progressively modified diesels the type rarely exceeded 20 knots. Nearly 350 of all types were built between 1931 and 1945.

R-Boats were designed as coastal minesweepers. They mounted a single 2-cm Flak, but by the end of the war the type was being used as a minelayer and also a Flak ship. The normal complement was one officer and 28 or 29 men, but with the increase in armament this increased to two officers and 36 to 38 men. In 1944 *R401* mounted a 3.7-cm Flak and three twin 2-cm Flak guns as well as 12 mines. The 83 *R-Boote* built at the end of the war displaced 148 tonnes with a full load and had a maximum speed of 21 knots, half that of the *S-Boote,* and a range of 990 nautical mines. The craft were 39.4m long, 5.7m wide and had a draught of 1.6m.

On D-Day between 50 and 60 *R-Boote* were available for operations, but air raids on Le Havre and Boulogne damaged or sank 14. *R49* was badly damaged by British MTBs while she was on a minelaying sortie from Le Havre on 6-7 June.

SINKING SHIP

All through the war, German coastal craft proved to be tough adversaries for Allied air forces as well as surface vessels. As the war turned against Nazi Germany, the risks of putting to sea increased, but like their U-Boat bretyhren, *S-Boote* and *R-Boote* crews continued to run the gauntlet of rocket-firing fighters and roving MTBs.

HIGH-SPEED GLADIATORS

FAST COASTAL CRAFT proved their worth during WWI, but only the Italian and German navies went on to develop the type in the inter-war period. The other naval powers concentrated on major units. The British in particular, in spite of their Great War successes with coastal motor boats, focussed on policing their distant Empire. So by 1939 the Axis had a considerable technological lead over their opponents.

The Germans developed the *S-Boot* under the noses of the Allied regulating authorities, in the guise of sporting-club colours. The Germans were also the only nation interested in developing a small diesel propulsion unit: no other country produced a satisfactory marine diesel,

and they had to rely on hazardous petrol engines with their highly volatile fuel.

Hull construction was typically of wood, overlaying a timber or light alloy frame. Only wood could withstand the stresses of high speed travel. Nevertheless, hard-used coastal craft need constant attention and had a short operational life. The development of the 21 inch torpedo dictated later design of torpedo boats. Close-in fighting led to the development of varying configurations of cannon and machine guns as the situation demanded. Radar was another great leap forward, and was vital in the vicious nocturnal encounters.

R-Boot (above)
The *R-Boote* were pressed into service in an increasing variety of roles as the war progressed. They saw action primarily in the Baltic, as convoy escorts and minelayers. Although they were fitted out with increasingly powerful diesels they could rarely manage more than half the speed of their more glamorous counterpart the *S-Boot*.

S-Boot (below)
The S-Boat's round-bilged hull design enabled the craft to maintain high speeds even in rough seas. Later models, as depicted below, were heavily armed and armoured. The raised forecastle enclosed the torpedo tubes: more guns were carried, including and extra weapon forward in the gun-pit between the torpedo tubes.

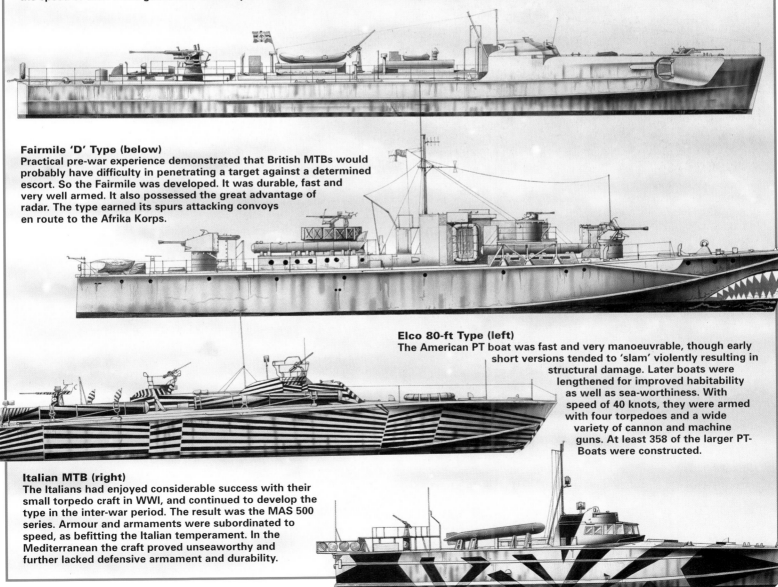

Fairmile 'D' Type (below)
Practical pre-war experience demonstrated that British MTBs would probably have difficulty in penetrating a target against a determined escort. So the Fairmile was developed. It was durable, fast and very well armed. It also possessed the great advantage of radar. The type earned its spurs attacking convoys en route to the Afrika Korps.

Elco 80-ft Type (left)
The American PT boat was fast and very manoeuvrable, though early short versions tended to 'slam' violently resulting in structural damage. Later boats were lengthened for improved habitability as well as sea-worthiness. With speed of 40 knots, they were armed with four torpedoes and a wide variety of cannon and machine guns. At least 358 of the larger PT-Boats were constructed.

Italian MTB (right)
The Italians had enjoyed considerable success with their small torpedo craft in WWI, and continued to develop the type in the inter-war period. The result was the MAS 500 series. Armour and armaments were subordinated to speed, as befitting the Italian temperament. In the Mediterranean the craft proved unseaworthy and further lacked defensive armament and durability.

Seen on its mobile rail launcher, the mighty A-4 rocket was one of the most astonishing advances in the history of weapons technology. But in spite of its unstoppable performance and the destruction it caused, the cost of the project nearly bankrupted the Third Reich.

VENGEANCE WEAPONS

As the war turned against Germany, its leaders placed their hopes in a series of 'wonder weapons' which would finally win the war for the Reich. In spite of some real scientific achievements, they hoped in vain.

ON THE NIGHT OF the 12 June 1944 – just six days after the Allied invasion of France – British anti-aircraft observers heard an unusual noise in the sky. The loud droning buzz came from a small, cross-shaped aeroplane trailing a tail of fire.

Travelling fast, it seemed to be heading for London. Those watchers did not know it but they were looking at the first manifestation of a new kind of warfare.

The tide of war had turned against the Nazis, and Hitler looked to desperate measures to strike back at the Allies. The strange flying bomb was just the first of his vengeance weapons. Soon another even more terrifying threat – the ballistic rocket – was to menace Allied cities.

As Allied armies closed inexorably on the borders of the Reich, Hitler and his followers began to pin their hopes upon two new 'wonder weapons'.

The V-1 was a pilotless flying bomb. Known to the Allies as the Doodlebug, or Buzz bomb, it carried a heavy warhead and was designed to strike at targets from a range of more than 200 kilometres. The Luftwaffe's planners felt that it would be all but impossible to stop. They were wrong.

But the V-1 was soon to be joined by another weapon against which defences were powerless. On 8 September, Chiswick in West London was rocked by a mysterious explosion. Over the next few weeks it became apparent that the buzz-bomb was not the only new vengeance weapon: the long-range ballistic missile had arrived in the form of the hypersonic V-2.

V-1 IN ACTION

The first aerial self-guided missile to be used in combat, this cruise missile got its popular designation V-1 from *Vergeltungswaffe* or 'reprisal weapon', though its true designation was Fieseler Fi 103.

It was also given the cover designation FZG 76 (anti-aircraft target 76).

Its development started in 1942 when *Generalfeldmarschall* Milch authorised the Schmidt pulsejet, a novel form of jet engine, to be used to propel a cheaply produced 'flying bomb'. The first powered flight was on 24 December 1942, and after many delays the bombardment of London began in the summer of 1944.

By April, 1944, *Flakregiment* 155 was in place in to France but it was understrength. This caused delays in setting up launch sites. Things changed after 6 June. V-1s and all necessary supplies were rushed to the forward zones after the Allied landings in Normandy.

The long-delayed operational debut came on the night of 12-13 June. It was an inauspicious beginning: so many launch sites had been damaged that only ten missiles were launched, of which seven crashed. Three days later it

was very different. On the night of 15-16 June, 244 bombs were fired from 55 sites, and by 21 June over 1,000 V-1s had droned and buzzed their way towards England.

The V-1 was most erratic and imprecise, but London was an ideal target.

Nobody who lived through the V-weapon bombardment of 1944 could forget the loud throb of the approaching missile, the sudden silence as the engine cut out, and the tremendous explosion a few seconds later as the missile hit the ground.

AIR-LAUNCH

Missiles were also launched from the air by Heinkel bombers. Although numbers were not high, these were active for most of the second half of 1944.

The start of the V-1 campaign was seen as a major success by the Luftwaffe. Congratulations poured in from all quarters, even from officials who had previously

opposed the scheme. In view of this change in fortune, Hitler himself approved the formation of two new V-1 batteries.

Allied air attacks on the sites themselves were not as successful as had been hoped. Attacks on supply routes were much more effective, and delivery of V-1s to the launch sites fell short of the Regiment's capacity for firing them.

Even worse, British ground forces were pushing north out of the Normandy beachhead, capturing sites along the way. By 1 September 1944 Operation *Rumpelkammer* was over.

In just over two months, more than 8,500 V-1s had been launched. However, the V-1 had never been as effective as the Germans believed. Fighter, anti-aircraft and balloon barrage defences proved to be increasingly effective countermeasures.

Just under half of the V-1s crossing the coast were destroyed

Vengeance Weapon 1, the world's first operational cruise missile, was a fairly crude unmanned aircraft which some members of the Luftwaffe staff thought would take the place of the bomber. Over 8,000 were launched between June and September, but about half were intercepted by British defences.

Inside the V-1

THE RATIONALE behind the development of the flying bomb is not really clear. In part, it was designed to meet one of the Luftwaffe's original mission requirements, to serve as very long range artillery in support of the Wehrmacht in attack.

However, by the time it came into service, the Wehrmacht was doing very little attacking. Another faction among the weapon's high-ranking supporters knew that German bomber programmes lagged far behind those of the Allies.

They had hopes that the V-1, which needed a minimum amount of development and construction, might prove a cheap alternative to the manned bomber. Whatever the reason, the development of the V1 went forward at an incredible pace.

In 1942 *Generalfeldmarschall* Erhard Milch, the Secretary of State for Air, visited the German Army Research Institute at Peenemünde. He was there to see a demonstration firing of A3 and A5 missiles.

Milch did not like the fact that the Army was making such progress in developing long-range weaponry. He issued a requirement for a rival long-range weapon for the Luftwaffe. An expendable unmanned aircraft would be quickest and easiest to develop.

Gerhard Fieseler Werke of Kassel drew up rough designs to fulfil the requirement. Fieseler's scheme was based upon use of the Argus As 014 pulse jet unit for propulsion. The pulse jet was a very simple concept: air from the intake passed through one-way valves, mixed with fuel and ignited.

The explosion closed the valves and burst out of the rear of the 'stove pipe'. Once the pressure dropped, the valves could open. The whole sequence repeated itself several times per second.

The Fieseler proposal was known as the Fi 103. It was accepted by the Luftwaffe High Command, and a team under former Heinkel engineer Robert Lüsser started on the design of the fuselage and control system. A development team was immediately established at Peenemünde. Its leader, engineer Temme, was given far-reaching powers to conscript whatever manpower or equipment he considered necessary.

The result was a small pilotless aircraft with a wing span of just over five metres. The Argus pulse jet was mounted above the rear of fuselage.

Simplicity was the key. The Luftwaffe stipulated that the flying bomb had to be easy to assemble and to maintain, and to use the minimum number of parts.

The missile had a small windmill in the nose which powered an air log. This measured the distance travelled, and at a predetermined distance, cut off the fuel to the engine. It also commanded the weapon

to dive. The air log gave erratic and imprecise measurements. However, it was to prove accurate enough to hit a target the size of London.

Also at Peenemünde, Section E8 was created, which was tasked with designing the launch gear, support vehicles and other ancillary equipment. The launch gear was important, since the pulse jet engine needed to be at flying speed before it would work.

To get the missile into the air, it was catapulted along an inclined ramp by a chemically-powered piston. It took less than a month to progress from the first glide test to the first powered ramp launch, which took place on Christmas Eve, 1942.

Over the next months, many missiles were launched, some even reaching the south coast of Sweden. In July 1943, one missile managed to hit within 800 metres of its designated target, more than 200 kilometres from launch.

Left: A Supermarine Spitfire rolls away after tipping the wing of a V-1 in flight. The missile's speed of up to 400 mph (690 km/h) was close to the maximum that piston-powered fighters could achieve at low level, but late-model Spitfires, Mustangs, Tempests and the new Meteor jets shot-down 1,847 flying bombs.

Below left: Initially, the V-1s were to be launched from huge concrete ramps built in the Pas de Calais. These proved easy to detect from the air, however, and an intensive bombing campaign destroyed most of the sites. Later V-1s were launched from simple wooden ramps.

by aircraft or anti-aircraft fire, and many went astray, exploding in open country. Unfortunately, those which did get through were enough to kill 6,000 people, 5,000 in London alone.

But if the V-1 could be countered by conventional means, against the V-2 there was no defence. The missile travelled so fast that it arrived and exploded before the whooshing sound of its dive onto the target could be heard by its unfortunate victims.

The Peenemünde A4 was unquestionably the greatest single thrust into the unknown in the history of technology, and its development resulted in a weapon against which there was no defence. At the same time, it it did little to stave off the defeat of Nazi Germany – indeed, the large resources committed to it might have been put to better use.

LONG HISTORY

Although the V-2 became operational after the Luftwaffe's much simpler V-1, development had in fact begun much earlier. German work on liquid-propellant rockets was inspired by the writings of Hermann Oberth, and practical experiments began in the 1920s, carried out by enthusiasts at the VfR (Society for Spaceflight). One of the leading engineers was a young Prussian aristocrat named Werner von Braun.

Engineering the V-2

THE TASK of engineering a scaled up A5 as a viable military rocket was daunting – to say the least. Whereas the test rocket had weighed just over one tonne, the A4 had a projected launch weight of around twelve and a half tonnes. Where the original A-3's engine produced about 1500kg of thrust, the A4's engine would need to deliver over 25 tonnes.

The rocket had a steel framework externally clad in rivetted steel plate. Lighter materials were available, but they would not have survived the massive aerodynamic and gravitational forces of hypersonic flight.

The shape of the missiles was reputedly based on that of the German army's 7.92-mm rifle bullet, which was known to be ballistically stable at supersonic speeds.

Power would be provided by burning a mixture of alcohol and liquid oxygen. The rocket carried over five tonnes of alcohol and four tonnes of oxygen, enough for around 70 seconds of powered flight.

By this time it would be travelling at over five and a half thousand kilometres an hour and would have reached a maximum altitude of around 90 kilometres.

The A4 needed a lot of fuel: over 100 kg per second. It was driven into the combustion chamber by a lightweight steam turbine powered by the explosive reaction of hydrogen peroxide and calcium permanganate.

Guidance and control of the missile presented even greater difficulties than the rocket motor. Keeping a rocket upright at launch is like balancing a stick in your hand: you have to be able to sense any changes in balance and apply a corrective movement to keep it stable.

Gyroscopes were used to detect any changes in attitude. They acted as directors to carbon vanes projecting into the rocket exhaust. Actuated by hydraulic servos, these vanes vectored the rocket's thrust, providing low-speed control. At higher speeds the missile was controlled and stabilised by the movable tail surfaces.

Although simple in theory, the control system had to react instantly to cope with gusting winds on launch. It had to tilt the missile to the correct angle so that its ballistic flight path would take it to the target.

The system also had to compensate for changes in aerodynamics as the missile accelerated through the sound barrier, as well as for the missile's changing weight and centre of gravity as fuel was burned.

Autopilots of the day were primitive, so the development team created one of the world's first analogue computers to handle guidance. It was not without its problems, however, and the first V-2s were fitted with an unsatisfactory interim autopilot.

By 1934 the army, forbidden long-range artillery by the terms of the Treaty of Versailles, was showing an interest. Army support meant funding for more ambitious rockets and facilities at the disused artillery range and research establishment at Kummersdorf. *Hauptmann* (later General) Walter Dornberger headed the army team, which in 1937 moved to remote Peenemünde on the Baltic coast. There, larger and larger rockets were built and tested.

THE V-2 FLIES

The mighty A4 rocket design was completed late in 1941, and the first A4 was fired on 13 June 1942. It exploded. The second A4, launched on 16 August, though only partially successful, was the first powered missile to fly faster than sound. The next A4, fired on 3 October, flew under full power for a minute, covering 190 km (118 miles).

Hitler ordered the rocket by the thousand as the V-2 (*Vergeltungswaffe* or Reprisal Weapon 2).

A stupendous production programme got under way. Initially located at Peenemünde, production was switched to the vast Mittelwerke slave mines after the RAF attacked the research site in August 1943.

Army firing troops were ready for operations in the autumn of 1944. The first operational V-2 launches took place on 6 September, when two missiles were fired against Paris.

Two days later, the sustained campaign against London began. For a while the British government, which had advised Prime Minister Churchill that such a rocket could not be built, and that the RAF should stop wasting time looking for it, told the public the explosions were caused by faulty gas mains.

Within days the truth had to be admitted, but Londoners just got on with winning the war.

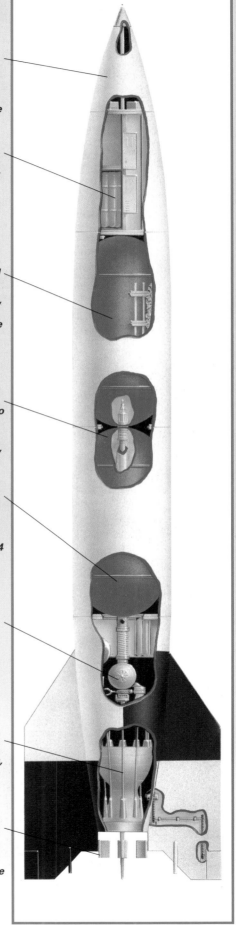

The nose of the V-2 carried a contact fuse which detonated the warhead – 910-kg of amatol high-explosive. Attempts to develop a proximity fuse were unsuccessful.

Behind the warhead was the main equipment bay, holding the accelerometers, telemetry and gyro systems, cryogenically cooled by liquid nitrogen.

The upper fuel tank contained over four tonnes of ethyl alcohol. Insulated by glass wool, the tank was filled early in the six-hour launching process, soon after the missile had been elevated onto its launching platform.

The feed valve at the bottom of the tank passed alcohol into the main feed pipe, which passed through the core of the main liquid oxygen tank. The feed pipe was also thickly insulated.

Over five and a half tonnes of liquid oxygen was pumped into the second main tank during the last two hours of the launch process. Because the tank was insulated the A-4 never developed the frost coating typical of post-war missiles such as the Atlas.

The fuels were pumped at high-pressure by a steam turbine. This was driven by a volatile mix of Z-stoff (calcium permanganate) and T-stoff (hydrogen peroxide). The high-pressure system was needed for the rocket to develop full thrust.

The alcohol and oxygen were fed into the combustion chamber by a ring of injectors, and ignited electrically.

Thrust was vectored by small graphite vanes which extended into the jet exhaust. The main fins gave aerodynamic stability once the missile was up to speed.

Above: The V-2 pilot production plant was set up south of Peenemünde early in 1943. These pre-production A4s are seen in the middle of the year, displaying at least three of the camouflage schemes under consideration for the rocket. Production was interrupted, however, when the RAF mounted a heavy raid a month later, on the night of 17 August.

Below: SS interest in the V-weapon programme saw production moved to a massive underground complex at Nordhausen. There was abundant slave labour from the Dora concentration camp, and tens of thousands of inmates were worked to death. This incomplete V-2 was discovered in the main tunnel of the complex after it was captured by the US Army.

They got quite used to hearing a sudden deafening explosion, followed by the long diminishing rumble, just like thunder, caused by the supersonic plunge of the missile through the sky.

Over 1,300 rockets were launched, mostly from wooded sites near The Hague in Holland. However, some were even launched from the city itself. This launch site was not far from the historic Palace of Peace in the centre of the town.

About 90 percent of the A4s actually reached the British Isles, killing nearly 3,000 people and causing considerable damage. Around 100 rockets blew up in flight or went astray as their guidance systems failed. One rocket actually went east instead of west, hitting the ground near Wiesbaden.

ATTACK ON ANTWERP

Advancing Allied troops had forced the Germans back from the North Sea ports in Belgium and Holland. The German high command decided to use the V-weapons in an attempt to prevent the Allies from using these ports to resupply their forces.

Pulling back to the Eifel mountains, the V-1 launch sites were prepared for operations against Antwerp, Brussels and Liège. Starting on 21 October more than 8,000 V-1s were launched during the Belgian campaign.

The damage they inflicted had little practical military effect. This was largely due to highly effective US Army radar-directed anti-aircraft guns which accounted for 95 per cent of the missiles fired.

The V-2s also took part in the campaign. Over 1,300 were fired against Antwerp, causing considerable damage to the city, but doing little to disrupt the flow of supplies.

A few V-1s, with their range extended to 200 miles, were fired against London during the early days of 1945, but activities were limited. V-2s continued to be launched against continental targets, until the suspension of all 'reprisal' weapon operations on the 27 March.

More than 30,000 V-1s were manufactured, and about 18,000 were fired or dropped in combat. Most of the remainder were destroyed in factories or in transit, though several hundred were found in underground factories at the end of the war. Over 4,000 V-2s out of the near 10,000 produced had been fired in anger.

WASTE OF MONEY?

Ultimately the V-weapons failed to provide Hitler with the vengeance he sought. They absorbed an enormous amount of Nazi Germany's resources, while providing little military return for the huge investment.

The V-1's potential was never really fulfilled. As so often happened under the Third Reich, personal feuds and inter-service rivalries meant that struggles for control were the norm. Senior commanders spent more time fighting each other than fighting the enemy.

The V-2 was far more influential. One of the greatest single achievements in the history of rocketry, it was the foundation of all post-war missile development. The Soviets, who captured Peenemünde at the end of the war, rounded up as many scientists as they could. They had great influence on Soviet missile development.

ROAD TO THE MOON

American rocket programmes were also given a massive boost by the German know-how. Many of the scientists were rounded up in an operation called Project Paperclip. They were sent across the Atlantic where they provided the core of the teams which were to develop the first intercontinental ballistic missiles.

It was the men behind the V-2, most notably Werner von Braun, who provided much of the early impetus for the American space programme. In just over two decades they would take man to the moon.

TARGET LONDON

Above: Many V-1s were destroyed by the anti-aircraft belt placed along the Kent coast. Directed by radar, hundreds of guns placed a curtain of shrapnel in the V-1's path, and over 1,800 bombs were brought down.

Left: Any bombs which passed the AA guns were intercepted by Allied fighters. This Hawker Tempest, probably from No. 486 Squadron, is about to open fire on a V-1. The squadron was to claim 223 V-1 kills.

Right: A V-1 flying bomb, its engine cut off by the simple autopilot, noses down over the West End of London. Several bombs caused devastating casualties when they hit crowded shops or apartment blocks.

Below: The result of a tonne of high explosive detonating after hitting the ground at more than four times the speed of sound. A V-2 hit this suburban London street late in October 1944, devastating a row of terraced houses.

Both the V-1 and the V-2 were ahead of their time – so far ahead, in fact, that existing technology could not produce a guidance system to match their performance. Although notionally accurate to within a few hundred metres, in practice they would be lucky to hit within five kilometres of a target. Fortunately for the Germans, London presented a target large enough that even V-1s and V-2s had a chance of hitting it. Between June 1944 and March 1945, 2,419 V-1s came down in London, with a further 3,403 impacting outside the city. Over 500 V-2s hit London in the same period, with a similar number missing.

TANK KILLERS

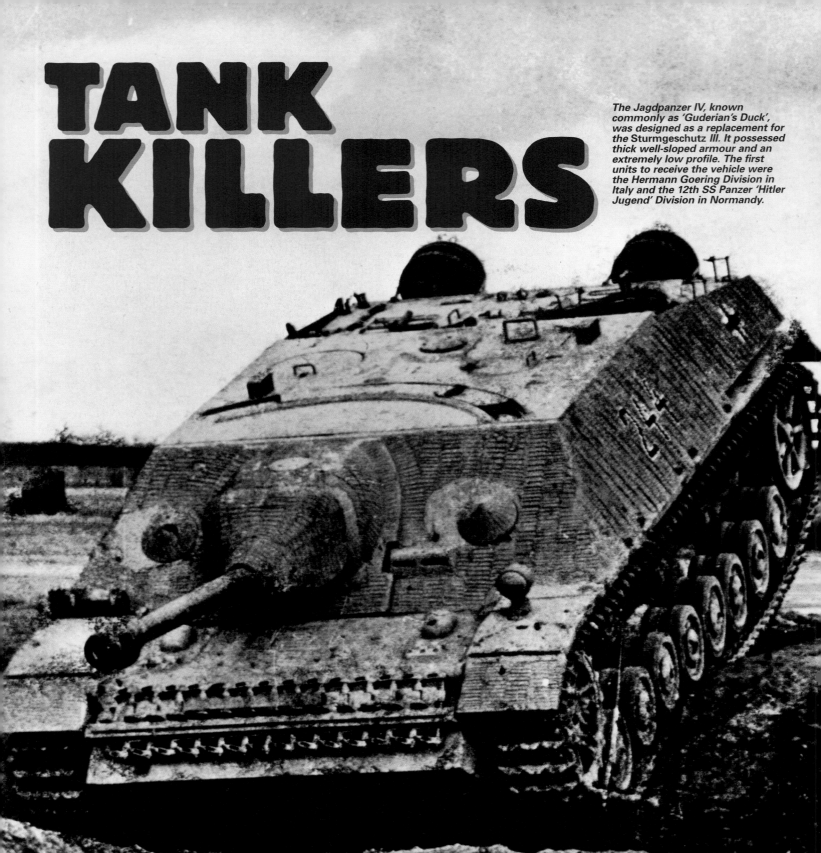

The Jagdpanzer IV, known commonly as 'Guderian's Duck', was designed as a replacement for the Sturmgeschutz III. It possessed thick well-sloped armour and an extremely low profile. The first units to receive the vehicle were the Hermann Goering Division in Italy and the 12th SS Panzer 'Hitler Jugend' Division in Normandy.

The *Panzerwaffe* had a rude awakening on meeting the Soviet T-34 in 1941. Germany suddenly had a pressing need for large numbers of cheaply produced heavily gunned vehicles. The solution was the Tank Killer.

T HE 'BATTLE OF the Bulge', Hitler's last desperate offensive in the west in December 1944 gave the German army's propaganda film units a final opportunity to show German panzers advancing. And what incredible tanks they were.

The assault involved the Wehrmacht's most powerful armoured vehicles: some almost twice the size of their British and American opponents. Many were not conventional tanks at all: designated 'tank hunters' they were armoured boxes with no turrets, the main armament projecting from the steeply-sloping front hull. They had already shown what they could do in Normandy. The 88-mm gun of the *Jagdpanther* could knock out any Allied tank at over 2000 metres. Backed into a wood and camouflaged, the tank hunter could remain unseen, even after it opened fire. Now the *Jagdpanthers* were on the offensive, clattering along snowbound forest tracks, enthusiastic grenadiers perched on their giant steel hulls. Other components of the new generation of armoured vehicles included the *Panzerjäger* IV, a turretless conversion of the *Panzerkampfwagen* (*Pzkfw*) IV. Easy to conceal, but also equipped with an 88-mm gun, it was built for defensive warfare, its low silhouette making it a perfect vehicle for ambush tactics. Also included in the offensive was a battalion of gigantic *Jagdtigers*: Tiger IIs with the turret replaced by an armoured box containing a 128 mm gun.

PANZERJÄGER

The *Jagdpanther* and *Jagdpanzer* IV were among the most effective armoured fighting vehicles of the war: able to take on superior numbers of Allied tanks and destroy them. However, the concept of the 'tank hunter' was born of desperation, not forward planning, and was ultimately a

symptom of industrial weakness.

In 1939, the German army went to war with two types of light and two types of medium tanks. Although used in combat during the Spanish Civil War, the 6-ton *Pzkpfw*. I had only been intended as a training tank, but Hitler's premature declaration of war saw it pressed into combat. Its armament of twin machine guns, and light armour severely restricted its operational effectiveness. However, some of the *Pzkpfw*. Is were modified to mount the Czech 47-mm anti-tank gun, a much more powerful weapon than the German army's then standard 37-mm Pak 38. Thousands of these Czech weapons were seized after the annexation of 1938/39.

The gunners only protection however was the gunshield, which left the crew extremely vulnerable to artillery fire. The vehicle's hull was protected by no more than 13 mm of armour. But it fitted out some

anti-tank battalions in the panzer divisions with a mobile and hard-hitting weapon system, superior to the towed weapons otherwise available. Another hundred or so were produced after the triumphs of 1940 and the *Panzerjäger* I saw action in North Africa and Russia until 1942.

T-34 TERROR

In the summer of 1941 the Germans had a nasty surprise. The latest Russian tanks, the T-34 and KV-1, were superior in every way to German medium tanks: better protected, more heavily-armed and able to traverse swamp, mud and snow thanks to their wide tracks and powerful diesel engines. The *Pzpkfw*. III and IV were consequently to be up-gunned, but an interim solution was to exploit the large numbers of old light tank hulls available to the Wehrmacht. By mounting the gun behind a shield, rather than inside a turret, these small hulls could carry

Above: The 70-ton Jagdtiger was the largest armoured fighting vehicle of the war. An adaptation of the striking King Tiger, and mounting a hugely powerful 128-mm gun it was nevertheless a failure, even in the defensive role for which it been designed.

Left: With a lack of tank chassis, the German army was compelled to find uses for the otherwise totally obsolete Panzer I light training tank. A common variation was to mount the Czech 47-mm anti-tank gun. The crew of three had only a gun shield as protection, and were vulnerable to shrapnel from above and behind. Some 400 Panzerjäger Is were produced.

much heavier guns than they were designed for. The end result was a series of purposely designed tank hunters, mounting ever more powerful armament.

These *Marders* (Marten) carried 75-mm guns in open-topped fighting compartments on the *Pzkpfw*. II or 38(t) chassis. Likewise, the *Hornisse* (Hornet) mounted an 88-mm gun in a similar box-like structure atop of a *Pzkpfw*. IV. This was re-named *Nashorn* (Rhinocerous) on Hitler's orders. The same conversion was later exploited to become the *Hummel* (Bumble Bee) 150-mm self-propelled artillery piece. There were many other conversions: some official, some extemporised during the desperate winter of 1941-2 when the *Ostheer* was fighting for its life. Half-tracks received boilerplate armour and carried a Pak 40 in an improvised mounting. Many captured French tanks were fitted with anti-tank guns in place of their turrets.

German Lash-ups

Above: In this photo from early 1944 Rommel reviews one of the less impressive elements of his French defensive network. Only 24 Marder Is based on the French Hotchkiss H39 were built. Mounting a 75-mm PaK 40 with muzzle-brake, they were only used in occupied France, for policing duties and briefly against the Allied invasion of Normandy.

Above right: The Char B1 was the biggest French tank in use in 1940, but its combat effectiveness was undermined by its one-man turret. Thick armour and reasonable speed made it a useful if ungainly-looking piece of mobile artillery. The conversion involved removal of the turret in the usual way and its replacement with a fixed mounting which housed a 105-mm howitzer (which was also fitted to the Hotchkiss chassis).

IN THE WAKE of the lightning conquests of 1939-40, the Wehrmacht's demands for self-propelled artillery soon outstripped factory production. The German economy was woefully unprepared for war in 1939, and the increasing strain put upon industry to kit out the ever growing number of divisions meant that equipment had to be scraped up from wherever it could be found.

The Army was crying out for motorised artillery to give close-up support to the fast-moving panzers. In 1940 the majority of artillery was still towed, and much of that by horses. Wehrmacht gunners therefore had to rely upon a series of inadequate improvisations. With typical ingenuity the Germans made use of their huge inventory of captured equipment, and produced a series of unusual hybrid fighting vehicle variants.

With practically all of the new materials pouring from the factories being earmarked for the East, the defences in the West were for a long time reliant upon equipment captured from the French and British in 1940. Although the resultant mutations were among the strangest looking vehicles ever to take the field, and were often of questionable tactical effectiveness, for their crews it was basically take it or leave it.

Above: The outstanding firepower of the 88mm gun, excellent mobility and a low elegant silhouette made the Jagdpanther a formidable opponent when correctly deployed, though its combat effectiveness was hampered by the limited traverse mount. Overall, the Jagdpanther was probably the best tank destroyer produced during WW2.

All were produced in tiny numbers. Some worked well, others were mismatches with high profiles and poor reliability.

The German army already had a turretless tank in service before the war. Designed and built as such, the *Sturmgeschütz*

(*StuG*) III was based on the *Pzkfpw.* III chassis but mounted a short 75-mm infantry support gun in a box-like fully enclosed fighting compartment. Its purpose was to provide direct fire support for the infantry while the 'proper' tanks (and, above all, anti-tank

guns) dealt with enemy armour. The concept was suggested in 1935 by former artilleryman, and future panzer general, Erich von Manstein. Manned by artillerymen, not tank personnel, the first *StuG* companies saw action in 1940. Expanded to nine companies, they took part in the invasion of Russia and their numbers increased rapidly thereafter. With many fewer parts than a turreted *Pzkfpw.* III, they were more reliable and easier to repair. Weight saved by having no turret enabled them to employ frontal armour with a thickness of up to 50 mm.

STURMGESCHÜTZ

Over 8,000 *StuG* IIIs were built between 1941 and 1945. This production rate and the vehicle's reliability meant that in 1943 and 1944 between a third and a half of the serviceable 'tanks' in Russia were actually *StuGs*. The chronic shortage of armour led to the *StuG* battalions being employed as substitute tank units, despite their intended purpose as close support artillery.

Once fitted with a long-barrelled 75-mm gun, their armament was equally capable of engaging armoured targets as well as infantry positions.

Employing them as substitute tanks was a misuse of resources since the limited traverse of their gun handicapped them in a mobile tank battle, and if they were engaging enemy armour, German infantry were deprived of their firepower. Nevertheless, the infantry preferred to be supported by the *StuG* than by the more famous heavy tanks: the Tiger's fuel consumption restricted its range and Tigers often had to break off action to refuel just when the foot soldiers needed them most.

In 1943 Hitler delayed the assault on Kursk until the summer so that the latest German tanks could be employed: 200 of the new *Pzkpfw.* V (Panther) medium tanks and 147 Tiger I heavy tanks. Even the unsuccessful candidate in the competition for the Tiger design was brought along: the 89 completed hulls of the Porsche heavy tank design

Stugs in action

DESIGNED TO A 1936 Wehrmacht requirement for an armoured support vehicle, the *Sturmgeschütz* or *StuG* first served in France in 1940 and fought in all theatres in both an artillery and tank destroyer role.

Originally attached to Panzer Grenadier units, it was eventually decided by industrial planners to incorporate the *StuGs* into the *Panzerwaffe*. This was a monetary and not a tactical decision. The *StuG* could never be a substitute for a real tank due to the absence of a turret. In its favour it was able to carry much heavier armour and armament than a conventional Panzer III.

In a typical panzer attack, *StuGs* would take on multiple roles. They would contribute to the initial barrage, before joining the main body of armour as it moved forward. StuGs would reduce enemy strongpoints such as bunkers or defended houses and, if opposing tanks appeared, it could switch to the tank killer role. However, if an enemy attack developed on their flank, the StuGs with their forward-facing guns were obviously terribly vulnerable.

The mixing of tanks and fixed gun platforms increasingly blunted the operational effectiveness of German armour, but in spite of their limitations the StuGs continued to give good service to the war's end.

Above: A StuG IIIF with a short 75mm gun and armoured skirts resists the Allied landings at Salerno. The StuG was based on the chassis of the Panzer III. The driver's station was unaltered from that of the tank, but behind him was now a very cramped compartment, which made fighting with hatches down an extremely arduous experience.

Above left: Units of the Leibstandarte *SS Adolf Hitler armoured division in Russia in the spring of 1942 prior to its withdrawal to France for a refit. It was in the role of close support vehicles, rather than ersatz tanks, that the StuG excelled. The commander and loader habitually travelled standing half-way out of their respective hatches, so confined was the vehicle's interior. Also in the photograph is a* Panzerjäger *I – a tank-killer based on the Panzer I chassis.*

were fitted with 88-mm guns in a fixed fighting compartment and used to equip two 'heavy tank hunter' battalions. Some were lost to mechanical breakdown, others to the fanatical bravery of Russian anti-tank squads (the absence of an onboard machine gun proved an embarrassing oversight). The survivors were withdrawn to Italy where they were used intended: long range anti-tank weapons.

'HUNTING CATS'

During 1944 the German army received its most deadly tank hunters. By mounting the main armament in a fixed fighting compartment rather than a turret, the Panther could take an 88-mm gun in place of its 75-mm weapon. The *Jagdpanther's* fighting compartment was protected by 100 mm of armour at the front, steeply sloped to make it invulnerable to most Allied tank guns except at point blank range. Weighing 46 tons, its 690 hp engine gave it a top speed of 46 km/h and it had a range of some 160 km.

The stalwart *Pzkfpw.* IV received similar treatment: the *Jagdpanzer* IV or 'Guderian's duck' as it was nicknamed weighed 25 tons, its 300 hp engine giving a top speed of 40 km/h. With 80 mm of armour at the front, it too was a tough proposition for Allied tank guns and better still, its height of just 1.85 m made it very easy to conceal. However, only about 400 *Jagdpanthers* and 1,000 *Jagdpanzer* IVs were built between 1944 and 1945: a combined total of less than the monthly production of American M4 Shermans or Soviet T-34s.

Plans were made for an improved *Jagdpanther* carrying heavier armament, but the war ended before any could be see active service. However, two battalions of *Jagdtigers* were in action by the end of 1944. The Tiger II was armed with an 88-mm gun: but by substituting the turret for a non-traversable, slab-sided box, the vehicle could mount a massive 128-mm gun capable of destroying even the Russian heavy tanks at long range. Unfortunately, these

Above: StuG crews were considered the elite of the artillery units and were issued special field grey uniforms. StuGs had accounted for an impressive 20,000 enemy tanks by the spring of 1944. Approximately 9500 StuG IIIs of various types had been produced by March 1945.

Above: Armaments minister Albert Speer test drives a Tiger chassis. In spite of Speer's undoubted genius for galvanising German arms manufacture, Germany could not produce tanks in sufficient numbers to offset losses. The result was the introduction of several stop-gap designs which down-graded the fighting effectiveness of the Panzer formations.

Below: The Elefant or Ferdinand was a marriage of the rejected Porsche chassis for the Tiger, and an 8.8-cm Pak 43 (longer-barreled and with a higher muzzle velocity than the gun used on normal Tigers). It first saw action at Kursk in 1943, where the lack of a machine gun made it vulnerable to Soviet tank-killing infantry. The main fighting compartment provided adequate space for the crew of six, but the huge vehicle was difficult to conceal and an easy target in open country.

Below: A battery of four Hummels stands ready for action on a Russian steppe in 1942. The Hummel or 'Bumblebee' was the first of a series of hybrids, combining components from Pzkfpw. IIIs and IVs. The close grouping of the guns and relative lack of camouflage demonstrates that the Luftwaffe still had superiority in the air at this time.

monsters weighed over 70 tons and proved mechanically unreliable. Like the Tiger II, they required a great deal of fuel, which was in short supply, and recovering a broken down *Jagdtiger* took the full power of a second – often resulting in another breakdown. They were also too heavy for standard army bridging equipment. Their 250 mm frontal armour kept out anything Allied tank crews could fire at them, but most were lost to mechanical failure and abandoned.

DIMINUTIVE GIANT

The most successful German tank hunter was not a giant, but the diminutive *Hetzer* or 'Baiter' (as in bull-baiter). This was an ingenious conversion of the old Czech *Pzkpfw* 38(t). Little more than two metres high, it weighed less than 16 tons yet its 75-mm gun could knock out most Allied tanks. It was unusually plentiful by German standards, with some 2,500 produced at the Skoda works by early 1945.

As the number of tank hunter units increased, *StuG* crews were transferred into them to provide a core of experienced personnel. General Heinz Guderian, Inspector General of Armoured Troops, planned to integrate the assault guns and the tank hunters during 1944-45. Infantry divisions were to receive companies – or whole battalions – of turretless armoured vehicles which would double as tank hunters and assault guns.

Just as the German tank hunters stemmed from the inferiority of their main battle tanks compared to the Russian behemoths, so the British and

Americans soon copied the idea. Western tanks were thin-skinned and under-armed compared to their German opponents. One British solution was to put the powerful 17-pdr anti-tank guns onto the old Valentine tank chassis; christened the Archer, it was used in 1944 and 1945. The US Army already had 75-mm guns on M3 half-tracks in the anti-tank battalions of its armoured divisions. These were progressively upgraded with the M10 and M36 tank destroyers; these vehicles had fully traversable turrets, albeit lightly armoured and open-topped.

'ANIMAL HUNTER'

The Russians reacted even more effectively: by the summer of 1943 they had mounted 152-mm (6-inch) howitzers onto the KV-1 chassis to produce a formidable tank destroyer/infantry support vehicle. The ISU-152 became known as the 'animal hunter' after the toll it took of Panthers and Tigers. From 1944 these were supplemented by large numbers of SU-85 and SU-100 tank destroyers. Based on the T-34 chassis, they mounted high-velocity 85 mm and 100 mm calibre weapons respectively.

The tradition endured after the war: among the first armoured vehicles ordered by the West German army was a light tank chassis with a 90-mm anti-tank gun projecting from the sharply angled hull front – an updated *StuG*. The famous post-war Swedish S-tank was designed at the outset as a turretless vehicle. An AFV design born of desperation had become a sub-species of combat vehicle enduring to the present day.

CZECH WORK HORSE

Above: The Marder III production line at BMM in Prague. The factory turned out around 500 of the conversions, which mounted the captured Soviet 76.2-mm gun or the 75-mm German PaK.

ALTHOUGH THE GERMANS made much use of captured enemy vehicles, adapting them for their own purposes, the only foreign design which they put into production, albeit significantly modified, was the Czech TNH P-S light tank. Entering service with the Wehrmacht as the *Pzkfpw. 38(t)*, it's simple chassis and reliable engine were adapted to be used in a wide variety of roles.

The *Marder* series was an extremely successful attempt at marrying PaK (anti-tank) weapons to the 38(t) chassis. There were two types produced. Both were designated *Marder* III, and they provided Panzer and Panzer Grenadier divisions with mobile and powerful tank-busting weaponry. Although largely replaced by better designed *Panzerjägers*, some Marders saw service to the end of the war.

The most effective conversion of the 38(t) was the *Jagdpanzer Hetzer* or 'Baiter' which was probably the best of its type produced during WW2. It served with the Swiss Army into the 1970s.

Below right: The Hetzer *used the same basic engine, suspension and running gear as the 38(t), allied to an armoured sloping hull, enclosing a four man crew. The resultant combination was small and low, yet it was well protected and had good cross-country performance. Its gun could knock out all but the heaviest enemy tanks.*

Below: The original Marder III *proved to be nose-heavy. This limited mobility, so in the interests of balance the engine was relocated at the front of the chassis, while the 'working platform' and the heavy weaponry it carried was moved to the rear. Production was based in Prague, and some 800 units were completed.*

Left: Over 1400 of the light Panzer 38(t) were produced up until 1942, when developments in tank warfare rendered this most successful vehicle obsolete for all but reconnaissance duties. Its chassis remained in production beyond WW2, being used in the Czech army.

Right: The 'Bison' was an open-topped self-propelled artillery piece carrying the 15-cm siG infantry howitzer and was used in the close fire-support role. Being an early conversion, the gun on the Bison was mounted well forward, the engine being retained at the rear.

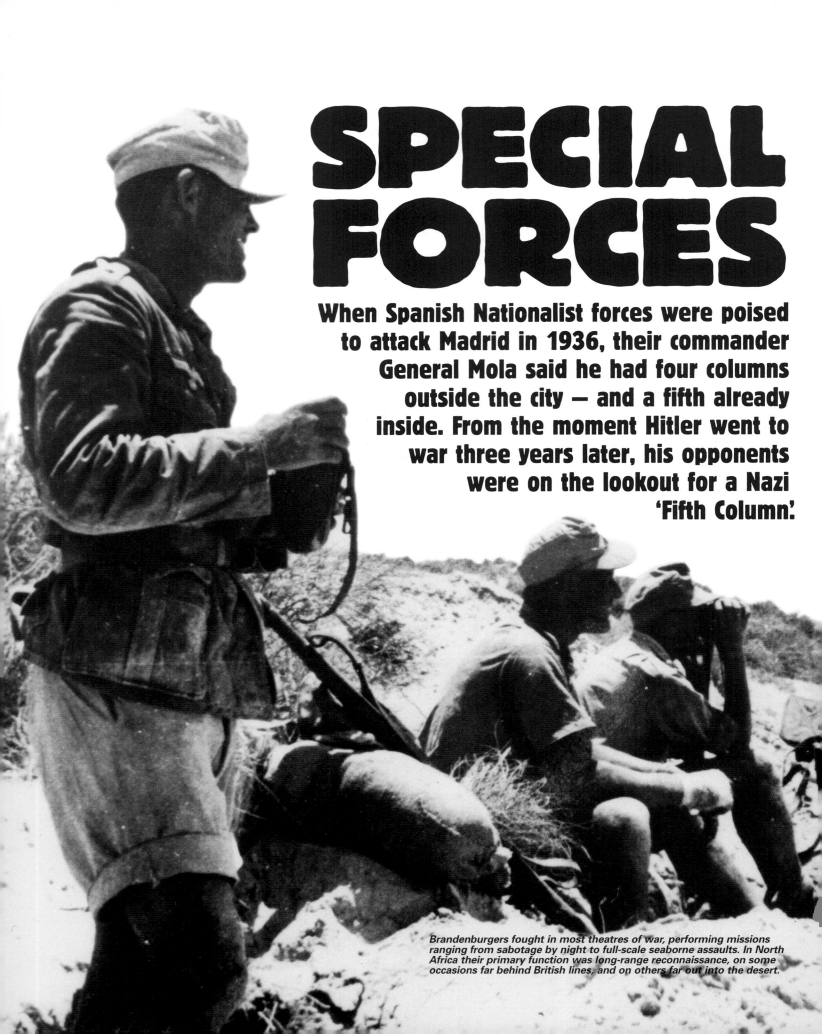

SPECIAL FORCES

When Spanish Nationalist forces were poised to attack Madrid in 1936, their commander General Mola said he had four columns outside the city — and a fifth already inside. From the moment Hitler went to war three years later, his opponents were on the lookout for a Nazi 'Fifth Column'.

Brandenburgers fought in most theatres of war, performing missions ranging from sabotage by night to full-scale seaborne assaults. In North Africa their primary function was long-range reconnaissance, on some occasions far behind British lines, and on others far out into the desert.

J OSEPH GOEBBELS' radio broadcasts added to the fear of fifth columnists. He called on *Volksdeutsch* – ethnic Germans – all over Europe to rally to Hitler.

Some helped the Germans during the invasion of Poland. The fall of Norway in 1940 was assisted by Nazi sympathisers led by Vidkun Quisling: he gave his name to those who collaborated in occupied Europe.

The blitz across France and the Low countries inspired widespread arrests of suspected fifth columnists. Military authorities knew that the strategically vital bridge over the river Maas at Gennep had been captured by some sort of special forces unit in advance of the main invasion force. A spy scare gripped Britain; immigrants and refugees were regarded with deep suspicion. The hunt was on for Nazi parachutists.

SPECIAL OPERATIONS

The paratroops who seized the bridge at Gennep had also captured the Belt bridge during the invasion of Denmark. They were not part of the Luftwaffe's elite *Fallschirmjäger* division

that parachuted into Holland, but a special unit reporting directly to OKW. Officially known as *Baulehrbataillon zbV* 800 (construction training/special duties battalion 800) they were christened 'Brandenburgers' after the state in which they were formed in 1939. The unit was subordinated to Admiral Canaris and the *Abwehr*. Recruited in company strength and expanded to a battalion in 1940, it included a high proportion of *Volksdeutsch* proficient in foreign languages. Allied special forces, such as the British SAS, would be created during the war for operations behind the lines, but the Brandenburgers were in action from the first day of Hitler's War.

'TRAINING' REGIMENT

By the end of 1940 the Brandenburgers were re-designated *Lehr Regiment Brandenburg zbV* 800 and expanded to include a parachute battalion and a battalion of marines. They were tasked with the capture of strategically vital points during the invasion of the Balkans. Detachments secured the bridge over the river Vardar in Yugoslavia while others guarded the Romanian oil wells at Ploesti, feared by OKW to be a target of Allied saboteurs. Brandenburgers spearheaded the assault on Russia in 1941, capturing the bridge over the Dvina at Daugavpils in Latvia and seizing

Above: Brandenburgers spearheaded the German attack on the Low Countries in May 1940. Their primary task was to take several bridges ahead of the advancing Wehrmacht, using Dutch greatcoats and helmets to deceive the defending forces until the moment of attack.

Below: Partisans in Serbia – or Brandenburgers in disguise? The Abwehr's *special operations unit specialised in covert operations in enemy uniform – an extremely dangerous mission, since capture almost invariably meant execution as spies.*

the city of Lvov.

The Latvian mission was nearly a 'bridge too far'. A company of Brandenburgers had parachuted behind the lines, dressed in Red Army uniforms. Speaking fluent Russian, they pretended to march across the bridge, then shot down the sentries and seized control of both banks. However, the German armoured column that was supposed to link up with them took longer than expected, and the Russians counter-attacked the bridge. The Brandenburgers fought savagely to hold their ground until the tanks arrived. Ironically, one of

their number, taken prisoner by German forces unaware of his identity, was photographed: his image, captioned 'Typical Bolshevik subhuman' was published in Signal magazine to the amusement of his comrades.

The Brandenburgers expanded to a division during 1942, although its units were scattered across all fronts, including North Africa, and seldom fought in greater than company strength. It trained for assaults on Soviet factories in the Urals or raids on the Caucasus oil fields, but served primarily as an intelligence gathering service. Small patrols, often including

Above: Special Units 287 and 288 were formed from the 11th Brandenburg Company. They began operations in North Africa in 1941, even though Erwin Rommel did not approve of 'special forces'. Among their planned operations was one to foment a nationalist rebellion in Cairo, and another was to seize bridgeheads over the Suez Canal.

Below: The Jablunka Pass Detachment was the first 'Brandenburger' unit to see action, on 26 August 1939. Commanded by Oberleutnant Albrecht Herzner, a force of 70 disguised Polish-speaking soldiers seized a key railroad junction in the Tatra mountains. However, radio-silence for security reasons meant that they did not find out the invasion of Poland had been delayed for four days, and when they did make contact they were ordered to slip back over the border.

Below: Hauptmann von Hippel of the Abwehr's Department II first proposed a special operations commando unit before the war. The first wartime operations were carried out by temporary units, but by November 1939 the first company was in training at Brandenburg, and by December von Hippel was in command of a battalion.

'turned' Russian soldiers, infiltrated behind Soviet lines to report on the location, strength and activities of Soviet forces. The risk of capture was high and these men faced a grisly fate in enemy hands. Their reports enabled OKW to enjoy excellent knowledge of the Soviet order of battle. From 1942 units from the Brandenburg division were also employed on anti-partisan duties.

SPYING ON PARTISANS

Russian-speaking soldiers would join Red Army partisan units in order to betray their operations. As the guerrilla groups were assembled from a wide variety of army units cut off by the German advance in 1941, it was possible to create a multitude of cover stories, but the risks and consequences of capture were terrible indeed.

The last and potentially greatest Brandenburger mission ended in obscure failure in November 1943. The *Abwehr* knew that Stalin, Churchill and Roosevelt were to meet at Tehran at the end of the month. Aided by agents from the *Volksdeutsch* community in northern Iran and by spies inside the Persian capital, they concocted Operation Long Jump: a plan to kill or capture 'the Big Three'. An assault team would parachute in near the city and be conducted to the conference area by the *Abwehr* team already in position. Unfortunately for the Brandenburgers, the operation was betrayed to the NKVD. Soviet agents captured some of the men in Tehran and the commandos were killed when their unmarked Junkers Ju-52 was bounced by Soviet fighters as it flew across the Turkish border.

The implication of the *Abwehr* in the resistance against Hitler led to its take-over by the SS in February 1944. The Brandenburg division was redesignated as a *panzergrenadier* division, to be employed as conventional mechanised infantry. Some men were transferred to the SS to join *Obersturmbannführer*

(Lieutenant-Colonel) Otto Skorzeny's commando teams, the Friedenthal *Jagdverbände* (Friedenthal hunting groups).

Skorzeny was an Austrian volunteer who joined 1st SS division *Leibstandarte* Adolf Hitler and served in its artillery regiment from 1940 until he was invalided out of Russia in December 1942. He returned to Vienna with the Iron Cross First Class and a fitness report that restricted him to home duties. Nevertheless, he transferred to 3rd SS division *Totenkopf* in early 1943, but suffered a relapse. A giant of a man with a prominent duelling scar, Skorzeny had attracted the attention of his superiors for his ruthlessness and bravery.

SS SPECIAL FORCES

When Himmler decided to follow the example of the SAS and create a special forces unit in the SS, he selected the fanatical *Obersturmführer* (Lieutenant) unaware how rapidly his services would be required. The unit was established on Hitler's birthday 1943 and began training at Friedenthal.

One British operation that particularly inspired Skorzeny was the attempt to kill General Rommel at his headquarters during the Desert War. Although the Desert Fox was not there at the time, the appearance of British commandos deep behind German lines had become a regular feature of the campaign in North Africa.

MUSSOLINI RESCUE

On 23 July 1943 Mussolini was overthrown by his army high command and arrested. In spite of numerous security measures taken by his captors, the Germans tracked him down. Skorzeny was ordered to the rescue, and in a daring raid freed the former dictator.

Hitler was jubilant. Goebbels milked the incident for all it was worth. Skorzeny was promoted and his unit enlarged. Feted in Berlin, he prepared several special operations that were

THE FÜHRER'S DAREDEVIL

OTTO SKORZENY'S MOST FAMOUS MISSION was the rescue of the deposed Italian leader Benito Mussolini. Hitler knew Italy was poised to change sides, and ordered the rescue of his fellow dictator so that the Fascist regime could be resurrected.

Skorzeny was summoned to Hitler, who took an immediate liking to this super-confident fellow Austrian. The Führer's judgement was not misplaced. Skorzeny flew to Italy where he travelled the country in a variety of disguises, depending on his own resources rather than German army intelligence. He tracked Mussolini to the Hotel Imperatore, a resort high in the Abruzzi mountains. It was thought to be impregnable to assault by anything less than a division.

On 9 September, as Allied forces landed in southern Italy, Skorzeny attacked the hotel by glider, leading 90 men drawn from his own command and from 7. *Fallschirmjäger* division. The daring assault took the Italians completely by surprise. Having secured the building and rescued Mussolini, the plan called for the fallen dictator to be driven to Aquila, where the airfield had been seized by a German parachute battalion. However, Skorzeny could not make contact with the Luftwaffe to coordinate the move, so was forced to resort to his back-up plan. A Fieseler Fi 156 Storch spotter plane put down on the tiny field by the hotel, and whisked Mussolini to freedom.

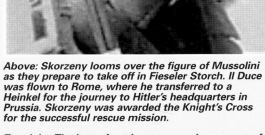

Above: Skorzeny looms over the figure of Mussolini as they prepare to take off in Fieseler Storch. Il Duce was flown to Rome, where he transferred to a Heinkel for the journey to Hitler's headquarters in Prussia. Skorzeny was awarded the Knight's Cross for the successful rescue mission.

Top right: The large Austrian commando was one of the most colourful figures to emerge from the Third Reich. His scarred face came from the tenth of 15 ritual sabre duels he fought as a student in Vienna. A Nazi party member from 1930, he was heavily involved in preparations for the Anschluss, and became something of a protege of Kaltenbrunner.

Right: Few of Skorzeny's planned missions ever took place. Usually daring, even foolhardy in conception, they faced both political and military opposition from more conventionally-minded superiors. One of the most ambitious was to have been launched in November 1943, when the three main Allied leaders were in conference in Teheran. Skorzeny intended to raid the conference, decapitating the anti-German alliance at one stroke.

Above: Operation Axis was the plan to seize Italian-held positions once the Badoglio government announced for the Allies. The 1st Company of the Brandenburger coastal raider battalion was based in Piraeus, and went into action in the Athens/Larissa area on 9 September.

Above: In one of the last major German successes of the Mediterranean campaign, the Brandenburgers spearheaded the German counter-attack to retake the Aegean islands of Kos and Leros, which had been captured by the British in September 1943.

overtaken by events and cancelled, including the abduction of Marshal Pétain and the assassination of Tito. In the capital on 20 July, he coordinated loyal Nazi units against the coup attempt that followed the bomb attack on Hitler's headquarters.

HORTHY MISSION

Skorzeny's next mission was to keep Hungary in the war. The Hungarian regent, Admiral Horthy was known to be negotiating with Stalin; the Red Army had seized passes over the Carpathian mountains and was poised to invade the Magyar heartland. If Hungary defected, Germany itself would be exposed to invasion. In an exemplary display of bluff and daring, Skorzeny succeeded in kidnapping Horthy's son in the middle of Budapest and drove a motorised column right into the palace. The Regent was removed and replaced by a puppet regime drawn from the Hungarian Fascist movement. Hungary remained a German ally until the end of the war.

On 16 December 1944 the German army launched its last great offensive of the war: Hitler's insanely ambitious attempt to repeat the triumph of 1940 by

attacking through the Ardennes forest. The plan called for a rapid breakthrough to the river Meuse, thence to Antwerp, cutting off the vanguard of the Allied armies.

Skorzeny was ordered to take the Meuse crossings before Allied engineers could blow the bridges. Leading a column dressed in American uniforms and driving captured US tanks and trucks, he was to bluff his way as far as possible and then fight once his unit's cover was blown. OKW issued a request for English-speaking volunteers.

'SPIES' CONTROVERSY

The decision to fight in enemy uniform was controversial. Under the internationally accepted rules of war, this meant execution if captured. It had never been an issue in Russia where both sides habitually executed PoWs, but would prevent a 'civilised' surrender in the style still possible with the British and Americans.

Skorzeny's 150th Panzer Brigade was compromised from the start. Only one of the promised M4 Shermans turned up in running order, and Skorzeny's men had to mock up several Panther tanks to look like Shermans. His adjutant spoke for them all when he observed that

these might just fool a GI – in the dark and at long range. Skorzeny was not happy: he had to be talked out of aborting the mission.

Ahead of his mechanised brigade, a number of four-man teams drove into the Allied lines in jeeps. Selected from his best English speakers, their attempts to impersonate GIs were not uniformly successful: one group stopped for gas and said 'petrol, please'. Neither word was in the vocabulary of a GI in a hurry and the Germans fled when their identity was challenged. They crashed and were arrested.

Three refused to speak even when threatened with a death sentence. As a result, they were executed by firing squad. Any qualms the US authorities might have had were soon removed by news of the massacre of American prisoners by SS men at Malmedy. One man broke and confessed all.

RUMOURS AND PANIC

The news started a new panic. Rumours multiplied, but the assumption was that Skorzeny was leading a band of cut-throats in Allied uniforms, their objective: the assassination of General Eisenhower. Anyone trying to pass through a US Army checkpoint

had to undergo a ludicrous process of question and answer. Many a British officer failed to know the difference between a linebacker and a wide receiver or know who Betty Grable had married. They found themselves under arrest. Eisenhower became a virtual prisoner in his own headquarters, his every movement covered by jittery MPs.

The rumours proved far more effective than 150th Panzer Brigade itself, which was stuck in traffic behind the German lines. The Meuse crossings remained tantalisingly out of reach. There was no prospect of seizing them by *coup de main*. On 21 December, Skorzeny's men were committed as part of an attack on the US 30th Division near Malmedy; they discarded their US uniforms and fought as conventional troops. Skorzeny was wounded and on the 28th the unit was withdrawn.

The story of Hitler's special forces thus began and ended with a panic hunt for Fifth Columnists. Skorzeny was tried for war crimes at Nuremberg and acquitted. His involvement in the escape of some SS officers to South America has never been proved. He lived in Spain until his death in 1975.

BATTLE OF THE BULGE

THE WINTER OFFENSIVE through the Ardennes at the end of 1944 was Germany's last throw of the dice. Hitler's generals amassed the largest and most powerful strike force since the great eastern front battles of 1943. Equipped with the latest weapons, three entire armies – including Sepp Dietrich's 6th SS Panzer Army and Hasso von Manteuffel's 5th Panzer Army – smashed into a weak point in the American front line. The German spearheads were directed at the port of Antwerp, their aim to divide the Allied forces.

The attack, shocking though it was to the Allies, could never have succeeded. The British, Americans and Canadians simply had too many men, too much equipment and a vast superiority in the air. After initial successes, the Germans quickly bogged down in the face of stiffening American resistance – resistance that was only strengthened by reports of the massacre of American prisoners at Malmedy. It was into this maelstrom that Skorzeny's special group of English-speaking, American-dressed volunteers was thrown. Skorzeny's men knew that if they fell into American hands, they risked being shot. Nevertheless, they went ahead with the operation.

Above: The German plan was to reach the Meuse on day one of the attack. One of the tasks allotted to Skorzeny's raiders was to seize key bridges over the river: however, the advance teams in Jeeps were rumbled before they could take their objectives, and the armoured force in American tanks which was supposed to support them was caught in traffic. Even if they had been successful and managed to take the river crossings, it would have been to no avail: unexpectedly fierce American resistance slowed the main German attack, already crippled by lack of fuel. Instead of being on the river by the end of day one, the leading Panzers were still 30 kilometres short of their objective on the 20th of December, four days after the offensive began.

Below and below left: Skorzeny survived the mission – wounded in action, he got back to the German lines and was hospitalised. Many of his men were less fortunate, and a number were captured wearing American uniforms. The members of one group refused to talk to the court martial which tried them, and were sentenced to be shot as spies. As a last request, Fahnrich Guenther Billing (below left), Feldwebel Manfred Pernass and Obergefreiter Schmidt asked for Christmas carols to be sung to them by captured German nurses.

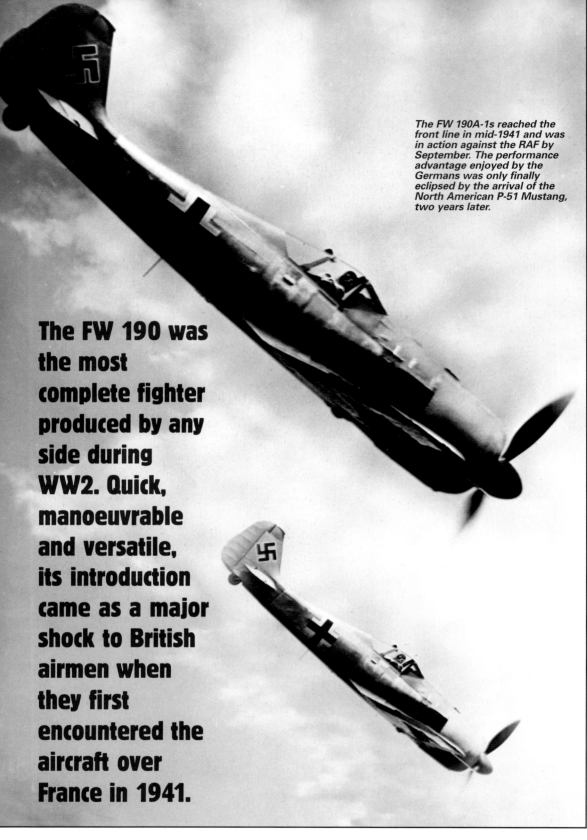

The FW 190A-1s reached the front line in mid-1941 and was in action against the RAF by September. The performance advantage enjoyed by the Germans was only finally eclipsed by the arrival of the North American P-51 Mustang, two years later.

The FW 190 was the most complete fighter produced by any side during WW2. Quick, manoeuvrable and versatile, its introduction came as a major shock to British airmen when they first encountered the aircraft over France in 1941.

Focke-Wulf Fw 190
BUTCHER-BIRD

THE FOCKE-WULF Fw 190 was first flown on 1 June 1939 and entered service with the Luftwaffe in August 1941. By the close of the war the Luftwaffe had received 16,724 aircraft of all types, placing it second only to the Bf 109 as the most extensively produced aircraft in the Third Reich.

The Fw 190 was designed as a response to a development contract for a new single seat fighter placed in the autumn of 1937by the *Reichsluftfahrt-ministerium* – RLM, or Reich Air Ministry – with Focke-Wulf *Flugzeugbau*. The first prototype flew on 1 June 1939. Engine changes followed and the first production model, the Fw 190A-1, began to leave the assembly lines in Bremen and Hamburg late in 1940.

CHANNEL DASH

The first aircraft were delivered to a *Jagdstaffel* based at le Bourget in May 1941 and during the summer the fighter appeared in action with *Jagdgeschwader* (JG) 26 commanded by Adolf Galland. Fw 190s clashed with RAF Spitfires on 27 September 1941 and in the action the RAF lost three aircraft. It was not until the Spitfire IX entered service almost a year later that the Fw 190 was seriously challenged. The Fw 190A-1 earned the unofficial name of *Würger* – Butcher Bird.

The fighter saw its first major deployment providing air cover for the battle cruisers *Scharnhorst* and *Gneisenau* and heavy cruiser *Prinz Eugen* in Operation *Cerberus/Donnerkeil* – the Channel Dash of 12-13 February 1942. The 190s of JG26 shot down six Fairey Swordfish torpedo bombers that attempted to attack the warships.

Over the next two years, Fw 190s appeared in increasing numbers on all major fronts, from the Arctic and Russia to the Mediterranean. In the defence of the Reich, the Fw 190A-5/U2 night fighter was fitted with anti-dazzle screens and flame shrouds over the exhausts and employed in *Wilde Sau* – Wild Boar tactics. *Wilde Sau* was a form of free lance night fighting co-ordinated with searchlights and was employed by JG 300, formed in July 1943, and subsequently by JG 301 and JG 302.

FIGHTER BOMBERS

In the west, 190s were used over the beaches of Dieppe in August 1942 and in 'hit and run' raids against targets in southern England. In these operations Fw 190 *Jabos* – fighter bombers – of JG26 attacked railway yards, factories and gasometers and claimed six coastal vessels. The installation of underwing drop tanks in September allowed the aircraft to fly deeper into southern England.

The Fw 190A-4/Trop was a tropicalised version of the fighter designed for use in the Mediterranean. It had filters for its engine intakes to screen out dust. The aircraft had a rack for a 250 kg bomb under the fuselage. The Fw 190A-5/ U15 was an experimental torpedo fighter that was fitted with a rack for a 1,000 kg LT 950 torpedo. The A-5/U16 was a special bomber destroyer version with 30 mm MK 108 cannon deployed. For flight training the Fw 190A-8/U1 was developed, this two seater first flew on 23 January 1944.

RAF WINDFALL

The RAF were able to assess their new enemy in a less hostile environment when on the evening of 23 June 1942 *Oberleutnant* Arnin Faber, the adjutant of III/JG2, landed his Fw 190A-3 at RAF Pembrey. The nine aircraft of Faber's *Staffel* had been in combat with Spitfires of the Exeter-based Polish Wing returning from a strike on Morlaix airfield. Faber may have mistaken the Bristol Channel for the English Channel – before he landed he made a series of victory roles over the airfield. The aircraft was rushed to Farnborough for evaluation and some of the design features

were incorporated into the Hawker Tempest.

About a year later an Fw 190A-4 in a temporary matt-black finish landed at RAF West Malling following a night intrusion mission. Eventually the RAF had three Fw 190s that were operated as part of the 'RAFwaffe'. This was a 'flying circus' of captured enemy aircraft known as Flight 1426 that was based at Collyweston, a satellite airfield of RAF Wittering.

The Fw 190B was a high-altitude interceptor powered by a 1,800 hp Daimler-Benz DB 603 liquid cooled engine. Six prototypes were built and the big belly-mounted Focke-Wulf turbo-superchargers earned it the nickname *Känguruh* – Kangaroo. A four-bladed propeller made efficient use of the additional power, and heights in excess of 13,000 metres were reached on test.

LANGNASE

The introduction of the superb Fw 190D led to the abandonment of the high-altitude programme. The Fw 190D entered service in 1944, and its 1,770hp Junkers Jumo 213A-1 in line engine – much longer than the compact BMW radial of the A-series earned it the nickname *Langnase* – Long Nose.

Large numbers of Fw 190Ds were used in Operation *Bodenplatte* or Baseplate, the Luftwaffe's final fling – a desparate and futile attack on Allied airfields in Belgium and Holland in January 1945. Though production remained high in 1944 and even into 1945, many of the new aircraft remained grounded due to lack of fuel.

STUKA REPLACEMENT

The Fw 190F and G were close-support and ground attack variants of the fighter. The 'F' model entered service in the winter of 1942-43, replacing the vulnerable Ju 87 in day, and later night, ground-assault *Gruppen*.

Fw 190Fs operated mainly on the Eastern Front, supporting

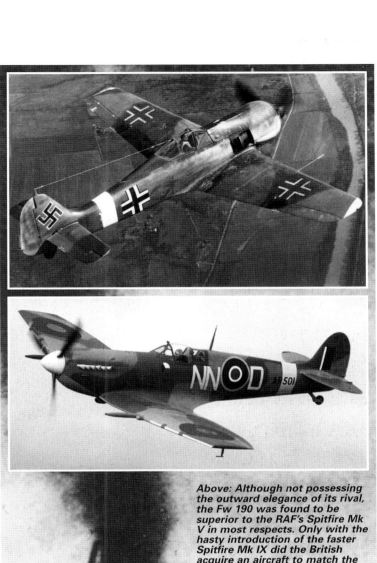

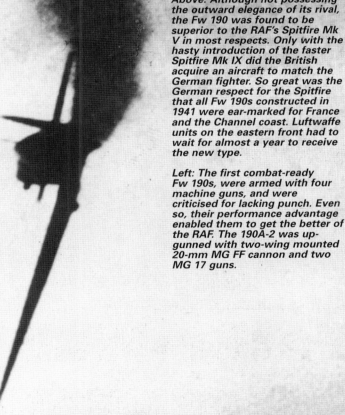

Above: Although not possessing the outward elegance of its rival, the Fw 190 was found to be superior to the RAF's Spitfire Mk V in most respects. Only with the hasty introduction of the faster Spitfire Mk IX did the British acquire an aircraft to match the German fighter. So great was the German respect for the Spitfire that all Fw 190s constructed in 1941 were ear-marked for France and the Channel coast. Luftwaffe units on the eastern front had to wait for almost a year to receive the new type.

Left: The first combat-ready Fw 190s, were armed with four machine guns, and were criticised for lacking punch. Even so, their performance advantage enabled them to get the better of the RAF. The 190A-2 was up-gunned with two-wing mounted 20-mm MG FF cannon and two MG 17 guns.

Weapons Carrier

Above: In spite of its modest size, the Fw 190 was capable of carrying a diverse and heavy load of weaponry. This included the ability to deploy a full-sized naval torpedo. The craft pictured here is the A-5/U14. 'U' is short for Umrüst-Bausätze or 'conversion kit'.

Above: Jagdbomber mit vergrösserter Reichweite was the official name for extended range fighter-bomber variants of the 190, universally shortened to 'Jabo-Rei'. This prototype Fw 190A-5/U-13 carried only two guns, a reduced weapons load, and two 300 litre fuel tanks.

Below: The Fw 190F was a ground-attack version of the basic A-type, and was equipped with extra armour to provide protection against light anti-aircraft fire from the ground. Seeing service particularly on the Eastern Front, this example carries eight 50kg bombs.

Below: The Pulk-Zerstörer was designed to disrupt USAAF bomber formations and was successfully used during the Schweinfurt raid of 14 October 1943. The pilot would fire the underwing 21-cm mortars at a bomber box, and then supporting fighters would move in for the kill.

Left: Fw 190Gs of I Gruppe, Schlachtgeschwader 2 'Immelmann'. Pictured in mid-1943, these aircraft were to play an important role in the German summer offensive at Kursk, alongside the slow and vulnerable Ju 87 Stuka they were to replace.

German withdrawals. They were also employed in smaller numbers in the Mediterranean and Italian campaigns in daylight actions against USAAF bombers over Germany, and in France. Fw 190s were heavily committed against the Normandy landings in 1944, Fw 190As equipping the veteran JGs 2 and 26, while about 75 Fw190Fs and Gs were used by *Schlachtgeschwader* SG 4 and SG 10.

Though there was a vital need for ground attack aircraft in Western Europe, the Luftwaffe high command was obliged to deploy nearly 600 Fw 190s on the eastern Front in anticipation of the Red Army's summer 1944 offensive.

PANZERBLITZ

The Fw 190F was armed with 2 cm cannon and 13 mm machine guns. It could carry 250 kg, 500 kg, 1,000 kg, 1,800 kg bombs, as well as SD-2 and SD-4 cluster weapons – the latter with a shaped-charge war head for use against tanks. In the final stages of the war they were armed with the 8.8 cm *Panzerschreck* and *Panzerblitz* rocket projectiles for anti-armour attacks.

The Fw190G actually appeared earlier than the 'F' series. It was fitted with bomb racks as standard and had the fuselage machine guns deleted. Its operational debut was in the final stages of the Tunisian

Long-Nose

ALTHOUGH ON ITS DEBUT in 1941 the Fw 190 was the fastest, most formidable fighter in the world, its performance fell away at higher altitudes, and was inferior to that of the Spitfire above 7000 metres. Once the Americans joined the war, it became clear that the Luftwaffe was going to need high altitude fighters to counter growing USAAF bomber strength. After initial experiments with superchargers, Berlin ordered Kurt Tank, the 190's designer and technical director at Focke-Wulf, to use the Junkers Jumo 213A engine – which had actually been developed for the Heinkel 111 bomber.

The Fw 190D was first delivered to combat units in August 1944. Tank had little faith in it – the 190D was only meant to be a stop-gap before Tank's favoured Ta 152 could come on line. But after initial reservations Luftwaffe pilots raved about the new type, considering it the best fighter in the air force. A match for any Allied fighter that it encountered, the *Dora* was restricted only by lack of fuel and the shortage of trained pilots. Many of the Fw 190Ds were wasted in low-level roles such as protecting Me 262 jets when taking off and landing.

Left: Dipl-Ing Kurt Waldemar Tank, the man behind the original Fw 190 design, was the Technical Director and chief of flight testing at Focke-Wulf.

Above: The first attempt to boost the Fw 190s high-altitude performance was the Fw 190B which had a turbo-boosted BMW radial, followed by the Fw 190C seen here. The 'C' model featured a Daimler-Benz DB603 engine, a four blade propeller and a massive supercharger.

In April 1944 a US Army pilot engaged an aircraft which he reported as an Fw 190 with a long nose. It became known as the 'Schnozzle' after Schnozzle Durante, the nasally unchallenged American comic.

campaign in North Africa and in the Battle of Kursk in July 1943.

The Fw190 pedigree lived on in the Focke-Wulf Ta 152H-1 high altitude fighter. It was in effect an improved Fw190D, but its new designation was a tribute to the designer of the Fw 190, Professor Dipl. Ing. Kurt Tank. The first aircraft reached front line squadrons in 1945 and were used in defence of Me 262 bases.

FOCKE-WULF ACES

Some of the 302 victories scored by Major Gerhard Barkhorn were scored flying a Fw 190; *Oberleutnant* Otto Kittel ranked up most of his 267+ victories in an Fw 190A-5; Major Walter Nowotny scored some of his 258 kills while flying a Fw 190 with JG 54 *Grunherz*. Nowotny would eventually be protected by Fw190D fighters when he

commanded the Me 262 equipped *Jagdgeschwader* 7, *Kommando* Nowotny in 1945.

Hans-Ulrich Rudel is best known as a Stuka pilot, but he also flew Fw 190s. Most Stuka pilots were withdrawn from the Eastern Front to learn the new aircraft, but Rudel taught himself on the new fighter bomber while continuing to fly operational sorties in his Stuka. "I finish up my self-training," he wrote, "by going out straight away on one or two sorties in the frontal area with the new type and feel quite safe with it." It is a tribute to a fine aircraft from the greatest ground attack pilot in history.

Fw 190 operations in the East were assisted by the poor early training of Soviet air crews. Although later Lavochkin and Yak fighters could match the 190 at low level, few Soviet aircrew could match German pilot skills.

A 2cm Flakvierling *38 SdKfz 7/1* anti-aircraft 'half-track prepares for action. When firing, the sides of the vehicle were folded down to provide a working platform around the gun. Later versions were fitted with an armoured cab, but the gun crew were never provided with similar protection.

HALF-TRACKS

Blitzkrieg was a new type of warfare based around the mobility and firepower of the *panzer*. But tanks alone are vulnerable to enemy infantry action, so covering troops had to be brought forward at the same speed as the armour. The Germans developed the highly mobile, armoured half-track as a solution to the problem.

MILITARY terminology often takes time to catch up with the changing nature of war. By the end of the 20th century, the infantrymen of most western armies were foot soldiers only in name: they rode to war in armoured personnel carriers (APCs) often fitted with turret-mounted cannon, machine guns and even anti-tank missiles. Various terms have been coined, 'armoured infantry', 'armoured cavalry' or 'mechanised infantry'. The vehicles themselves are now split between lightly armed APCs and MICVs (Mechanised Infantry Combat Vehicles) which are quite capable of fighting it out with older types of tank.

In battle, the infantry would dismount to fight on foot according to circumstances. The British army, reluctant to regard its vehicles as anything more than transports, tended to operate out of the vehicle most of the time. The soldiers of Soviet-trained armies were reluctant to get out at all – something that cost the Arab forces dearly in their 1973 war with Israel.

MOBILE WARRIORS
The driving force behind the transition from foot soldiers to mechanised warriors was the German army of World War II,

whose own terminology combined the old and new in memorable style. The infantry units of the tank divisions were christened *panzergrenadiers*. Their half-tracked vehicles were the most distinctive of the war.

CONCENTRATED POWER

While the British and French persisted in regarding the tank as primarily an infantry support weapon, to be distributed in small units among the infantry divisions, the German army followed the Soviet lead. The *Reichswehr's* secret training programme on the Red Army tank grounds paid enormous dividends. German tanks were to be concentrated in discrete armoured divisions, with accompanying infantry, artillery, anti-tank, anti-aircraft and even re-supply columns all mounted in vehicles, with as high a proportion as possible capable of off-road movement.

Half-track vehicles were already in service as artillery tractors. Their cross country capability was not as great as a fully tracked vehicle, but they were cheaper and quicker to manufacture, being essentially trucks with the rear wheels replaced by a track unit. It was a short step to consider them as infantry transports for the *panzer grenadier* regiments.

HANOMAGS

The idea was to fit a lightly armoured shell to a half-track chassis. Development began in 1937; Hanomag undertook the design of the chassis while Büssing-NAG produced the armoured body. The vehicle used as a basis for the design was the three-ton prime mover, the Sd Kfz 11. Designated the Sd Kfz 251, Allied sources later referred to as the Hanomag; the German army's term for such vehicles was *Schützenpanzerwagen*, abbreviated to SPW. Series production commenced in June 1939 and continued until September 1943.

The basic infantry carrier was fitted with a 7.92 mm machine

The SdKfz 251 was developed as an offshoot of the German half-tracked artillery tractor. It acted as an armoured personnel carrier for infantry accompanying the newly formed panzer divisions. It could carry up to 12 soldiers, and was armed with two MG34 machine guns.

HANOMAGS IN ACTION

ALTHOUGH GERMAN INDUSTRY produced some 15,000 SdKfz 251s or Hanomags for the armed forces, this figure fell way below the number needed to fully equip her nominally motorised units.

Throughout the war the German Army suffered from so chronic a shortage of equipment that when Hanomags went into action its logistics requirements met by a quartermaster's nightmare of captured French or Soviet vehicles. Although nominally designed to carry 12 troops, it rarely did. In the real world, there was barely room in the troop compartment for eight infantrymen in full combat gear.

The role of the Hanomag companies evolved rapidly during the war. In the early Blitzkrieg years the Grenadiers often operated on their own. With the Panzer units punching through enemy defences and into their rear areas, the Grenadiers had to cover the dangerously exposed flanks of the tank units against counter-attack. This would involve dismounting from their vehicles to adopt defensive positions, only later to re-embark once the enemy had been neutralised.

From 1942, with the advent of more heavily fortified positions, tactics were reversed. Tanks were increasingly vulnerable to fortified anti-tank positions, and so worked in close cooperation with the *panzergrenadier* units. It was now the infantry's task to scout forward of the tanks to disperse enemy tank-killing squads, watch out for minefields and generally be the eyes of the nearly blind tankers.

By 1945 the roles had changed again; desperate times evoked drastic responses and Hanomags were fitted with heavy artillery pieces to act as tank hunters.

Below: Pictured here with BMW motorcycle and sidecar in the foreground and the Panzer V 'Panther' to the rear is the SdKfz 251/7. Produced for use by combat engineers, it carried specialist equipment such as a light assault bridge that was slung along the top of the hull.

Above: Panzergrenadiers armed with MP40 sub-machine guns deploy from the rear of a Hanomag. It was intended that all motorised troops be so equipped, but as in many other areas German production fell short of requirements.

Right: The SdKfz 251/16 mittlere Flammpanzerwagen was introduced in 1943. It stowed 700 litres of fuel, fired from flame-throwers either side of the hull.

Left: The blistering desert heat meant that infantry were not capable follow the Panzer forces on foot. From their initial deployment in North Africa in 1941 Rommel's forces, later designated the Afrika Korps, were composed wholly of mobile units. This facilitated the bold, hit-and-run tactics and sweeping flank manoeuvres favoured by Germany's most celebrated commander. Fully motorised infantry divisions were never to reach other theatres, due to the inability of Germany's hard-pressed factories to satisfy production demands.

Below: A Panzergrenadier unit in East Prussia in March 1945. By this time the German army was fighting increasingly defensive operations on every front. The personnel carrier was up-gunned to provide better infantry support for the individual Kampfgruppe (battle group). The German army had to be more mobile than ever to fill the breaches wherever they occurred in the line.

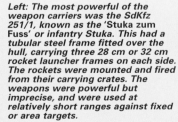

Left: The most powerful of the weapon carriers was the SdKfz 251/1, known as the 'Stuka zum Fuss' or infantry Stuka. This had a tubular steel frame fitted over the hull, carrying three 28 cm or 32 cm rocket launcher frames on each side. The rockets were mounted and fired from their carrying crates. The weapons were powerful but imprecise, and were used at relatively short ranges against fixed or area targets.

Right: The SdKfz 251 variant armed with the 2 cm Flak 38 never received a formal designation as so few examples were produced. As with most weapons carriers it had sides which folded down when deployed for action, to provide room for the gun and its four-to-six man crew . Produced during 1942 only, the vehicle saw action almost exclusively on the Eastern Front, both as a Flak gun and in the infantry support role.

Above: In spite of its non-sequential designation, the 12-tonne SdKfz 8 was the first half-track to enter service with the Wehrmacht. One of the most important of German artillery tractors, it is seen here on parade, towing modernised 15-cm K16s. Production ceased in 1944.

Above: The eight-tonne SdKfz 7 was most famously paired with the 88mm gun. In its tractor form it had space for up to 12 men and their kit. At its peak in 1942 there were over 3,000 examples in service. Many surviving vehicles were appropriated in 1945, and were used by the Czechs and Allies for several years after the end of the war.

Below: The Wehrmacht's main tank recovery vehicle was the SdKfz 9. Though able to handle vehicles up to the weight of a Panzer IV, the 50 or more tonnes of a Tiger needed two or three tractors working in tandem.

gun behind a small armoured shield at the front. A second machine gun was located at the rear, on a high-angle mounting. The two-man crew remained in the vehicle, but the infantry section in the open troop compartment deployed via twin rear doors. The second most numerous sub-class looked almost identical, being the ammunition carriers for the tank and artillery units as well as the machine gun and mortar companies of the *panzergrenadier* battalions. There were numerous other variants, some developed in 1939-40, others right at the end of the war on Hitler's personal orders.

There was only one problem with the Sd Kfz 251: there were never enough of them. The numbers built fell far short of the quantity needed to equip every *panzergrenadier* unit. In general, only one of the four or six *panzergrenadier* battalions in a panzer division would be mounted in half-tracks; the bulk of the troops remained in lorries. This severely reduced the ability of the *panzergrenadiers* to fight in conjunction with the tanks. Their unarmoured trucks were vulnerable to enemy fire and had only limited cross-country mobility. The battalion in half-

tracks could not be everywhere at once. Ironically, the balance between 'armoured infantry' and tanks that the proponents of the panzer divisions intended was achieved to some extent during the war – because the number of tanks in each formation was often far short of the authorised strength.

'FIRETEAM'

The success of the Sd Kfz 251 in the APC role led the army to demand a similar vehicle for its reconnaissance units in 1939. The troop carrying requirement was reduced to half a squad (*Halbegruppe*), or a 'fireteam' in modern parlance. The basis for the new vehicle was the Sd Kfz 10 1-ton prime mover; Büssing-NAG were responsible for the armoured body while Demag built the chassis. Hitler's 'stop-start' approach to industrial management imposed delays on all military production in 1940 so it was not until the summer of 1941 that the first of these new APCs appeared. Designated Sd Kfz 250, some 4,250 were built before manufacture ceased in October 1943. They were the mainstay of the panzer divisions' reconnaissance units and appeared in almost as many variants as the Sd Kfz 251; ammunition carriers, command vehicles, fire support vehicles and mortar carriers were all built.

Dissatisfaction with the Sd Kfz 222 four-wheeled armoured car's performance in Russia led to the experimental fitting of the 222's 20 mm gun turret to a number of Sd Kfz 250s in March 1942. This hybrid proved very successful and the Sd Kfz 250/9 entered mass production to replace the Sd Kfz 222.

18-TON MONSTER

The German army's range of half-track artillery tractors ranged from 1-ton vehicles towing light anti-tank or anti-aircraft guns to 18-ton monsters designed to pull the heaviest guns or to serve as recovery vehicles. Even these were overloaded by the heavy tanks

Above: Fast, reliable and robust, the SdKfz 250 leichter Schützenpanzerwagen was very popular and remained in production until the end of the war. The variant depicted is the command and communication model as used by Erwin Rommel.

Right: In spite of the efforts of Goebbels' propaganda departments and most Hollywood war films, German divisions were by no means totally mobilised. Leg-work and natural horse-power continued to predominate over the combustion engine.

introduced from 1942: it took two or three Sd Kfz 9s to tow a Tiger tank out of mud!

One of the most successful half-tracks was never designed as such. The Opel Maultier was simply the standard Opel army truck with Horstmann tracked suspension in place of the rear wheels. Over 4,000 were made, primarily for service on the Russian front.

Hitler's devotion to minutiae led him to interfere in the procurement programmes of all three armed services, but most particularly with the army. The Russian winter was a ghastly experience for the men, but inflicted serious attrition on the army's unwieldy and inefficient motor transport. Hundreds of different models of vehicle, culled from all over Europe created a spares nightmare.

In May 1942 Hitler decreed that a new, 'no frills' series of half-tracks be built to replace the existing 3- and 5-ton tractors. The *Schwere Wehrmacht-schlepper* (sWS) was entrusted to

Büssing-NAG and prototypes were ready by early 1943. Orders were placed for over 7,000 but no more than 150 were built in 1943 and fewer than a thousand were completed by the end of the war. The sWS served in many roles, from self-propelled anti-aircraft guns to *Panzerwerfer* (where it supplemented the version based on the Maultier). A modified version continued in production at the Tatra works in Czechoslovakia after the war .

MOBILE FLAK

Perhaps the most unusual (and certainly the hardest to pronounce) of all wartime half-tracks was the *Feuerleit-panzerfahrzeug für V-2 Raketen auf Zugkraftwagen 8t.* The *Zugkraftenwagen 8t* was a conventional half-track built as a self-propelled flak unit, with either the 20 mm *Flakvierling* (quadruple) mounting or a single 37 mm Flak 36. Introduced in 1943 it was also used – in very limited numbers – to carry the 50 mm Flak 41. The V2 ballistic missile was designed to be fired

from mobile launching units, thus avoiding the problem of the V1 which had fixed firing ramps exposed to Allied air attack. Fitted with a high, box-like armoured superstructure, the *Feuerleitpanzerfahrzeug für V-2 Raketen auf Zugkraftwagen 8t* was the mobile command post for these rocket units. It could tow the base plate unit from which the actual rocket was fired.

INFINITE VARIETY

German half-tracks, like German tanks, aircraft and even lorries, were manufactured to very high standards and in many versions. This imposed its own limitations on manufacturing output, especially when compared to the prodigious quantities of simpler American and Russian equipment that they faced on or above the battlefield. One comparison will suffice. The tracks on the US Army's M3 half-track consisted of two steel cables with reinforcing crossbars, moulded into a single unit by vulcanized rubber. They had a wear-life of about 1,500 miles but were easily and cheaply replaced. The tracks on a German half-track consisted of individual steel cross pieces held together in a continuous link by a series of pins, each pin held in place by a pair of needle bearings. The German tracks were better engineered, stronger and longer lasting – but labour intensive, expensive to make and just as easily destroyed in battle.

Above: From late 1942 Panzer formations were equipped with their own dedicated rocket artillery units. The soft-top Maultier truck was made available and was refitted with a full suit of armour. The unit mounted a 10-barrel launcher and was designated the 15-cm Panzerwerfer 42.

Below: Designed for use with airborne units the Kettenkrad was first used in 1941. After Hitler's rejection of the airborne concept, the vehicle's original role became redundant and so it was deployed as a supply vehicle in difficult terrain.

Below: The only weapons carrying version of the 18-tonne SdKfz 9 prime mover was produced in 1943. It mounted an 88-mm Flak 37, and was used on the Eastern front and in France. This example was equipped with an armoured cabin. The vehicle is depicted in firing mode – the sides of the rear firing platform are folded down as a working platform for the gun crew and the small outrigger arms are deployed for stability.

From Goliath to David: German Half-tracks

Right: SdKfz 9
This 18 tonne Leviathan was by far the largest of all WW2 half-tracks. Its origins were in a 1936 requirement for a vehicle to support the panzer divisions and act in a recovery role. Two types were therefore produced. It towed he heaviest German artillery pieces including the massive 24-cm K3. It was made obsolescent as a tank recovery vehicle due to the ever increasing tonnage of the Panzers, and production halted in 1944.

Right: SdKfz 250/10
The vehicle was developed following a mid-1930s requirement for a one tonne half-track to provide mobility for infantry and other units operating with panzer divisions. First seeing action in 1940, production continued until 1944. Later models had redesigned hulls to facilitate manufacture and cut down on the amount of raw materials required. Variants included a communications vehicle and mobile observation post, as well as a number of specialised weapons carriers.

Left: SdKfz 251/20 'Uhu' (Infrarotscheinwerfer)
Another of the seemingly endless variants of the basic 251 model, used to support Panther tanks fitted with infra-red night vision aids. The IR searchlight on a Panther had a range of only 400 metres, but the massive *Beobachtungsgerät* 1251 in the 251/20 could illuminate targets 1500 metres away. The *Uhu* ('Owl') commander controlled five IR-equipped Panthers in a night engagement and was a concept with tremendous potential. However of the 600 ordered in August 1944 no more than 60 are believed to have been completed.

Right: *Maultier* (Mule)
German trucks proved to be totally unequal to the demands made of them during the winter of the Russian campaign in 1941-42. It was therefore decided to produce a low-cost half-track to take over many of the trucks' duties. This was achieved by simply taking Opel and Daimler-Benz trucks from the production lines and bolting on a tracked assembly composed of Panzer II tracks and running wheels. Many of the latter were available as the light tank was being phased out at that time.

Left: Sdkfz 2 *kleines Kettenrad*
The SdKfz 2 was developed for use by German paratroopers as a light artillery tractor. Entering service in 1941, after airborne units had become almost exclusively ground troops, the *Kettenrads* were used on all fronts as cross-country utility vehicles. They had an impressive road-going speed of 80km/h.

GERMAN ROCKETS

The 28cm and 32cm Wurfkörper rockets were awkward, bulky and their poor ballistic shape further decreased their range. But their payload was awesome and if the rocket hit a target the results were catastrophic.

Rocket artillery has a long history dating back to ancient China, but by the start of the twentieth century this type of ordnance had been largely overlooked. In 1941 the Wehrmacht became the first army to reintroduce the weapon – to devastating effect.

Above and below: German rocket artillery was not employed during the first blitzkrieg campaigns in the West. This was because most of the Nebelwerfer had been assigned to the chemical warfare units. These were being held in reserve to wage gas warfare if the fighting had taken such an horrific turn. Some rocket artillery was released in time for Operation Barbarossa, but large numbers were not deployed until the late summer of 1941 when Russian Katyushas rudely awakened the Wehrmacht to the weapon's potential when used in quantity.

ROCKET ARTILLERY dates its origin to the ancient Persians and Greeks. However, the Chinese were the first to use the technology on a wide scale, followed by the Mongols. Rockets reached Europe in the 13th century but were not deployed significantly until the 16th and 17th centuries. Rockets was subsequently used in most conflicts prior to the 20th century but were sidelined by developments in conventional artillery.

Rockets were used in World War I primarily for signaling and were also fired from French aircraft against hydrogen-filled observation balloons. In the 1920s and 1930s however Germany and the Soviet Union began to re-explore the military potential of rocket artillery.

German rocket artillery were widely known to the Allies as 'Moaning Minnies' or 'Screaming Mimis' because of the distinctive howl from the rocket motors of the 15-cm six barrelled projector. This weapon had the more formal title of *Nebelwerfer* or Smoke Projector.

The name was a hangover from World War I, where heavy calibre mortars were employed to lay down smoke or gas. In World War II rocket projectiles could be used to deliver smoke, but more commonly they were employed with high explosive (HE) warheads. In addition to HE, *Nebelwerfer* fills included incendiary liquids and there were huge stocks of rocket projectiles containing lethal chemicals – 18,600 15-cm chemical rockets were captured at H Muna St Georgen in 1945 – though even Hitler did not resort to their use.

'SHOOT AND SCOOT'

The weapon was feared and respected by the Allies for its ability to deliver five or six projectiles simultaneously onto a target. The rockets had a high blast effect and were devastating against troops in the open. For the *Nebeltruppen* – Smoke Troops, the major drawback of the weapon was its firing signature. Dust was kicked up around the launch site and a long trail of smoke marked the flight of the rocket. This could attract counter battery fire – in the East Soviet forces even responded with their own *Katyusha* rockets. *Nebeltruppen* became expert in 'shoot and scoot' tactics – firing and then hitching up the projectors and moving out of the area very quickly.

Training for *Nebeltruppen* was undertaken at Celle south of Stettin and, as the numbers of regiments increased, at Munster-Nord. The soldiers who operated these specialised weapons wore a distinctive burgundy red *Waffenfarbe* arm colour as piping on their epaulets and forage caps. On the lower left sleeve they had the trade badge of an upright mortar round in white surrounded by a wreath of white oak leaves on a blue-green oval background.

The first rocket equipment, the *Nebelwerfer* 42 with its 28/32-cm rockets, entered service in 1940. It was a comparatively simple towed weapon that arrived too late to see action in the campaign in France. The launcher consisted of a frame that took six 32-cm rockets, while inner rails would take the smaller 28-cm rounds. The 28-cm HE rocket weighed 82 kg and had a maximum range of 1925 metres; the 32-cm

Below: This impressive display of pyrotechnics was photographed on the night of 24 – 25th March 1944 as the British and Americans prepared to cross the Rhine. The western Allies made effective use of rocket artillery, but in much smaller quantities than the Germans and Russians.

"MOANING MINNIE"

The Wehrmacht were the first to use rocket artillery in World War II, though the honour is often wrongly attributed to the Soviets. Four German Army Nebelwefer regiments were among many artillery units that opened fire on 22 June 1941 at 3:15am, beginning Operation Barbarossa. The Red Army used rocket artillery for the first time on 14 July 1941, firing at the rail station at Orsza on the Minsk-Moscow route, which had been captured by Army Group Centre.

GERMAN ROCKET ARTILLERY grew into a formidable weapons system. It was capable of quickly laying great concentrations of smoke, or massed fire across target areas. Besides the enormous blast and destruction wrought on enemy targets, the distinctive screaming sound of the rocket motors loaded additional psychological pressure onto troops on the receiving end of a barrage.

The inherent inaccuracy of rocket projectiles meant that volume of fire replaced accuracy. The *Nebeltruppen* favoured an approach based on General Guderian's favourite maxim *Klotzen, nicht Kleckern* – "Kick them, don't spit on them.'

As the war progressed the Germans employed rockets in preferebnce to conventional. This was for two main reasons: the projectors were easy to handle compared to cannon firing similar warheads, and they were also far easier and cheaper to make.

Above: In comparison with field guns rocket artillery was deficient in range and accuracy. The noise and smoke generated by the flight of the rounds made it relatively easy for an enemy to locate the firing unit.

incendiary rocket of 79 kg, but with a maximum range of only 2200 metres. Though the 28/32-cm NbW 41 rockets were powerful projectiles, their comparatively short range meant that the equipment was not used in large numbers.

RUSSIAN DEBUT

A year on, the *Nebelwerfer* 41 equipped with 15-cm rockets was fielded in Russia. It would be employed throughout the war and would even be used by French forces after 1945.

The rocket was of an unusual design, with the motor in front of the warhead. This was designed to ensure that on impact the motor fragmented. The rocket consisting of seven WASRAG R61 (Diglykol-Dinitrate) propellant sticks ignited by an ERZ.39 initiator vented through 26 angled venturi in a ring about two thirds of the length of the body. The maximum velocity was a slowish but respectable 340 metres a second. The maximum range was 6,900 metres.

The 15-cm rockets were later mounted on the half-track Sd Kfz 4/1 *Maultier* – Mule. However this was a stopgap until the 15-cm *Panzerwerfer* 42 entered service in 1944. Using the same ten barrelled launcher as the Sd Kfz 4/1 Maultier the *Panzerwerfer* 42 used the *Schwerer Wehrmachtschlepper* chassis and could carry 26 rockets internally and ten in the projector. These vehicle-mounted projectors were grouped in independent armoured companies – *Panzerwerferbatterie*, composed of two platoons each with four projectors.

HUGE PAYLOAD

The 21-cm *Nebelwefer* 42 was trialled in 1942 and entered service in 1943. It was essentially an expanded version of the 15-cm NbW 41, with five larger barrels mounted on the same carriage. To fire, a 0.3-amp current was sent down a six core cable using a hand generator via a junction box on the right hand side of the projector. The *Nebelwefer* 42 fired only HE ammunition. The rocket weighed 112.6 kg at launch had a velocity of 320 metres a second and a maximum range of 7,850 metres. The rate of fire was five rockets in eight seconds and three salvos of five rockets in five minutes.

The carriage weighed 1100 kg in travelling mode. The rockets weighed 127 kg, and had a maximum velocity of 230 metres a second after launch and a maximum range of 4,550 metres. The rate of fire was six rockets in ten seconds and two salvos of six rockets in five minutes.

The 30-cm *Raketenwerfer* 56 that was introduced into service in 1944 used the carriage of a 5-cm Pak 38. By fitting special liners to the launch rails it could also fire 15-cm ammunition. The system weighed 1004 kg in travelling mode and had a rate of fire of six rockets in ten seconds and two salvos of six in five minutes.

PACKING CRATE LAUNCH

The 28-cm, 30-cm and 32-cm rockets were delivered to front line units in *Packkisten* – simple open frame packing crates and with some modifications these became very effective one shot launchers. The simplest field rocket launcher was the *schweres Wurfgerät* 40 that consisted of six crates for 28/32 missiles fixed to a frame that could be adjusted from +10° to +45°. This mounting gave the missiles a maximum range of 2200 metres from the

Above: Crews used a simple open site to aim this highly inaccurate weapon. The 15-cm and 21-cm projectors were provided with traversing and elevating gears, powered electrically.

Above right: HE, smoke or a mixture of the two would then be loaded into the five firing tubes. This procedure would take around two minutes for a practiced crew.

Right: After loading the crew retired to slit trenches 10 to 15 metres away. The rockets were fired by remote control using a hand generator. Electric pulses were sent along a cable to a plug and socket on the right of the mounting. The rockets were fired in two-second intervals that could be judged by the firer since one turn of the firing handle fired one rocket. The sequential firing was to prevent the weapon from being overturned by the rocket's blast.

M4 Sherman tanks launch a broadside from their T-34 60-tube launcher known as *Calliope*. The tubes were manufactured of plywood and could only be used a few times before disintegrating. The launcher nonetheless provided tank units with awesome close-range firepower.

The mounting of rocket artillery on to a self-propelled platform not only provided an armoured gun-platform for the crew but allowed the weapon to be removed from its firing position at great speed. The rockets could be reloaded in under a minute. Most units saw service with the Waffen-SS.

32-cm and 1925 metres for the 28-cm. Four rockets could be fired in six seconds using this system. First used operationally on the Eastern Front in 1941 it was nicknamed the *Stuka zu Fuss* – Stuka on Foot or Ground Stuka.

'HOWLING COW'

The *schweres Wurfgerät* 41 differed from the sWG 40 by being constructed from a tubular steel framework that weighed 110 kg and could launch the 28/32-cm and 30-cm rockets from their crates. Elevation was from +10° to +45° and rockets could be mounted singly or in banks of four that could be fired in six seconds. This too was known as the *Stuka zu Fuss*, though the sWG 41 was sometimes called the *Heulende Kuh* – the Howling Cow.

The most successful mobile launcher for 28/32-cm and 30-cm rockets was the *schwere Wurfrahem 40*. This was a metal framework fitted over and along the sides of an SdKfz 251 armoured half track vehicle. Designed by J. Gast KG of Berlin in 1940, it entered service that year. The frames holding the *Packkisten* could be elevated

from +14° to +50° and six rockets could be launched from their crates in ten seconds. In action the rockets were not loaded onto the sWR 40 until the moment of launch because this made the vehicle too wide. Normally the load consisted of five 28-cm rockets and one 32-cm incendiary rocket.

The vehicle was aimed at the target, brakes applied, rockets bolted at the correct angle and the crew retired ten metres. The rockets fired in a staggered succession starting with the left rear through to the right front.

ORGAN MUSIC

There were three types of rocket unit within the German Army: the *Werferabteilung (Mot)* – Rocket Projector Brigade (Motorised) – equipped with the 15-cm *Nebelwerfer* 41; the *schwere Werferabteilung (Mot)* or Heavy Rocket Projector Brigade (Motorised), equipped with either the 21-cm *Nebelwerfer* 42 or the 28/32-cm *Nebelwerfer* 42 or 56; and the *Gebirgswerferabteilung* – Mountain Rocket Projector Unit.

The *Werferabteilung (Mot)* consisted of a unit staff and staff battery and up to three batteries

each with six projectors. The staff was composed of the Abteilung Headquarters, Reconnaissance/ observation platoon, Survey section, Maintenance unit, Administrative staff and Signals staff. For local defence an anti-tank unit armed with either four 3.7-cm or 7.5-cm Pak was attached. It had 14 officers, 101 NCOs and 440 soldiers with 109 motor vehicles and nine motor cycles. In action a 15-cm *Werferabteilung* was supposed to cover a front of 1,200 metres, though in practice with each battery covering 200 metres it was usually 800 – 900 metres. A 15-cm *Werferabteilung* carried 1728 HE rounds and 432 smoke. Each battery thus had 432 HE and 108 smoke.

The *Abteilung* were linked together to form a *Werfer-regimenter*. This normally comprised a Regimental HQ or HQ battery, two 15-cm *Abteilung*, one 21-cm *Abteilung* and a light projector column (usually a 15-cm detachment) for special tasks. A regiment had 1,876 personnel, 12 anti-tank guns, 54 rocket projectors, 374 motor vehicles and 37 motor cycles.

A *schweres Regimenter* was

one in which more than one *Abteilung* was equipped with the 21-cm *Nebelwerfer* 42 or larger. The normal establishment for one of these heavy units was two 21-cm or 28/32-cm (later 30-cm) *Abteilung* and one 15-cm *Abteilung*. The *schwere Werferabteilung (Mot)* 21-cm carried 900 HE rounds – ten salvoes or 180 for each battery. The 30-cm projector battery carried 600 HE enough for three salvoes. The 28/32-cm battery carried 450 28-cm HE and 150 32-cm Incendiary rounds.

HALF-TRACK SUPPORT

Both the 15-cm and 21-cm equipped *Abteilung* were supported by the *Nebelkraft-wagen* (Sd Kfz 11/1) half track vehicle that carried the launcher crew and, in interchangeable stowage bins along the side, either 36 15-cm rockets or ten 21-cm rockets.

The *Gebirgswerferabteilung* equipped with the 10-cm *Nebelwerfer* 35 and 40 carried 1899 HE and 1269 smoke rounds. The *Nebelwerfer* 35 and 40 were mortars with a range respectively of 3,025 and 6,350 metres. However mountain

The most widely used rockets in WORLD WAR 2 were the Russian 'Katyushas.' Generally mounted on trucks, they provided the Soviet Army with awesome fire power. Because of the distinctive moaning sound made by the missiles in flight, the Germans dubbed the weapon 'Stalin's organ'.

troops in operations in the Caucasus in 1942 deployed standard rocket equipment.

By the autumn of 1944 manpower shortages had led to *Werferregimenter* being reduced to two *Abteilungen*, and though nominally motorised the projectors were often towed into action by horses.

SHOCK WAVE

The *Werferregimenter* and smaller units were not normally part of any Army divisional establishment but were allotted to the various armies, corps and divisions by the OKH. Only the Waffen-SS Panzer Divisions had organic *Werferabteilung* each equipped with 18 projectors.

The Waffen-SS even copied the Soviet *Katyusha*. They produced the 8-cm *Raketen-Vielfachwerfer*, a 24-rail launcher mounted on an ex-French Army *Somua* half track that fired a 6.9 kg fin stabilised rocket. In trials early in 1944 it was established that the 8-cm rocket was superior to the 15-cm. However this conclusion may have been biased by political pressure.

ROCKET DUEL

NEARLY ALL THE MAJOR protagonists in World War II made operational use of rockets to some degree. They were mainly used to supplement existing weapons, but the Soviets soon discovered that the rocket could at times be regarded as a weapon in its own right.

Technologically the Germans were the most advanced, but they used rockets only in a supporting role to flesh out artillery barrages.

The Red Army used rockets in the forefront of every offensive to repel the Germans from its soil. Some of the Soviet rocket types were still in service all over the world until the mid 1980s.

The rocket was capable of swinging the balance on the battlefield, and did just that in the Eastern conflict. In the west the British and Americans occasionally used them to devastating effect to reduce bunkers and strongpoints.

The original stimulus to British pre-war rocket design had been the need to develop an anti-aircraft weapon. Although unsuccessful in its designed role, it was used as the basis for some interesting designs, such as this 24-pdr air-portable rocket projector.

The Junkers Ju 88 vies with the British Mosquito as the most versatile combat aircraft of World War II. Designed as a specialised high-speed bomber, it proved suited for virtually every type of combat mission, and was built in greater numbers than all other Luftwaffe bombers combined. These are Ju 88A-4 bombers, one of the most numerous of all variants, serving with III Gruppe of Lehrgeschwader 1 in the Mediterranean in 1941/2.

JUNKERS Ju 88 SCHNELL BOMBER

'The Fuhrer does not ask me what kind of bombers I have. He simply wants to know how many' – Hermann Goering

ON 10 MARCH 1935 the British *Daily Mail* published an interview with *Reichsmarschall* Hermann Goering in which he admitted what defence analysts had known for years: Germany had defied the terms of the Versailles Treaty by establishing a military air arm. The Luftwaffe, whose formation had been officially announced the preceding day, had existed in secret for some time.

In April Hitler nationalised Germany's leading aircraft manufacturer, Junkers. The firm, in which the government had acquired a 51% stake in 1933, was already supplying military transport versions of its Ju 52 airliner. Its most famous aircraft, the Ju 87 Stuka dive bomber, was poised to enter series production. The next Junkers aircraft, the

Ju 88, was never a public name like the Stuka, but it was destined to play a far more significant role in the war.

Like other major air forces in the mid-1930s, the Luftwaffe developed a series of twin-engined bombers that were capable of out-pacing the biplane fighters still in widespread service. The Dornier Do 17 and Heinkel He 111 both began life as civil aircraft with an eye to future military applications and both were tested in action during the Spanish Civil War. But the pace of technological progress was extraordinarily rapid during this period. The need for a purpose-built bomber to replace them both was apparent even as they entered service. The

objective was to increase both speed and bomb load, and the RLM (*Reichsluftfahrtministerium* – German air ministry) issued a demanding specification for just such a machine. The initial design for the Ju 88, the *Schnellbomber* (fast bomber), comfortably exceeded the specifications. The fifth prototype established an international speed record in 1939, carrying a 2,000 kg (4,409 lb) payload at an average speed of 517 km/h (321 mph) over a distance of 1,000 km (621 miles). This was very close to the maximum speed of the Hawker Hurricane which equipped the majority of RAF fighter squadrons at the time.

Professor Hugo Junkers, the aging head of the company, was

Above: An early Ju 88A runs up its engines before taking off for a mission over England. The aircraft carries a pair of SC 500 (500-kg) bombs on racks between the engines and the fuselage. Two internal bomb bays carried a maximum of 28 smaller 50-kg high-explosive bombs.

Right: The Ju 88 had been designed as a fast bomber able to use its speed to keep out of trouble. However, it proved vulnerable to more modern single-seat fighters, and Junkers had to squeeze extra defensive armament into the bomber's already crowded cockpit.

replaced. The professor had been due to retire anyway, but his open opposition to Hitler saw him ejected forthwith. He was replaced by Dr Heinz Koppenberg, a ruthless manager from the steel industry.

INDUSTRIAL OVERLOAD

Koppenberg did his best to overhaul the labour-intensive manufacturing methods he discovered in the aviation business. However, he never fully overcame traditional working practices or the culture that led to a non-aviation engineer at Henschel to query whether it was really necessary to have eleven different types of countersunk rivets on the same aircraft.

American methods of mass-production were never adopted and German aircraft would continue to require more man-hours and more skilled labour than their US equivalents. Productivity was hampered even more severely by constant changes to the design dictated by the air ministry.

The outbreak of war failed to shake German industry into high gear. Indeed, Hitler switched production priorities to the army and navy during 1940, reducing aircraft production across the board. Even the belated mobilisation of industry achieved by Albert Speer did not make the best of the civilian sector. The giant Opel car plant began to manufacture parts for the Ju 88, but never built a complete aircraft despite huge resources and a skilled labour force.

ALLIED FLEXIBILITY

By contrast, British factories switched from buses to tanks or aircraft in accordance with pre-war plans. In America, the contrast was even greater: General Motors built Grumman carrier aircraft, while Ford built complex B-24 bombers at the specially-built Willow Run facility. In 1944, the factory reached Henry Ford's self-imposed target of one four-engined bomber an hour!

Junkers Ju 88A-5

Bombsights
The Ju 88 had two sets of bombsights. The bomb aimer had a sight in the nose for use in conventional bombing attacks. The pilot also had a sight for use in dive-bombing attacks. Mounted on the cockpit canopy, it swung to one side when not in use.

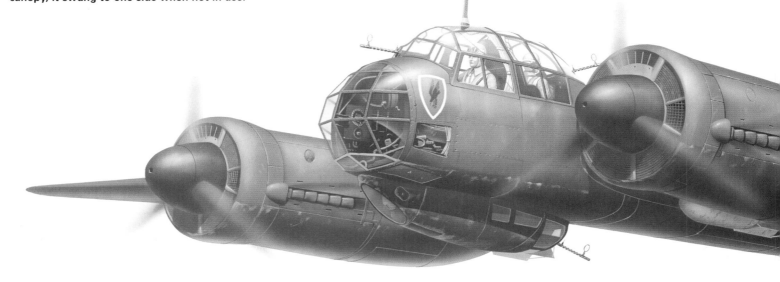

Powerplant
The A-5 model of the Ju 88 was powered by two of the same Jumo 211 G-1 engines used in the original production models, mated to the more efficient wing developed for the Ju 88A-4. It actually preceded the A-4 into service, due to development delays in the production of the latter's more powerful Jumo 211J engines.

Below: British engineers examine a captured Ju 88. The cramped cockpit for the four-man crew was noteworthy: The Germans accepted slightly less efficiency and increased vulnerability to a single hit, believing in the morale value of having the crew in close contact.

Under the lackadaisical Goering and tragically miscast Ernst Udet, the Ju 88 was subject to continuous interference by various interested parties. It required the construction of 100 prototype and pre-production aircraft between 1936 and 1939 before the Ju 88 entered service. There were some 250,000 technical changes made between the flight of the first prototype in December 1936 and the completion of the sixth in 1938.

NEEDLESS COMPLEXITY
This was typical of the pre-war Luftwaffe, which continued to change the specification of aircraft after they were taken into service, even over very small production runs. For instance, though only 500 Arado Ar 68 fighters were ordered, they were delivered in a dozen variants that featured four different types of power plant and three different radio sets.

At least the Ju 88 was merely delayed. The Ju 89 heavy bomber, planned for 1942-44 was cancelled after its champion, *Generalleutnant* Walter Wever was killed in an accident in a Heinkel He 70. While British and American plans for four-engined heavy bombers matured, the Luftwaffe was committed to a strategy of medium bombers only. And whereas the Heinkel He 111 and Dornier Do 17 were conventional level bombers, the Ju 88 had to double as a dive-bomber. Large slatted dive-brakes were added under the outer wings. Four 500 kg (1,102-lb) bombs could be carried on hardpoints under the wings; maximum load was 28 SC50 50 kg (110-lb) bombs. Problems with overloading on the final pre-production aircraft led to wing-spar failures and undercarriage collapses. Even the first service aircraft had to be flown carefully.

The four-man crew were squashed together in the same style as the Dornier Do 17. The

150

9.Staffel, Kampfgeschwader 30 Gilze Rijen, Holland, 1941

Unit markings

This Junkers Ju 88 wears the codes of KG 30, which was the first unit to take the *Schnellbomber* into action in September 1939. For much of the war the *Geschwader* concentrated on anti-shipping missions in the North Sea, from bases in Holland, Denmark and Norway.

Mine warfare

The Luftminen Type B was a dual purpose weapon for use as a mine at sea or as a delayed action bomb on land. It was parachute-retarded, to ensure that the weapon was not damaged when it entered the water and to avoid premature detonation on land.

Junkers Ju 88A-4

Powerplant: two 1,350 hp Junkers Jumo 211J-1 engines
Performance: maximum speed 470 km/h (292 mph) at 5300 m (17,390 ft); maximum cruising speed 400 km/h (248 mph) at 5000 m (16,405 ft); maximum range 2730 km (1,696 miles)
Weights: empty equipped 9860 kg (21,737 lb); maximum take-off 14000 kg (30,865 lb)
Dimensions: span 20 m (65 ft 7 in); length 14.4 m (47 ft 2 in); height 4.85 m (15 ft 11 in); wing area 54.5 m2 (586.6 sq ft)
Armament: one forward-firing 7.92-mm machine gun, one forward-firing 13-mm machine gun, up to 2 x 13-mm machine guns aft and one or two in the ventral gondola. Maximum bombload 4000 kg (4,409 lb)
Ju 88 production:
Sept-Dec 1939: 69, 1940: 2538, 1941: 3348, 1942: 3661, 1943: 3654, 1944: 3286, 1945: 355
Total: 16,911

Since it was manufactured by several sub-contractors on many different sites, final production figures are uncertain. Figures given by different sources range from 14,780 (including 104 prototypes) to just under 19,000 (Henschel figures).

British felt that this made sense from a morale point of view – the isolation of rear-gunners in certain RAF bombers was notorious. However, the crew compartment in the German aircraft was terribly cramped.

CREW COMPARTMENT

The pilot sat high on the left with the bomb aimer low on the right; on some versions the latter sat up higher, doubling as a second pilot. The engineer was seated behind the pilot and facing aft so he could man the rearward-firing 7.92-mm machine gun(s). The radio operator sat alongside, but lower in the fuselage, ready to squeeze into the gondola to operate the rearward-firing 7.92-mm belly gun.

The ambitious 1938 RLM production programme called for 54 bomber squadrons, all equipped with Ju 88s by the spring of 1942. Supplemented by 4 squadrons of He 177 heavy bombers and 8 with Stukas (to be

replaced by Messerschmitt Me 210s) the 7,327 Junkers bombers would provide the main striking force of the Luftwaffe. However, it took longer than anticipated to tool up factories, expand the labour force and secure the raw materials. It was against this background that Goering saw off attempts to revive heavy bombers, observing "the Fuhrer does not ask me what kind of bombers I have. He simply wants to know how many." More realistic production targets were set in August 1939: the Ju 88 was still earmarked as the main bomber with a target total of 2,460 to be complete by April 1941 and production to continue at 300 per month thereafter.

SLOW PRODUCTION

It was one thing for Goering's advisors to conjure up a vision of the world's largest air force, with swastikas on every fin. It was another to actually do it

Below: The only defence of a Ju 88 bomber against a multi-gunned single-seat fighter single diving down from astern was a pair of machine guns at the rear of the cockpit. A single gun in the ventral gondola also provided some protection to the aircraft's underside.

Manufacturing output crept up, but failed to soar. On the eve of the war, 31 August 1939, there were only eighteen Ju 88s in the Luftwaffe's first line inventory, compared to nearly 800 He 111s and 250 Do 17s. Both Heinkel and Dornier types were kept in

production during 1940 to compensate for the shortfall in Ju 88 numbers – in fact, the Heinkel He 111 remained in production almost to the end of the war.

The Ju 88 acquitted itself well during the campaign in the West in 1940. It was the best of the

Left: The prototype Ju 88 first flew on 21 December 1936. By 1938 it had been declared the winner of the Luftwaffe's Schnellbomber or 'Fast bomber' competition – in spite of the fact that this aircraft crashed in April 1937, very early in the test programme. Orders for production tooling were placed in 1938, with subcontracts going to Arado, Heinkel, Henschel, Dornier and Volkswagen.

Above: Even as Junkers was delivering plans of the Ju 88 to the Reichsluftfahrtministerium in 1936, the company was suggesting an improved model with more powerful engines and an enlarged, streamlined crew compartment. The Ju 88B seen here remained a prototype, but it was to be developed into the powerful Ju 188.

Right: After 1940 the Ju 88 became the mainstay of the Luftwaffe's bomber force, and the aircraft and its crews featured heavily in the numerous colour propaganda magazines the Germans published.

Below: The Ju 88A-17 was a variant of the standard bomber adapted for torpedo attacks. It could carry a pair of 750-kg LT F5b torpedoes, fitted to racks under each wing root.

Below: The seventh Ju 88 prototype was used to test the aircraft in the Zerstörer or heavy fighter role. It proved highly successful, and the RLM ordered it into production as the Ju 88C. Over 3,000 were built as night fighters and long-range day fighters. The original prototype is seen here after being converted into a high-speed communications aircraft.

Mistel: Flying bombs

The Mistel *S3* was a training version of the combination, which mated a Ju 88A-6 with a Fw 190A-6. The two aircraft used fuels of different octane rating, so it would not have been a practical proposition as an operational machine. Combat versions mated the FW 190 with the airframe of the Ju 88G night fighter, with a modified nose carrying a 3800-kg shaped-charge high explosive warhead. This is a captured example being evaluated by the RAF after the end of the war.

ONE IMAGINATIVE use for ageing airframes was as guided bombs. Codenamed *Mistel* (Mistletoe), this involved piggy-backing a fighter on to a pilotless Ju 88 packed with explosives. On later versions the cockpit of the bomber was removed and an extended nose fitted with a long stand-off fuse was installed in its place. Once within sight of the target, the pilot in the fighter aimed the whole combination then released the Ju 88. Initial attacks in May 1944 were conducted against Allied shipping, by night. Plans were laid for a mass raid on the Royal Navy fleet base of Scapa

Flow in December 1944: 60 Mistel combinations were to fly from Denmark to make a night attack. The mission was loaded with risk – the lumbering *Mistel* combinations would have been slaughtered had British night-fighters intercepted them. It was never put to the test: the mission was cancelled "due to bad weather." An even larger raid early in 1945 was also cancelled as the Red Army overran many of the *Mistel* combinations on their airfields. The target had been the major Soviet tank factories – an important target, but one which the Luftwaffe was attacking four years too late!

Above: The prototype Mistel *linked a Messerschmitt Bf 109F-4 to a Ju 88A-4. Flying early in 1943, the concept seemed to have promise. In July 1943 Junkers were instructed to prepare 15 old A-series bombers for* Mistel *use. The first operational unit was a staffel of KG 101, which mounted its first attack on Allied invasion shipping in June 1944.*

German bombers launched across the Channel that summer, but its defensive armament had to be increased during the Battle of Britain because even the *Schnellbomber* proved vulnerable to attacking Hurricanes and Spitfires.

SELF-DEFENCE

Improvised arrangements of up to four machine guns were common, but since they had to be aimed and fired individually, feeding from 75-round drums that gave just 3 seconds of fire, their effect was more psychological than practical.

A revised cockpit layout inside a bulbous, all-glazed nose had been on the drawing board since 1936. The Ju 88B was finally flown in 1940, its rearward

armament including a 13-mm machine gun with limited traverse and a 7.92-mm machine gun in a turret. Longer wings and a number of other improvements gave it a very different look: sufficiently so for Goering to re-designate it as the Ju 188 in May 1942. "Now," he quipped, "We can demonstrate to England that we also have something new."

The Ju 88 was the most versatile German aircraft of the war, rivalling the Mosquito in the range of missions it could fly. Over 40 variants were completed, and reconnaissance aircraft, bombers and fighters underwent constant improvements. From 1942 the Ju 88 was the most numerous type of bomber in the Luftwaffe, supplanting the He 111 which was increasingly used

as a transport.

The British were well informed about the capabilities of the Ju 88. A bomber which crash-landed in the summer of 1940 was restored to airworthy condition by the RAF and flown early in 1941. In July 1941 a Ju 88A-6 landed by mistake at an airfield near Bristol and the crew were overpowered before they realised they not flown home but had been flying on a reciprocal bearing. The crew of a Ju 88A-5 made the same error four months later, putting down at the RAF airfield at Chivenor in North Devonshire.

DEFECTORS

Two Ju 88 crews defected. In July 1943 a Rumanian pilot flew to Limassol, Cyprus with a

brand-new Ju 88D-1. And in an incident still subject to much speculation, a crew from an elite Luftwaffe night-fighter squadron flew their Ju 88R-1 to Dyce, near Aberdeen, apparently by prior arrangement. Met by an escort of RAF Spitfires over the Scottish coast, *Oberleutnant* Heinrich Schmitt, *Oberfeldwebel* Paul Rosenberger and *Oberfeldwebel* Erich Kantwill signalled their colleagues in 10./NJG 3 they were ditching in the North Sea after an engine fire. Their advanced night-fighter, complete with FuG Lichtenstein radar, was minutely examined and Schmitt and Rosenberger later broadcast on British radio. Preserved at RAF St Athan, their aircraft is one of only 3 Ju 88s to survive to the present day.

NIGHT FIGHTER

JUNKERS DEVELOPED a *Zerstörer* (destroyer) version of the Ju 88 in 1940, just as the limitations of the Bf Messerschmitt 110 were becoming obvious over Britain. The new fighter proved timely – although showing its mettle by day in long-range operations over the Bay of Biscay, it was as a nocturnal predator that the Ju-88C really made its mark. Ultimately, over 3,000 C-series night fighters were delivered, later versions being equipped with radar and upward-firing cannon. Gun armament increased from 13-mm machine guns to up to six 20-mm cannon. One short burst at close range was enough to bring down a heavy bomber. Some of these valuable aircraft were hazarded in daylight when incessant American raids stung Goering into ordering a maximum effort in the summer of 1944. Their appearance in American gun cameras was in some cases the first time the Allies had seen these nocturnal hunters, but in spite of their heavy armament they were not a major threat. The combined weight of their radar and cannon had a performance penalty which meant that the Ju 88 stood little chance in a fight with the P-51 Mustangs and P-47 Thunderbolts now escorting the American heavies.

Above: This Ju 88C-6c is equipped with Lichtenstein FuG 202 BC and FuG 220 SN-2 radar. Pilots accepted the performance penalty from the forest of aerials because the powerful SN-2 had a minimum range of 400m while the older BC's minimum was 200m.

Left: Non-radar-equipped versions of the Ju 88C were used as 'train busters' on the Eastern Front. This Ju 88C-6 has had its gun-equipped nose painted to resemble a relatively harmless bomber, presumably to deceive Soviet fighter pilots.

Below: The ultimate development of the Ju 88 was the Ju 388, built in reconnaissance, bomber and night fighter versions. Supremely capable, they came too late to make any difference to the air war, and none were to see operational squadron service.

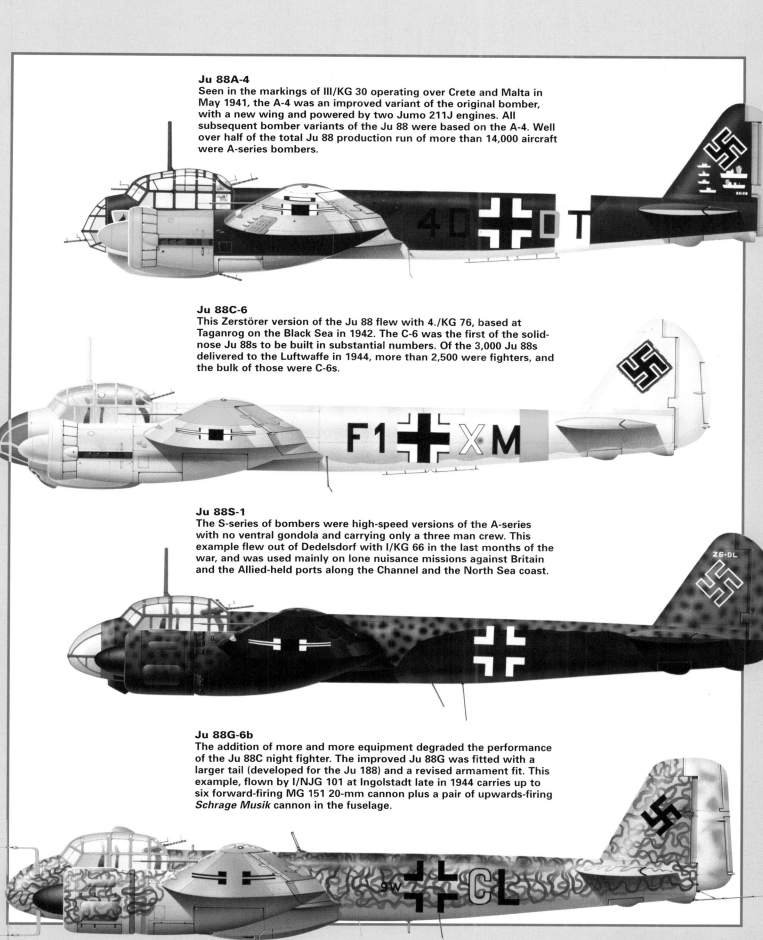

Ju 88A-4
Seen in the markings of III/KG 30 operating over Crete and Malta in May 1941, the A-4 was an improved variant of the original bomber, with a new wing and powered by two Jumo 211J engines. All subsequent bomber variants of the Ju 88 were based on the A-4. Well over half of the total Ju 88 production run of more than 14,000 aircraft were A-series bombers.

Ju 88C-6
This Zerstörer version of the Ju 88 flew with 4./KG 76, based at Taganrog on the Black Sea in 1942. The C-6 was the first of the solid-nose Ju 88s to be built in substantial numbers. Of the 3,000 Ju 88s delivered to the Luftwaffe in 1944, more than 2,500 were fighters, and the bulk of those were C-6s.

Ju 88S-1
The S-series of bombers were high-speed versions of the A-series with no ventral gondola and carrying only a three man crew. This example flew out of Dedelsdorf with I/KG 66 in the last months of the war, and was used mainly on lone nuisance missions against Britain and the Allied-held ports along the Channel and the North Sea coast.

Ju 88G-6b
The addition of more and more equipment degraded the performance of the Ju 88C night fighter. The improved Ju 88G was fitted with a larger tail (developed for the Ju 188) and a revised armament fit. This example, flown by I/NJG 101 at Ingolstadt late in 1944 carries up to six forward-firing MG 151 20-mm cannon plus a pair of upwards-firing *Schrage Musik* cannon in the fuselage.

The German Army's schwere
Granatwerfer 34 gained an
enviable reputation among Allied
frontline troops for its accuracy
and rate of fire. It was also very
robust and easy to manufacture.

INFANTRY
SUPPORT WEAPONS

The Flammenwerfer *35 in action against an enemy strongpoint. The model's components were largely unchanged from WWI. The equipment weighed a substantial 35.8 kg and so was often carried into action by two men. Carrying enough fuel for 10 seconds of use the weapon remained in production until 1941.*

The modern battlefield, with its uncertain dynamics, necessitates infantry carrying their own artillery. The German army was the first to realise this.

Infantry support weapons are those that are part of the battalion's inventory and are not 'on call' like artillery or air power. In the mobile battlefields of World War II infantry could not count on any artillery unit being close enough to give support in case of trouble.

DEDICATED WEAPONRY

Therefore, the natural solution was to give the infantry their own dedicated heavy weaponry. This consisted of mortars, flame-throwers, anti-tank weapons and light artillery.

The classic infantry support weapon is the medium mortar, and the German army was well equipped with the 8-cm *schwere Granatwerfer* 34. The weapon was carried into action as a three man load, consisting of base plate, barrel and bipod. It entered service in 1934 and was still in use at the end of hostilities. A wide range of ammunition was developed including the 8-cm *Wurfgranate* 39 'bouncing bomb', as well as conventional HE, smoke, target illumination and target marking ordinance. The mortar weighed 56.7 kg in action and could be elevated from 40° to 90°. It's range of traverse was from 9° to 15°.

The range of a mortar shell is controlled by the amount of propellant or charge. THis is typically rated between 1 and 6, 6 being the maximum. The charge is placed into the firing tube prior to loading the shell. The minimum range for the 3.5 kg shell on Charge 1 was 60 metres and the maximum on Charge 5 was 2,400 metres.

HEAVY MORTARS

The 12-cm *Granatwerfer* 42, which entered service with the German army in 1942, started life as the Russian Model 38 heavy mortar. On the Eastern Front, the big mortar fired a heavier bomb further than any mortar in the German inventory.

Initially, captured weapons, designated 12-cm Gr.W.378 (r), were pressed into service and then the 12-cm GrW.42 was produced capable of firing both Russian or German ammunition. On Charge 1 it could fire a 15.8 kg bomb to 300 metres, and on Charge 6 to 6,025 metres. The 12-cm GrW.42 had a two wheel carriage that could be attached to the base plate and could be gravity- or trigger-fired. This versatility made it a popular weapon and even replaced infantry guns in some battalions.

The *Gebirgsjaeger*, or Mountain Troops, had a number of lightweight guns, some of which were deployed in conventional operations by line infantry. The 7.5-cm *leichte*

Above: The 5-cm leichte Granatwerfer *36 was one of the standard Wehrmacht light mortars of the early war years. However, it proved too complex and expensive for wartime production.*

Gebirgs Infantriegeschutz 18. L/11.8 weighed 440 kg in action and fired a 5.45 kg or 6 kg shell out to 3,550 metres. It could also fire a 3 kg hollow-charge shell in an anti-tank role. The spoked-wheel variant could be broken down into six or ten loads for pack transport. The heaviest load weighed 74.9 kg. Waffen-SS troops used a version with pneumatic tyres.

The replacement for the 7.5-cm *leichte Gebirgs Infantriegeschutz* 18. L/11.8 7.5-cm was the 7.5-cm *Gebirgsgeschutz* 36. L/19.3.

This gun was designed by Rheinmetall in 1935. It entered service in 1938. The gun incorporated the unusual features of variable recoil and large muzzle brake.

GERMAN INGENUITY

As the war swung against Nazi Germany, there was a search for improvisation and expedients to keep soldiers in the front line supplied with weapons. Two of these were the 7.5-cm IG 37. L/22 and the 7.5-cm IG 42. L/22. These weapons used the 7.5-cm Pak 37, a captured cut-down Russian gun. It was mounted on the carriage of the obsolete 3.7-cm Pak 35/36, or the carriage of the captured Russian 27-mm Model 1930 anti-tank gun that had been used by the Germans as the 3.7-cm Pak 158(r). A muzzle brake was fitted, and the gun could fire a wide range of ammunition including

a hollow-charge shell in an anti-tank role.

RECOIL FREE

The design principles of the recoilless weapons that were widely used by NATO from the 1950s to the 90s can be traced back to the 7.5-cm *Leichtgeschutz* 40. L/10. This gun first saw action in Crete in 1941. It was a recoilless weapon that used an open breach with a venturi. It shared these features with the later 7.5-cm *Ruckstossfreie Kanone* 43. the 10.5-cm *Leichgeschutz* 40. L/13, the 10.5-cm *Leichgeschutz* 42. L/17.5 and the 10.5-cm *Leichgeschutz* 43. The case of the shells that it fired had a frangible plastic base. THis feature ensured that on detonation, the gas that projected the shell forward was ejected through the venturi to the rear. In conventional artillery buffers and recuperators absorbed a shell's recoil energy. This made the gun very light. The 7.5-cm *Leichtgeschutz* 40. L/10 weighed 145 kg in action. It had a maximum range of

Above: Opponents feared the accuracy and rate of fire of the German 8-cm sGrW34. But this reputation owed more to the thorough training of the crews than to design excellence.

Below: The Waffen SS grenadier in the foreground is armed with a Kar 98K rifle fitted with a Schiessbecker grenade launcher. This fired an array of fin-stabilised grenades of limited range.

SIG 33 IN ACTION

ONE OF THE conclusions drawn from analysis of tactics on the WWI battlefield was the need for an infantry battallion to have its own integral artillery fire support. The manpower to handle these weapons was to come from within the batallion itself. This would enable the infantry battalion to supply some measure of its own fire support besides that usually provided by artillery batteries. There would also be an advantage in response.

The *schwere Ingfantriegeschütz* or sIG 33was not accepted for service, however, until 1936. In the early years of WWII few sIGs were used by mechanised divisions so they were usually horsedrawn.

Although designated as a gun, the weapon was actually deployed as an howitzer. After about 1943 it began to be replaced by a German copy of the Soviet 120-mm mortar which was much easier to handle.

Below: German artillery crew prepare a firing position for their sIG 33. Although hampered by excessive weight, in action the gun had sufficient range for most fire-support activities (4,700 metres), and its ordinance was powerful enough to deal with most strongpoints.

Above: A Waffen SS-crewed sIG 33 in action on the Eastern Front in winter conditions. The wheels of this gun have rubber tyres. This denotes that the weapon was towed by some form of mechanised tractor.

Below: Soviet soldiers prepare to disable a pair of captured 15-cm sIG 33 howitzers. The weight of these infantry support pieces meant that they were often left behind in the fluid fighting in the East.

6,800 metres with a 5.83 kg shell. The 7.5-cm *Ruckstossfreie Kanone* 43 fired a 4 kg shell up to 200 metres, but was normally used at 300 metres, and it weighed only 43.1 kg. It was issued in small numbers but was not popular with its users.

AIRBORNE GUNS

The 10.5-cm *Leichgeschutz* 40. L/13, introduced in 1943, was intended for paratroopers and could be broken down into four loads for delivery by container. On the ground it was towed by the half-track, the SdKfz 2

kleines Kettenrad. The gun weighed 388 kg and fired a 14.8 kg HE shell to 7,950 metres. The performance of the 10.5-cm *Leichgeschutz* 42. L/17.5 and the 10.5-cm *Leichgeschutz* 43 were identical to the *Leichgeschutz* 40. L/13, but the former weighed 552 kg and the latter 523.7 kg. This increase in weight was the result of using steel rather than light alloys. The *Leichgeschutz* 43 was only produced in small numbers, but was a good infantry weapon since it could be broken down into 10 loads without the use of any tools

other than the elevating and traversing hand wheels.

The tactical drawback with all these weapons was the back-blast. This meant that the crew had to position themselves to the side when it was firing. The dust that could be kicked up by the blast would also give away a gun's position.

STOVE-PIPE

The German infantry entered the war with a simple 7.92-mm anti-tank rifle, the *Panzerbüschse* 38 and 39. However, as the war developed, there was a need for

more powerful and versatile weapons. This led to the development of a wide range of rocket-powered projectiles. The 8.8-cm weapon, designated the *Raketenpanzerbüchse* 43 or 54/1, had the propaganda name of *Panzerschreck*, or Tank Terror, though it was known by the soldiers as the *Ofenrohr*, or Stove Pipe. The *Raketenpanzerbüchse* was a larger version of the American Rocket Launcher M1 (Bazooka) The Rp 43 weighed 9.2 kg and the Rp 54 10.5 kg. The compact Rp 54/1 weighed 9.45 kg. All

Above: A solitary soldier in a fox hole sets out his anti-tank weaponry. Alongside the Teller mine is a Gebalte Ladung, a makeshift adaptation of the standard stick grenade. When the central grenade exploded, it sympathetically detonated about 1.20 kg of explosives.

Left: 7.5-cm leichtes Gebirgsinfanteriegeschütz 36 in firing mode. It could be broken into eight loads. Though at 750 kg the gun was rather heavy, it was popular with mountain gunners for its stability in action and general ease of handling.

Below left: The Germans made extensive use of flamethrowers during the battle around Verdun in 1916. Here a Wehrmacht flamethrower team practices for the second round in 1939.

weapons fired the Rp 4322 or Rp 4992, a 3.3 kg hollow-charge, rocket-propelled projectile, out to a maximum range of 151 metres or 201 metres respectively. The 0.667 kg explosive warhead on these rockets could penetrate up to 21 cm of armour.

'TANK DEVIL'

A less sophisticated but widely used anti-tank weapon, the *Panzerfaust,* was a single-shot weapon that fired a rocket-propelled, hollow-charge bomb. It first appeared late in 1942 and by the end of 1943 was in widespread use. The *Panzerfaust* 30 *klein* had a range of only 30 metres, but its 680 gram charge could penetrate 140 mm of armour at 30°. When the charge weight was increased to 1.58 kg, and the bomb diameter to 15 cm the penetration went up to 200 mm at 30°. The range was increased to 60 metres and later 100 metres by the provision of larger warhead. By the end of the war work was underway to

increase the range of the *Panzerfaust* even further. But defeat came before the reusable *Panzerfaust* 250 could get beyond the testing stage.

TANK HUNTING

Tank hunting could be undertaken with some very unusual weapons. These included the *Panzerwurfmine* (L). This consisted of a 1.35 kg grenade with a hollow-charge warhead, which contained a 50/50 mix of RDX and TNT. Four canvas fins deployed from the handle to ensure that the grenade hit its target correctly, so effectively deploying the shaped-charge warhead. It looked odd, and had a range of about 30 metres. It was effective enough however, and the Soviet Army copied it after the war. Despite its success the type was not copied closely by the other Allies. The Americans often misused them, thinking they were meant to be thrown in the same manner as an over-sized dart.

Goliath

THE GERMANS EXCELLED at invention, even if the end result of their creativity had limited practical value. The 'Goliath' was one of the more memorable designs. It was a remotely-controlled demolition device constructed by the German automotive manufacturer Burgward. The Goliath, operated by a specialist *Deutsche Fernlenk Truppe,* was produced in both petrol-engined and electrically-powered versions. The vehicles were employed in a variety of roles, including mine clearance and anti-tank operations. They were used successfully during the suppression of the 1944 Warsaw Uprising. Some 7,500 units were produced.

Above, left and below (picture sequence): Stills from a training film for Goliath operators, demonstrate the anti-armour role of the demolition robot.
Large numbers of Goliaths were produced towards the end of the war (above). Germany could no longer match the numberless masses of enemy armoured vehicles, and resorted to ever more desperate counter-measures. After unpacking (left), the units were received by the specialist troops who transported the weapon on a simple carriage, so conserving batteries or fuel.

Above: After unloading, the robot would then be camouflaged, and its crew would wait in ambush for a suitable opportunity. With target selected, the device would then be directed by remote control to within range, when it would then be detonated.

Left: Soviet armour rarely fell victim to the Goliath. Russian tactics from 1943 on, were to send infantry forward with their armour to neutralise German anti-tank squads. The robot was extremely vulnerable to small arms fire, and the remote cable telegraphed the position of the operators.

PANZERFAUST

THE 'PANZERFAUST' or Tank Devil was a revolutionary invention by Dr Langweiter of Hugo Schneider AG. It was the German's answer to the huge problem posed by the Soviet T-34. By 1943, over 200,000 were being produced per month.

Left: Desperate to halt the Allies, the Nazis set up the Volkssturm. Men previously considered unsuitable for frontline combat were armed with Panzerfausts and, with the minimum of training, were thrown into the battle.

Right: This volunteer demonstrates that the correct way to hold the weapon was under the arm to allow the propellant exhaust to vent safely to the rear. Aiming was problematic, being reliant on a flip-up leaf site which had to be aligned with a pip on the projectile body.

Above: The Panzerschreck (tank terror) was a German copy of the American M1 bazooka. The small shield was used to protect the firer from the back-blast of the rocket motor. The effective range was about 150m, but it was essentially a close-in weapon and target tanks had to be 'stalked' for the crews to get within range. One hit was usually enough.

MAGNETIC MINES

The *Haft-Hohlladung* 3 kg was a magnetic mine with a TNT shaped-charge warhead. To operate it the soldier used the three powerful magnets on the outer edge of the cone to fix it to the side of a tank. He then pulled the friction-igniter which gave him between four and seven seconds to escape. The Germans developed a special cement coating, or *Zimmeritt*, for their tanks that prevented captured magnetic weapons from being used against them.

If specialised anti-tank grenades were not available, there was always the standby of the *Gebalte Ladung*. This was an explosive charge constructed from the heads of six stick grenade warheads which were wired around a central grenade.

BOILING FIRE

The Germans had pioneered the use of flame-throwers in World War I at Verdun, and used several types in World War II.

The *Flammenwerfer* 35p flame-thrower had a range of 25 to 30 metres and fuel for 10 seconds of use. It had a single trigger that operated the pressurised nitrogen tank which ignited the oil in the fuel container. The model was superseded by the *Flammenwerfer* 40 and 41, a cylindrical 'lifebuoy-type' flame-thrower. It had a similar range to the *Flammenwerfer* 35, but about half the fuel capacity. The *Flammenwerfer* 41 was ignited by passing hydrogen over a heated element, that in turn set the oil fuel alight. Five blasts could be fired producing a flame of about 700° to 800° Centigrade. The *Flammenwerfer* 42 dispensed with a gas tank that often froze in Russian winters. It used 10 rimless 9-mm blank pistol cartridges for ignition. The fuel was sufficient for five to six blasts, each lasting three seconds with a range of 25 to 35 metres.

Towards the end of the war the *Einstossflammenwerfer* 46 was introduced. It had originally been developed to a requirement from the Luftwaffe parachute arm. It was a single-shot disposable weapon, and provided a one-second burst about 38 metres long. It saw action in the fighting in Berlin in 1945.

'USER-FRIENDLY'

Like so many of the weapons designed and developed before and during World War II, those intended for infantry support were often innovative and 'user friendly'. However instead of concentrating on simplicity of design and volume production the major munitions manufacturers were permitted to expend time and effort on what could in some cases be described as novelty designs.

Left: The first type of Panzerfaust to enter widespread service was the Panzerfaust 30. The number referred to the 30m range. The short range of the early weapons was a great disadvantage to the firer, who had to get dangerously close to the target tank. Final versions boasted a range of 100m.

Below: The Panzerfaust exactly suited the German defensive tactics of 1943–45. Allied tank crews feared the weapon. It was available in huge numbers, and if aimed properly from the correct distance, every German could have at least one Allied tank to his credit.

THE EXCELLENCE OF Soviet tanks came as a nasty shock to the Germans in 1941. German anti-tank guns could not take out a Soviet tank at anything but point-blank range. A race began to develop a complimentary infantry anti-tank system. Bigger guns were quickly produced but these were bulky weapons needing large crews and a vehicle to tow them.

When the Panzerfaust first appeared in late 1942 it was unique. The manufacturer's design brief was to provide soldiers with a personal anti-tank weapon. What emerged was a recoilless gun that incorporated rocket principles. The weapon was meant to be cheap and simple. It was little more than a holllow tube that projected a hollow-charge grenade. The hollow-charge worked by means of the so-called Munroe effect. The warhead had a copper-lined, cone-shaped hollow interior with the open end facing forward. This ensured that when the head was detonated, the optimium distance form the armour plate, the explosive force went forward. A thin-focused jet of molten metal and supeheated gas attacked the tank's armour plate at around 6000m per second. This jet melted a hole in the armour, and hot-gas and vapourised metal would either kill the tank crew outright or explode the ammunition.

Below: The Panzerfaust projectile could penetrate up to 200 mm of armour set at an angle of 30˚. Any Allied tank was vulnerable. Tank crews therefore added extra protection to their vehicles, including piling sandbags around the hulls and welding on spare track.

LUFTWAFFE GROUND TROOPS

In September 1942 Hermann Goering called for Luftwaffe volunteers to fight as ground troops in Russia. Like Heinrich Himmler, Goering would have his own private army.

Left: Although the bulk of the Luftwaffe's manpower had always served on the ground – a million men in flak and searchlight batteries – it was not until the Stalingrad campaign that large numbers of Luftwaffe troops were used in fighting divisions.

Right: If all air force ground troops had the skill and courage of these Fallschirmjäger, then the Luftwaffe field divisions would have won a fighting reputation to match the Waffen-SS. Unfortunately for Goering's ambitions, most of his troops were poorly trained and badly led.

GOERING'S PRIVATE ARMY

"WHOEVER joins this corps," Goering announced, "has to do so with a bold heart. If he shows courage in combat, the soldier can expect promotion and decorations." Some 250,000 men answered his call. By the time their leader surrendered in 1945, most lay dead in the Russian snow.

Goering had been asked by Hitler to comb out 50,000 personnel who could be spared from air force duties. The German army desperately needed replacements. The annual call-up had already been brought forward to compensate for the 750,000 casualties suffered in 1941. Now, at the height of the summer offensive, intended to give Germany control of the

Caucasus and Russia's oil supplies, front-line army units were far below establishment. And a bloody battle of attrition was developing along the Volga, where the 6th Army struggled to capture Stalingrad before winter.

FIRST GROUND TROOPS

Luftwaffe ground troops were already at the front, however. At the height of the manpower crisis in the army's first winter in Russia, Goering had volunteered to organise some infantry regiments to help hold the line. Seven Luftwaffe Field Regiments were created in January-February 1942. Four battalions strong, with attached heavy mortars and a battery of 88 mm guns, they had a useful but limited impact across a frontline running from Leningrad to the Crimea.

One LwFR participated in the

relief of the Demyansk pocket. Regiments 1,2,3 and 4 were combined into a battlegroup by General Meindl. 'Division Meindl' was engaged through 1942, taking part in anti-partisan operations after a long spell at the front around Kholm. Part of the division was amalgamated with 5. LwFR to form the first Luftwaffe field division, 1.LwFD, that autumn. Division Meindl was redesignated 21.LwFD in early 1943.

NOT WELCOME

Senior officers, notably von Manstein and Warlimont, were loud in their opposition to what they saw as a misuse of manpower. They argued that the same number of men, integrated into existing army units, would have greater impact than the hasty assembly of new formations with

inadequate numbers of trained officers and NCOs.

Goering's hapless volunteers were greeted with the same cold shoulder encountered by the SS in 1939-40, but had neither the time, the training, nor the equipment to repeat the success of Himmler's men.

Goering's field divisions were poorly equipped. Forever short of motor vehicles, they relied on horse-drawn transport; their artillery often consisted of obsolete weapons from the First World War.

UNDERSTRENGTH

With four to six battalions of infantry (each of three companies), minimal administrative and logistic staffs and reconnaissance companies on bicycles (where they had any form of transport), they were

165

Above: The first of the newly-formed Luftwaffe Field Divisions arrived on the eastern front just in time for the battle of Stalingrad. The poorly-trained and poorly-equipped troops were thrown straight into action.

Below: After suffering severe losses in the fight against front line Soviet tank armies, many of the Luftwaffe units were assigned to the less demanding but no less bloody partisan war.

equivalent to half a standard German army division.

That was before taking into account the fact that their training standards were far below those of the regulars. There were too few officers and NCOs who knew their business and they were rushed into action before they had a chance to learn. They were not kept together, but fed in piecemeal according to the crisis of the moment. The first ten divisions were hurried to Russia, some to join the doomed attempt to relieve Stalingrad, others to man the frozen trenches of Army Group North.

SLAUGHTERED

Three of Goering's divisions were destroyed within days of their arrival. 8.LwFD detrained at Morozovsk on 25 November and marched through a blizzard to reinforce the front at Stalingrad. But the front had collapsed. There were no friendly troops on the steppe, just hordes of T-34s which made short work of the air force soldiers. General Manstein assigned the survivors to fight alongside an army infantry division. He did the same with 8.LwFD after it suffered catastrophic losses during the attempted breakthrough to the 6th Army.

The Soviet offensive at Stalingrad was actually the smaller of two gigantic attacks intended to break the back of the Wehrmacht. The unfortunate volunteers of 2.LwFD were directly in the path of Marshal Zhukov's frontal assault on the German 9th Army in the Rzhev salient. Even a full-strength army division would have been hard-pressed, but the rout of another Luftwaffe unit merely confirmed the generals' worst fears.

Army criticism increased, lamenting the waste of manpower in badly-trained, poorly equipped units that only existed because of Goering's political clout. Most of the surviving divisions were transferred to anti-partisan operations while their future was debated.

General Meindl wanted to convert them into specialist assault units to work with the panzer divisions. General Petersen wanted to exploit them as a recruitment pool for his airborne divisions. Field Marshal von Manstein advanced the Army's view that they should be incorporated into the regular army. On 20 September, Hitler decided in favour of the Army.

Goering's attempt at replicating Himmler's success with the Waffen-SS was over. The divisions became part of the Army, which immediately embarked on the wholesale replacement of the units' officers. The Luftwaffe retaliated by retaining a specialist personnel, many of whom were transferred to the parachute or flak divisions. However, by the summer of 1944 the Luftwaffe was obliged to transfer personnel to the Army. Some were even sent to reinforce the SS. The SS panzer corps in Normandy included hundreds of replacements drafted in from the air force.

ATLANTIC WALL

Five field divisions occupied stretches of the Atlantic Wall. 16. and 17.LwFD were destroyed in the battle for Normandy; 18. LwFD was sent to the front in August 1944 and all but wiped out in the prolonged retreat from northern France to Holland. The luckiest of Goering's divisions was 14. LwFD which was part of the disproportionately large garrison maintained in Norway. It never saw action.

In contrast to the dismal history of the field divisions, the Hermann Goering Division had an excellent reputation. Built on a core of former paratroops with a draft of 5,000 Luftwaffe conscripts to bulk it out, the division regarded itself as an elite unit. It remained part of the Luftwaffe, but its uniforms, equipment and ethos were closer to those of the Waffen-SS.

Before it was fully assembled, a major part of the division was shipped to Tunisia in November 1942 and acquitted itself well in the winter campaign. There it stayed however: lost along with

Earth-bound Airmen

THE LUFTWAFFE already had combat units apart from its paratroopers. One of Goering's earliest decisions as Prussian Minister of the Interior was to establish a paramilitary unit within the police. Intended to crush political opposition, *Landespolizeigruppe General Goering* was expanded into *Regiment Hermann Goering* when conscription was reintroduced in March 1935. It became part of the Luftwaffe and increased to two *Jäger* (light infantry) battalions plus engineer and motorcycle reconnaissance companies. In 1938 the *Jäger* battalions were broken up to form Germany's first parachute battalion; the remainder of the regiment was converted into an anti-aircraft unit. However, on 1 March 1942 the regiment was expanded once again to form the 'Reinforced Hermann Goering Regiment': three infantry battalions with supporting artillery, engineer and reconnaissance units. It was expanded into a brigade on 21 July and on 17 October its units in southern France officially became a division.

Top: Members of the Hermann Goering Division hitch a ride with a Fallschirmjäger *motorcycle combination in Tunisia. Within three months the bulk of the division's members were to be killed or captured.*

Right: The division was reformed just in time for the Allied landings in Sicily. There it won a reputation as an excellent fighting unit; the Italian campaign which followed added further to its battle honours.

Above: Although only two of the six Fallschirmjäger divisions were airborne qualified, the reputation of the parachutists was such that members of all of the other units considered themselves an elite, and they proved to be highly effective on all fronts.

Below: A Luftwaffe soldier lies dead in a Normandy farmyard, his unfired Panzerfaust by his side. Some of the Luftwaffe units on the invasion front fought extremely hard and well, while others – second line units which had been garrisoned on the Atlantic wall – offered little resistance to the overwhelming power of the Allied assault.

some 250,000 Axis personnel when *Panzerarmee Afrika* had to surrender in May 1943. Some key members of the division were evacuated to Sicily and a skeleton formation remained in southern France. The division was officially reformed on 15 July in Sicily, but it was already in action again.

On 10 July 1943 the Allies invaded Sicily. US troops poured ashore at Gela, where they were met the following day by a ferocious counter-attack spearheaded by the Hermann Goering division, ably supported by 15. *Panzergrenadier* and the Italian Livorno divisions. Halted by naval gunfire and heavy air attacks, the Germans fell back into the hinterland to conduct a successful rearguard action back to Messina. The division was evacuated to mainland Italy.

The division was well placed to deal with the inevitable sequel, the Allied landings at Salerno. The Hermann Goering division counter-attacked again, the skill and bravery of its troops disguising a lack of numbers and threadbare logistical arrangements. The battle was followed by another rearguard action until the division was taken out of the line for rest and refit. While the division occupied its next defensive position,

Oberstleutnant Julius Schlegel negotiated the removal of the paintings, medieval manuscripts and sculptures that resided in the monastery at Monte Cassino. For three weeks Schlegel's men laboured to remove artifacts, including a relic of St. Benedict.

GOERING'S OWN

In January 1944 the division was re-titled *Fallschirmpanzerdivision* Hermann Goering. Sadly depleted by the winter battles and counter-attacks at Anzio, the division suffered heavy losses in June, defending the approaches to Rome. In July it was withdrawn from Italy to be flung into the German counter-attacks outside Warsaw where the Red Army's massive offensive threatened to breach the Vistula.

In September, Goering's 'parachute panzer division' became *Fallschirmpanzerkorps* Hermann Goering but this did not represent the doubling of strength the corps title implied.
The division was split in two, additional infantry battalions were added, but a critical shortage of men and equipment was never overcome. The corps fought in the defence of East Prussia in January 1945, was evacuated from the Memel pocket in March and the survivors scattered between Pomerania and Denmark. A vestigal element fought on as part of *Panzerkorps Grossdeutschland* until surrendering to the Russians in May.

GOOD AND BAD

Units of Goering's 'private army' had wildly different fortunes. In the paratroops and the Hermann Goering division, the Luftwaffe had some of the finest combat units of the war. But Goering's attempt to establish an independent army along the lines of the Waffen-SS was a hideous failure with tragic consequences for the men so hastily driven into battle. It took the Army a year to persuade Hitler to abolish the Luftwaffe Field Divisions, during which time tens of thousands of soldiers paid for Goering's ego with their lives.

Goering's Failure

Above: At the height of his power, Hermann Goering was second only to Hitler in Nazi Germany. But his rival Heinrich Himmler used the SS to build an immensely powerful state within a state. After the Luftwaffe's failure in the air, Goering sought to do the same.

Below: Goering visits a Luftwaffe training unit in the summer of 1944. By this time, his dream of a private army was shattered – his troops had largely been absorbed by the army and the SS, and their officers replaced by men with no loyalty to the Reichsmarschall.

GOERING KNEW his star was on the wane. Hitler blamed him for failing to subdue Britain in 1940 and now his old boast that nobody would bomb Germany had come back to haunt him. RAF Bomber Command had mounted its first 1,000 bomber raid. The increasing intensity of British raids led ordinary Germans to make disparaging remarks about the Luftwaffe in general and Hermann Goering in particular – Himmler's security apparatus passed selected titbits around Hitler's court. By providing his Führer with 100,000 men, not the 50,000 he was asked for, and by promising to assemble them in powerful new divisions, Goering sought to reverse his political decline. His subsequent role in the decision to hold on to Stalingrad after it was encircled should be seen in the same light. Still Hitler's designated successor, he was prepared to risk hundreds of thousands of German lives to salvage his reputation.

Goering authorised the establishment of XIII. *Fliegerkorps* in Germany. Commanded by *Generalleutnant* Meindl, it was to oversee the creation of 22 divisions. *Generalmajor* Petersen, the veteran commander of 7. *Fliegerdivision* in Russia, was appointed Inspector of Luftwaffe Field Divisions. It was intended to get ten divisions into action as soon as possible, with another eleven planned for 1943. Divisions 2, 3, 4, 5 and 6 were formed at Gross-Born in northern Germany; divisions 7,8,9, and 10 were formed at Mielau in East Prussia. The impact of the airborne forces on the Luftwaffe Field Divisions was important. Paradoxically, as the likelihood of another German airborne assault receded, the parachute forces expanded, earning a reputation as formidable fighters from Leningrad to El Alamein, Tunisia and Cassino. They attracted a steady flow of volunteers of the highest calibre from throughout the Luftwaffe.

LIGHT FLAK
Battlefield air defence

The Wehrmacht was well aware of the value of an efficient anti-aircraft defence. At the outbreak of war, the German armed forces were better shielded from air attack than any of their opponents.

ROM THE beginning of the war, the German *Flugzeug Abwehr Kanone* (FLAK, or anti-aircraft gun) made a major contribution to the Axis cause. The German abbreviation entered the vocabulary of the Allies, as USAAF bomber crews referred to their heavy body armour as 'Flak Jackets,' and in the latter half of the 20th Century became universally used to describe anti-aircraft fire.

The function of light flak was engage low-flying aircraft at close-range. If the volume of short-range fire forced attacking bombers and fighter-bombers to higher altitudes they could be engaged by heavy calibre weapons like the 8.8-cm Flak.

The 7.92-mm MG 34 and later MG 42 general-purpose machine guns were the lightest weapons that could be effectively used in an AA role. The MG 34, erroneously known to the Western Allies as the 'Spandau,' was the German infantry's standard machine gun in 1939. With a muzzle velocity of 755 metres a second it had an effective ground range of 2,000 metres, though against aircraft this reduced to around 1000 metres. It had a cyclic firing rate of up to 900 rounds per minute, and was fed by a 75-round saddle drum magazine or by 50-round non-disintegrating belts.

The MG 42 replaced the MG 34 during the war. It was much cheaper to make, using stamped metal and spot-welding to speed manufacture. It had a similar muzzle velocity and range, but had a much higher cyclic rate of 1,550 rounds per minute.

Rate of fire is important when engaging a fast moving aerial target, and the MG34 was much more effective when used in pairs on a *Zwillingslafette* 36. An MG *Doppelwagen* 36 – a horse- or vehicle-drawn limber large enough to accommodate one man with twin MG 34s – was part of the German army inventory in 1939-40, but the mount was often installed on vehicles and railway wagons.

The German army did not use heavy machine guns, but to provide heavier anti-aircraft support the 15-mm *Maschinen-gewehr* 151/15 was adopted. Originally a Luftwaffe gun mounted in aircraft like the Bf 109 and FW 190, it became available as heavier armament was fitted to fighters. Output was diverted to bolster AA defences from the summer of 1944. The gun was mounted on the SdKfz 251/21 half track – essential because the Mauser design was electrically powered and required a 22-29 volt DC supply. Each vehicle carried 3000 rounds in readiness.

Weapons with a calibre of 2 cm were much more effective in the anti-aircraft role. Still small enough to have a high rate of fire, the projectiles they fired were

Continued on page 174

Light flak guns were fitted to a variety of moving platforms. The decline of German air power meant that flak defences had to be more and more mobile.

FLAK ACTION

THE GERMAN LIGHT FLAK arm was built from scratch in the 1930s. It had to work out its own internal arrangements and operating policies. This had to be done within the factional realities within Nazi Germany – one of the basic tenets of the Third Reich was that no single organisation could have sole control over any particular function. So, as the Wehrmacht was re-arming for its new air-defence role, the Luftwaffe was busy doing the same. There was supposed to be a division of responsibilities, with the Luftwaffe being responsible for defence of the Reich, whilst army light flak formations were to defend the field armies. This did not happen and new equipment procurement caused ongoing interservice squabbles. These increased as Waffen-SS units entered the equation. A unit bound for the field would often find its equipment and ammunition hijacked by another unit. The army formations would usually find themselves at the bottom of the pile.

Right: Crews obtained their initial training at schools scattered around Germany. The main emphasis was upon teamwork, special attention being given to the ammunition changers.

Below: A flak crew trains on a Panzer IV mounting a 3.7 cm Flak 36. Light flak units were divided into motorised and non-motorised types. The former were intended to move into the field with major formations.

Right: The 2 cm Flak 30 engages 'enemy' aircraft at the 1935 Nuremberg rally. The gun was a Rheinmetall-Borsig design which entered service with the Wehrmacht the same year.

Below left: A 2 cm Flak 38 mounted on a SdKfz 7/1 half-track defends a port installation in the south of France. This combination was first introduced in 1941 and had a crew of 10.

Below: Getting guns into and out of action was a relatively easy task. Flak 38s were transported on tubular steel trailers with special lifting and lowering mechanisms.

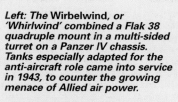

Left: The Wirbelwind, or 'Whirlwind' combined a Flak 38 quadruple mount in a multi-sided turret on a Panzer IV chassis. Tanks especially adapted for the anti-aircraft role came into service in 1943, to counter the growing menace of Allied air power.

Below: The Flakvierling 38 housed on an armoured train in Eastern Europe in March 1944. This superb gun was used to equal effect against ground and air targets. The gun used a variety of ammunition including high explosive and armour-piercing rounds.

Bottom: A 2 cm Flak 38 in action in the Western Desert in 1942. The Mauser-designed gun overcame the twin weaknesses of the Flak 30 – its slow rate of fire and a tendency to jam.

The Flak 30 used 20-round magazines. It usually had a crew of five, one of whom would operate a stereoscopic rangefinder. It was frequently used to engage ground targets.

Above: *A Luftwaffe crew mans a 2 cm Flak 38 from a fixed position in Italy in June 1944. Although the gun's high rate of fire increased the chances of producing a hit, the projectile's small explosive charge was unlikely to ensure a one-shot 'kill'.*

Below: *This light half-track, designated the SdKfz 10/4, mounts a 2 cm Flak 30. Highly mobile, the main drawback of this design was the very limited armour protection for the crew.*

large enough to carry a significant explosive charge. Weapons in service at the outbreak of war included the Flak 30, the Flak 38, the lightweight *Gebirgsflak* (Geb Flak) 38 and the four-barrel *Flakvierling* 38. All were recoil operated and could fire single shots or bursts fed by twenty round box magazines. A light armoured shield could be fitted when used in the field, but this was normally discarded on guns used in the defence of the Reich. The guns were equipped with one of three types of magnifying optical sight, the *Linealvisier* 21, *Flakvisier* 38 or the *Schwebekreisvisier* 30/38. German optical sights gave AA gunners a marked advantage compared to simpler metal ring sights fitted to many Allied guns.

MOBILE FLAK

The Flak 30 weighed 483 kg in action. It could fire high explosive (HE) or armour piercing (AP) ammunition. The maximum vertical range was 2,100 metres and horizontal 2,700 metres. Practical rates of fire was 120 rounds per minute. The Flak 38 was an improved version, being 80 kg lighter yet having double the rate of fire.

Light Flak guns were mounted on a variety of wheeled and half track vehicles including the

SdKfz 251 and the SdKfz 10. The *Leichte Flakpanzer* 38(t) of 1943 was the first fully tracked vehicle to be used as an SP AA gun, being a Flak 38 mounted on the rear of a modified PzKpfw 38(t) tank chassis.

The *Flakvierling* 38 was developed by Mauser for the Kriegsmarine and consisted of four Flak 38s on one mount. It had three seats, one for the gunner who fired the weapon using two pedal triggers, and two seats for the loaders. It had a triangular base onto which it was lowered using levelling jacks. It was widely used on self propelled and ground mounts by the army and Luftwaffe and was fitted in flak towers throughout the Reich and occupied Europe.

FURNITURE VAN

The SdKfz 7 half track was used as the chassis for the *Mittler Zugkraftwagen 8(t) mit 2 cm Flakvierling 38* or *Selbstfahrlafette 2 cm Flakvierling 38*. Later versions had greater armour protection for the driver and gun crew.

The chassis of the PzKpfw IV was used for two very effective SP mounts for the Flakvierling 38. The *Flakpanzer IV (2cm Flakvierling 38) auf Fgst PzKpfw IV Möbelwagen* earned its nickname of 'Furniture Van' from the hinged, slab-sided 10 mm

The most basic form of protection against low-flying enemy aircraft was the machine gun. The multi-purpose MG 34 was the standard secondary armament on most German fighting vehicles.

thick armoured shields that dropped down when the gun came into action. It came into service in 1943. The *Flakpanzer IV (2cm) auf Fgst Pz IV/3 Wirbelwind* or 'Whirlwind' that entered service at the end of 1943 was a better designed SP AA gun.

ALLIED AIR MENACE

Larger and harder-hitting than the 2-cm weapons, the Luftwaffe's 3.7 cm guns were necessarily slower-firing. During the war the Germans fielded four guns in this calibre – the Flak 18, 36, 37 and the Flak 43.

The Flak 18/36/37 operated by barrel recoil and residual gas pressure and had a practical/ cyclic rate of 80/160 rpm (Flak 18) and 120/160 rpm (Flak 36/37). The guns were clip fed from the side and fired HE-tracer, HE-incendiary-tracer, Armour Piercing HE, HE-incendiary and HE projectiles.

Though the Flak 43 looked externally similar to the earlier guns, it was in fact a ground based version of the Rheinmetall MK 103 aircraft cannon. Gas operated, it had a practical and cyclic rate of 180/250 rpm. The guns had a maximum vertical range of 4,785 metres and horizontal of 6,490 metres.

The SP mounts for the 3.7 cm Flak included half tracks and tank

chassis. The SdKfz 6 and SdKfz 7 were the most widely used. Early models had open topped cabs, but later these were fully armoured. The PzKpfw IV was used for two SP systems, the *3.7 cm Flak 43 auf Sf IV Möbelwagen* and the *3.7 cm Flak 43 auf Sf Ostwind* (Eastwind).

In addition to German designed and built weapons, captured light AA guns were widely used. Two of the most successful were the Swedish designed 40 mm m/36 light AA gun – better known as the Bofors Gun after the factory where it was designed – and the Soviet M-39 37 mm gun, which was itself a copy of the Bofors.

ARMY UMBRELLA

The M-39 had a crew of eight and weighed 2,000 kg in action. It fired clips of five rounds and in an anti-tank role could penetrate 46 mm of armour at 500 metres. The Swedish m/36 Bofors gun weighed 2150 kg and fired clips of four rounds. It had a cyclic rate of fire of 120-140 rpm and a practical rate of 70 rpm.

The flat trajectory and high velocity of light flak made them ideal weapons for close support and in the early years of the war they were employed more against ground targets than enemy aircraft. Fighters and flak made

Below: The Flak 38 was treated with great respect by its opponents. Allied units pressed it into service at every opportunity – late in 1944 the US Army even issued its own operating manual.

the front line battlefield a lethal area for slow flying French and British light bombers committed against armoured columns and transport nodes during the invasion of France in 1940.

From 1943 onwards when the Luftwaffe no longer dominated the skies over Germany and Europe, the huge volumes of

tracer thrown up by light flak units were among the few deterrents to marauding Allied fighter bombers. Light flak sited on flat roofed buildings and flak towers were deadly threats to low-flying USAAF and RAF fighters and light bombers, since it could fire almost horizontally at them as they approached a target.

Flying knights
of the reich

WW II Luftwaffe Aces

Germany without doubt fielded the best fighter pilots of World War II. In both East and West, the *Experten* of the Luftwaffe hacked Allied planes out of the air by the thousand.

FIGHTER 'aces' were fêted by both sides during World War I. Their individual, knight-like exploits made a welcome contrast to the anonymous slaughter of the trenches.

Five enemy aircraft was the threshold for 'ace' status, although a number of outstanding pilots achieved personal 'scores' far in excess. In Germany, ever-higher scores were demanded before the award of the coveted *pour le mérite* – the Empire's highest award for gallantry also known as the 'Blue Max'. It did not grace Hermann Goering's neck until 1918, when he had shot down more than 20 enemy aircraft.

From 1939 Goering would preside over a similar system as Hitler's top fliers competed for the *Ritterkreuz,* the Knight's Cross of the Iron Cross. As in World War I, thresholds had to be raised several times, and superior grades of *Ritterkreuz* were introduced to cope with the soaring victory tallies of the Luftwaffe aces, known as *experten.* Thirty-five German aces shot down 150 or more Allied aircraft; the top ten *experten* destroyed 2,552 between them.

TACTICAL ADVANTAGE

The Luftwaffe had a head start over its opponents thanks to Hitler's intervention in the Spanish Civil War. The Condor Legion included a number of future top-scoring aces, including Werner Mölders who brought down 14 Republican aircraft.

Combat experience in Spain led the Luftwaffe to jettison some First World War tactics and develop new ones. This was to be the Germans' greatest advantage at the beginning of the Second World War. They had a first class fighter aircraft in the Messerschmitt Bf-109 – but the British Spitfire was its equal, and in capable hands, the Hurricane could more than hold its own. However, the RAF remained wedded to pre-war tactics well

Goering's 'PIN-UP' Boys

WHETHER THEY LIKED it or not, many 'aces' found themselves popular icons, inundated with fan mail and a vehicle for government propaganda.

The National Socialists were obsessed with hero worship. The pilot's life was superficially glamorous and the *Experten* became role models for young German boys.

Far left: Werner Mölders was the top-scoring ace of the Spanish Civil War. The first recipient of the Knight's Cross with Oak Leaves and Swords, he had 115 kills when he died in 1941.

Left: Hans Joachim Marseilles, the highest scorer in the Western theatre, was feted as the 'Star of Africa' by the Nazi press.

added a chin turret to their B-17s, but Mayer's tactic remained in use until the end of the war.

Some Focke-Wulf Fw 190s were fitted with up to six 20-mm cannon, giving them every chance of destroying a bomber in a single pass. But they were slower and less manoeuvrable as a result, requiring fighter escort to protect them from Allied single-seaters. Using R4M unguided air-to-air rockets involved a similar trade-off between firepower and performance.

Regardless of weapon fit, or fighter type, a minority of pilots accounted for a large proportion of kills. At least 15 *Experten* shot down over 20 USAAF four-engine bombers each, and three destroyed over 30.

into 1940. British squadrons persisted in flying in tight three-plane 'vics' that required the pilots to concentrate on formation flying. They should have been checking the sky, most notably towards the sun. German fighters flew in looser pairs and four-ship formations known as *schwarme*. Dubbed 'finger four' by the British, who eventually copied it, the *schwarm* consisted of two pairs positioned like the fingers of an outstretched hand.

A number of German pilots ran up impressive victory scores against the British. Werner Mölders scored 31 kills during the Battle of Britain and another 22 in the West before he was posted to Russia. Major Helmut Wick became the top-scoring ace of the time on the morning of 28 November 1940, shooting down another Spitfire for a total of 56 kills. But Wick's total was quickly passed: *Hauptmann* Hans-Joachim Marseille eventually scored 158 kills, 151 over North Africa; on one occasion he shot down 17 RAF aircraft in a single day.

AERIAL MASSACRE

Victories for the Luftwaffe fighter pilots became scarce after the Battle of Britain. But the drought was only temporary. New and vastly richer killing

grounds soon presented themselves. Opportunities came in North Africa, and from June 1941, the 'anti-Bolshevik crusade' began in the East.

WAR OVER THE REICH

Two years on, the Luftwaffe's primary role had evolved into home defence. British heavy bombers attacked the Reich by night; US bombers struck by day. The nocturnal air war produced its own aces, including two pilots credited with over 100 kills.

The day war initially pitted the fighters against unescorted American bombers. The bombers flew in close formations so that a fighter could be brought under fire from a frightening number of heavy machine guns. However, if a bomber could be detached from the formation, it could be destroyed with far less risk to the attacking fighters.

This was formally recognized by the German 'scoring system' that charted a pilot's progress towards the highest gallantry awards. The destruction of a four-engine bomber was worth 3 points, but to separate one from the formation was still worth 2. Shooting down a fighter was worth 1 point. Twenty points earned the German Cross in Gold; 40 points garnered a Knight's Cross.

> "As long as I can shoot down the enemy, adding to the honour of the *Richthofen Geschwader* and the success of the Fatherland, I will be a happy man. I want to fight and die fighting, taking with me as many of the enemy as possible."
>
> **Major Helmut Wick, 57 victories, killed in action 28 November 1940, aged 25.**

Oberstleutnant Egon Mayer discovered that the best method of attacking the US bomber formations was from directly ahead, and slightly above, – '12 O'clock High'. Fewer of the bombers' guns pointed forward and a burst into the cockpit was the most certain way to bring them down. However, the closing speeds were terrifying and the fighter had, at best, one second in which to shoot before he had to break away or collide with his target. The USAAF eventually

TABLES TURNED

The appearance of North American P-51 Mustangs over Berlin signalled the likely outcome of the war, although Goering denied their existence as if he could wish them away.

During 1944 many of the *Experten* ran out of luck. Allied fighters were as good as or better than their German opponents, and there were many more of them. Allied pilots went into battle after extensive training whereas new Luftwaffe pilots were flung into action with less and less preparation. Allied fliers reported a steady drop in the average quality of their opponents, although an encounter with one of the *Experten* was always a disagreeable surprise.

JET DEBUT

In the last months of the war, a number of aces came together to form JV44, a squadron of Messerschmitt Me 262 jets. This elite unit pitted the world's first operational jets, flown by some of the world's greatest pilots, against overwhelming odds. Adolf Galland, ace pilot and *General der Jagdflieger*, said after his first test flight that a couple of hundred Me 262s could halt the Allied bomber offensive in a matter of days. But immature technology could not compensate for numerical inferiority. Rushed into service, the Messerschmitt's engines had an average life of ten hours; they were unreliable, vulnerable to flameout and the loss of one engine usually triggered a fatal spin.

Even with these handicaps, 22 Me 262 pilots became jet aces. *Oberst* Heinz Bär's 16 kills have yet to be surpassed by any jet flier. Lacking effective jets of their own, the Allies ambushed the Me 262s near their bases. With half of all Me 262 losses occurring in this way, pilots had to slip back to their airfields as close to the deck as they dared, at what became known as 'Knight's Cross height'.

Several aces were honoured after their death by having their unit named after them. Werner Mölders (115 victories) was the first to be so commemorated; ironically, he died as a passenger when the Heinkel taking him back to Germany for Ernst Udet's funeral crashed. *Oberst* Walter Oesau (123 victories) of JG1 was shot down and killed after a long battle with a P-38 over the Ardennes in May 1944.

EAGLE IN FLAMES

Kommando Nowotny was unusual in that it was named after the ace before his demise. He had joined JG54 as a new pilot just before the invasion of Russia, and between June 1941 and October 1943 he was credited with 255 kills. The 22-year-old Austrian, holder of the Knight´s Cross with Oak Leaves, Swords and Diamonds, was then taken off operations. However, a year later Nowotny got himself appointed to take over a unit testing the Me 262 in combat.

He took charge, transforming an unsuccessful outfit into an elite unit that impressed General Galland when he visited on 7 November. The next day, Nowotny was caught by a Mustang as he nursed his Me 262 back to the runway on only one engine. USAAF Lieutenant Stevens only had time for a short burst before pulling away to

TANK BUSTER

ALTHOUGH NOT a fighter ace, Hans Ulrich Rudel was one of the most remarkable men to fight for Hitler's Luftwaffe. Flying an extraordinary total of 2,530 combat missions in the obsolete Junkers Ju 87, he destroyed 523 Soviet tanks, 800 other vehicles, one battleship, a cruiser and a destoyer as well as countless other targets. He also gained nine air victories whilst flying the Focke-Wulf Fw 190.

Shot down 30 times, he rescued six aircrew members from hostile territory and was wounded five times. He was the only man to win the Knight's Cross with Golden Oak Leaves, Swords and diamonds.

After the war Rudel, an unrepentant Nazi, lived in Argentina whilst supporting extremist right-wing organisations in the FRG. In 1976, two Luftwaffe generals were compelled to resign for failing to prevent Bundeswehr officers from participating in a Rudel testimonial. He created a final scandal in 1982 when Luftwaffe planes took part in an unofficial fly-past at his funeral.

Right: Rudel demonstrates the optimum attack angle to destroy a Soviet T34 tank.

Below: The charismatic and outspoken Oberleutnant Helmut Wick (left) discusses tactics during a break in the Battle of Britain.

RED MIST

THE RUSSIAN AIR FORCE proved a very soft opponent and the source of thousands of easy 'kills'. Beginning the war with inferior aircraft and a desperate shortage of radio equipment, they were little more than targets to the vastly superior Luftwaffe.

Stalin had one of his air force generals shot for complaining about the poor quality of Soviet aircraft, so every flier from the most junior pilot to regimental commanders knew they could expect no mercy from their superiors. The result was an aerial massacre that lasted until 1944. Russian casualty rates were so high that only a tiny fraction of pilots lasted long enough to win the experience necessary to survive.

By mid-war, German units on the Eastern Front included a formidable number of men with over 500 combat missions logged in the same aircraft. The top seven *experten* were all eastern front fliers, at their head the lethally effective *Major* Erich Hartmann who shot down 352 Allied aircraft (345 Soviet machines plus seven US Mustangs at the end of the war). Whereas Mölders received the *Ritterkreuz* after his twentieth victory in May 1940, by 1944 some pilots with JG52 in Russia did not receive the award until they had shot down over 100 enemy machines.

Above: A pilot paints the twelfth 'kill' on the tail of his Messerschmitt Bf 109F during the initial phase of disastrous eastern crusade. The lack of red stars denotes that the first four victories were scored in the West.

Above left: Luftwaffe personnel examine the wreckage of a crashed Ilyushin Il-2 Stormovik ground attack aircraft in the summer of 1944.

Normandy in 1944. Two youthful pilots discuss a recent sortie in the foreground as mechanics wheel a Messerschmitt 'Gustav' under cover. Enthusiasm could not compensate for lack of experience as ever younger pilots were thrown unprepared into battle.

avoid the flak defences, but the jet burst into flames and spun in.

GERMAN TURNCOAT

One ace the Luftwaffe tried to forget, both before and after the war ended, was *Oberfeldwebel* Franz-Josef Beerenbrock. Awarded the Knight's Cross with Oak Leaves after his 100th kill in August 1942, he was forced to crash-land behind Russian lines on 9 November after a dogfight in which he accounted for three Soviet aircraft. He became one of the founders of the BDO or *Bund Deutscher Offiziere* – the anti-Nazi organization formed in Russia from German prisoners-of-war. Beerenbrock was half-Russian himself, and his old unit

SIMPLY THE BEST

reported a marked improvement in Soviet air force tactics shortly after his capture. Whether he had 'gone Red', as was rumoured in JG1 has never been established. He remained silent on the subject after his return to West Germany in 1949.

STRENGTH IN DEPTH

For every *Experte* with a score in triple figures, there were dozens of pilots with high scores by Allied standards – and it should be noted that the German procedure for verification was actually tougher than that of their enemies.

Horst Petzschler was a typical example: a 20-year-old enlisted man, he volunteered for the Luftwaffe in April 1941 and completed his training nearly two years later. Assigned to fly FW 190s in the ground-attack role on the Russian front, he scored his first victory on 11 May 1943, shooting down a Yak-7. His next two kills were achieved six months later, both on 10 November. There was another 6-month gap before he shot down two more Soviet aircraft in May 1944. Thirteen kills followed in the next four months when he served with JG3. By the time he flew to internment in Sweden on 4 May 1945, *Oberfeldwebel* Petzschler had shot down a fascinating variety of Allied aircraft: six Il-2s, four Pe-2s, three Yak-9s, three Lagg-5s, two P-51 Mustangs, two Yak-3s, one Lagg-7, one B-17 Flying Fortress, one B-24 Liberator, one A-20, and one MiG-3.

He was downed 13 times himself: Soviet anti-aircraft fire forced him to bail out once and to crash-land eleven times, and he had to take to his parachute after losing a fight with a P-51 over Magdeburg. He was awarded the Iron Cross first and second class.

Nearly half the top-scoring *Experten* were dead by May 1945. But the greatest of them all, 25-year-old Erich Hartmann, survived ten years in a Russian prison camp to return to Germany and play a major role in shaping the new West German air force.

Above: With 352 'kills', Erich Hartmann (1922-2000) was the most successful fighter pilot in the history of aerial combat. This picture, taken on 2 October 1943, shows Staffelkapitän Hartmann with his Messerschmitt Bf 109G on the Eastern Front.

Right: Hartmann's record is all the more remarkable since he did not make his combat debut until October 1942, and he had under 30 victories by the summer of 1943. His unit, JG 52, was the Luftwaffe's highest scoring, with some 11,000 'kills' acredited.

Below: Hartmann, dubbed 'the Black Devil of the Ukraine' by the Russians, receives his Brillanten (Diamonds) from Hitler at Rastenburg on 26 August 1944 in recognition of his then tally of 300 victories. Imprisoned for 10 years by the Soviets, he returned to Germany in 1955 when he joined the Bundeswehr, becoming Kommodore of the 'Richthofen' Jagdgeschwader.

Night Fighters
Electronic Warriors

German fighters forced the RAF out of the sky over the Reich for long periods of the night war.

THE LUFTWAFFE formed its first night fighter unit in 1939: a token *staffel* of Messerschmitt Bf 109Ds. The formation was expanded to become a *gruppe* (IV/JG 2) in 1940, and scored its first kill in July when one of the pilots intercepted an RAF Whitley. He admitted it had been pure luck that he saw

the bomber. The Bf 109s carried no airborne radar, and liaison with ground radar stations was haphazard. Pilots had tantalising glimpses of enemy aircraft, illuminated by searchlights; but if a bomber was 'coned' by the lights, it would be targeted by anti-aircraft guns and it was a bold night fighter that ventured closer. *Fliegerabwehrkanone,* or flak, remained Germany's

primary defence against nocturnal air raids for some time to come.

DAY FIGHTERS BY NIGHT

Single-seat fighters built for daylight operations had severe limitations as night fighters. The flat perspex panels of the Bf 109's canopy reflected the light from searchlights, making it hard to see anything. If a pilot

A late-model Messerschmitt Bf 110 night fighter is jumped by a Mosquito intruder of the RAF. The British and Germans waged the world's first high-technology war in the skies over Germany. Although the RAF had great success in hunting down the German fighters, the Luftwaffe had even greater success wreaking havoc among the streams of British heavy bombers who were pulverising the Reich.

found a bomber, his fighter was likely to be travelling so much faster that he had but a few seconds to aim and fire before he roared past and the bomber evaded into the night.

NIGHT DESTROYERS

After the conquest of Denmark, one *staffel* of IV/JG 2 was based at Aalborg, co-located with Messerschmitt Bf 110Cs of 'destroyer' squadrons I/ZG 76 and I/ZG 1. Wolfgang Falck, commander of I/ZG 1, wrote a report on the success of his Bf 110s in intercepting at night, working in cooperation with searchlights and ground radar. In June he was appointed to be the commander of the newly created NJG 1 after *Oberst* Josef

Kammhuber became 'Air Officer for Night Fighters' on the Luftwaffe staff. RAF Bomber Command was stepping up its campaign of night raids and Goering himself had staked his reputation on stopping it.

The first Bf 110 night fighters had no modifications for their new role, other than a coat of black paint which was believed to be the best camouflage at night. They bore a badge based on Falck's family coat-of-arms, designed by *Oberleutnant* Victor Mölders (brother of the top-scoring ace, Werner). The Bf 110 had a good rate of climb and a service ceiling of 32,000 feet. British bombers typically flew over Germany at 18,000 feet. With a top speed of more

than 300 mph, the Bf 110 could easily overhaul bombers reported by ground radar stations. The Hampden, the fastest British bomber then in service, had a maximum speed (when loaded) of only 254 mph. The Bf 110's cannon and machine-gun armament was powerful enough to bring down a bomber with a single pass.

BF 110 WORKHORSE

Built in successive dedicated night fighter versions, the Bf 110 remained the primary German night fighter until 1944 and was still in widespread service at the end of the war. It proved able to take the addition of radar, a third crewman to operate it, and heavier cannon

armament. Climb rate and maximum speed were reduced, but the aircraft still retained a healthy performance margin over enemy bombers.

In daylight it was a different story, however, and Goering's decision to order the night fighters up against the US 8th Air Force reveals just how out of touch he had become. On 4 February 1943, eight Bf 110s of IV/NJG 1 were ordered to attack a formation of US B-17s: they claimed three bombers shot down but all eight night fighters were damaged by defensive fire and were unavailable for operations that night. Overruling protests by several COs, Goering insisted his night fighters join the day battle.

Airborne radar

DURING 1942, British monitoring stations became aware of references by German night fighter crews to a device called 'Emil-Emil'. Suspicions were aroused that this might be some form of airborne radar, but the RAF had no idea of its frquency. One monitoring station in Norfolk picked up a likely transmission, and on 3 December a Wellington equipped with suitable receivers was sent on the world's first electronic 'Ferret' mission. It was attacked and badly damaged by a German Ju 88 night fighter, but managed to transmit the vital information and return to crash land in the sea off the Kent coast.

Six months later, a *Nachtjagd* crew defected, landing their Ju 88R at Dyce in Aberdeen. It carried 'Emil-Emil', more properly known as the FuG 212 Lichtenstein C1 airborne interception radar.

This was the start of two years of a fierce but unseen struggle in the night, with the British introducing countermeasures to each new Luftwaffe radar which appeared, while the Germans frantically developed new radar systems in an attempt to by-pass the latest British countermeasures.

Above left: A Dornier Do 217N-2 carries an early radar array, used by both the prototype FuG 202 and the production FuG 212 Lichtenstein radars. Under ideal conditions, it had a maximum range of about four km and a minimum range of 200 m.

Left: This Bf 110G-4 has the improved FuG 220 Lichtensten SN-2B. Although accurate, it had a minimum range of 500 metres, so a smaller FuG 212 C-1 was also fitted for close-range work.

Above: The angled dipole antennae on this Heinkel He 219 indicate that it carries a Lichtenstein SN-2d radar, the last version of the FuG 220 to see large-scale operational use.

Within weeks, USAAF P-47 Thunderbolts escorting the B-17s caught and slaughtered several night fighter squadrons. Ludwig Becker, with 43 kills the leading night fighter ace, was among the dead, his Bf 110 standing no chance against the more manoeuvrable P-47.

EARLY CONVERSIONS

Experiments with other aircraft were carried out during 1940. Eighteen Dornier Do 215 bombers (export models of the Do 17 on order for the Swedish air force) were converted to night fighters in the same way the RAF had converted some of its Blenheims. Nine Dornier 17Z-10s were completed with the nose of a Ju-88C. Supplied to 5/NJG 1, they packed a powerful punch: four MG FF 20 mm cannon and four 7.92 mm machine guns. They also carried the *Spanner-Anflage* (trouser press) infra-red searchlight, designed to pick out the exhaust gases in the wake of a distant

bomber, enabling the night fighter pilot to take aim through a special gunsight. Introduced in June 1940, it proved impractical as the maximum range was only about 200 metres.

AIRBORNE RADAR

The Do 17Z-10s also carried *Funk Gerät* (FuG) Lichtenstein C1 airborne radar. Lichtenstein operated on a frequency of 490MHz with a 620 mm wavelength. Four double pairs of dipole aerials bristled from the aircraft's nose, reducing its maximum speed. The radar had a range of between 3000 and 5500 metres, with a minimum of 200 metres, depending on conditions. Its search angle was restricted to a 24-degree arc. Three scopes were provided for azimuth, ranging and elevation. It was far from 'user friendly', but experienced operators could direct their pilot on to a bomber provided ground control vectored them approximately into the right area.

Although performance was similar to that of their prey, results were sufficiently encouraging for night fighter variants of the larger Dornier 217 to be produced. The Do 217N combined the nose of the Do 217J-2 with the airframe of the maritime bomber, the Do 217M. The main production version was the Do 217N-2 on which the dorsal turret was omitted to save weight. It was in a Do 217 that *Oberleutnant* Ludwig Becker (4/NJG 1) scored the Luftwaffe's first aerial victory using the combination of ground control airborne radar. On the night of 16 October 1940 he shot down a Wellington off the Dutch coast.

DEFENCE OF THE REICH

The Kammhuber line was to be Germany's shield until summer 1943. By then the Dorniers were being retired in favour of Ju-88s and Bf-110s. The Dornier was already underpowered, making the loss of an engine on take-off

or landing extremely dangerous, and the addition of more radar, radio equipment and cannon did nothing to help. Its 'greenhouse' canopy also had a tendency to dazzle the crew when searchlights veered too close.

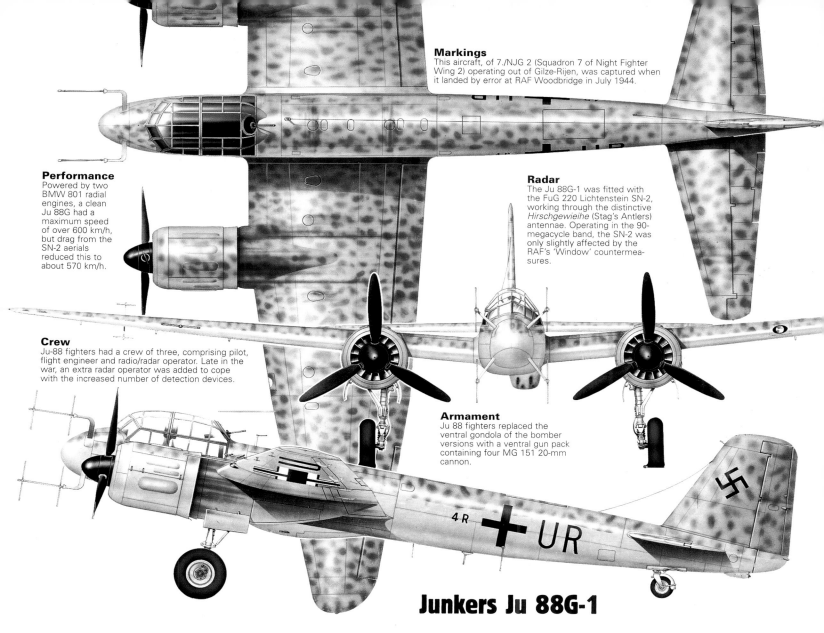

Performance
Powered by two BMW 801 radial engines, a clean Ju 88G had a maximum speed of over 600 km/h, but drag from the SN-2 aerials reduced this to about 570 km/h.

Radar
The Ju 88G-1 was fitted with the FuG 220 Lichtenstein SN-2, working through the distinctive *Hirschgewieihe* (Stag's Antlers) antennae. Operating in the 90-megacycle band, the SN-2 was only slightly affected by the RAF's 'Window' countermeasures.

Crew
Ju-88 fighters had a crew of three, comprising pilot, flight engineer and radio/radar operator. Late in the war, an extra radar operator was added to cope with the increased number of detection devices.

Armament
Ju 88 fighters replaced the ventral gondola of the bomber versions with a ventral gun pack containing four MG 151 20-mm cannon.

Junkers Ju 88G-1

Another German bomber proved more promising in the night fighter role. The original Junkers Ju-88 *schnellbomber* had evolved into several sub-types. The Ju-88C-2 was a long-range fighter version that served with one *staffel* of KG30 during the Norwegian campaign. Its solid nose housed a 20 mm cannon and three 7.92 mm machine guns. In July 1940 the *staffel* was ordered back to Germany and incorporated into the night fighter arm as 4./NJG 1. Successive dedicated nocturnal variants followed, until the Ju-88 was the primary German night fighter. Heavier and bulkier radar equipment, radios and weapons led to stability problems, overcome in the final Ju-88G sub-series which incorporated the larger

vertical and tail surfaces of the Ju-188 bomber. The usual liquid-cooled Jumo 211 engines were replaced by BMW 801D air-cooled powerplants.

Ju-88 night fighters ventured over Britain during the 1940 Blitz. Reasoning that it would be easier to intercept British bombers over their own bases rather than in the black vastness of the sky over Europe, NJG 1 flew a number of intruder missions that continued into 1941. These led to the first night fighter versus night fighter engagements.

FIGHTER vs FIGHTER

On 18 August 1940 a Ju-88C was intercepted near Chester and shot down over the North Sea after a long chase by a Blenheim Mk 1F flown by Pilot

Officer Rhodes. However, one German intruder nearly killed Bomber Command's most famous pilot, Guy Gibson. Then flying a Beaufighter night fighter, he was ambushed while coming into land at Wellingore on 8 April. His brakes shot away, the Beaufighter careered off the runway; his radar operator was injured but Gibson escaped without a scratch.

INTRUDER TRAP

Night fighters clashed over Germany as Bomber Command's offensive gathered pace. On the night of the Peenemunde raid, RAF night fighter ace Bob Braham led four Beaufighters on the fringe of the bomber stream. Sure enough, the German radar operators identified them as stragglers –

the best target – and vectored five Bf 110s from IV/NJG 1 to intercept them over the Frisian Islands. The result was a disaster for the Luftwaffe. Braham shot down two of the Germans and one of his flight brought down a third. One of the surviving Bf 110s was damaged by German flak and the other aborted due to engine failure.

The bane of the German defences was the de Havilland Mosquito: the 'wooden wonder' that could carry the bomb-load of a Flying Fortress to Berlin and back – at twice the speed and for half the price. Too fast and agile for the standard German night fighters to catch, it served as a pathfinder bomber and as an intruder. The German response was twofold: the first Luftwaffe night fighter to be

Above: This Junkers Ju 88G-1, which Obergefreiter Mäckle landed by mistake in Suffolk, proved an intelligence goldmine. It proved to RAF Bomber Command that Luftwaffe night fighters carried sensors to home in on British Monica tail-warning radars and on H$_2$S navigation radars.

Above: Fortunately for the Allies, fewer than a dozen Me 262B-1a/u1 night fighter conversions of the two-seat version of the German jet made it into service. It was equipped withthe FuG 218 Neptun radar.

Below: The Junkers Ju 388J would have been an extremely potent high-altitude night fighter. It was expected to enter service in January of 1945, but manufacture was halted in December 1944.

built as such from the outset, and the development of jet-powered interceptors.

The original design for the Heinkel He 219 *Uhu* – 'Owl' – was for a twin-engine multi-role fighter/fighter-bomber/torpedo-bomber. But it was offered to the Luftwaffe in the wake of the Battle of Britain, which had cost the *zerstörer* squadrons dearly. Erhard Milch, who was striving to reduce the number of aircraft types in service, opposed its development. However, General Kammhuber used the special powers granted him by Hitler to force the project into service.

NIGHT OWLS

He recognised that the aircraft had the makings of a first class night fighter and it was for this role that the final design was optimised. Further delays ensued, partly caused by RAF Bomber Command flattening the Heinkel factory at Rostock and destroying most of the documentation. Milch seized on every negative report to frustrate the He 219, but it won competitive trials against the Ju-188 and Do-217N. Major Werner Streib, *Gruppen-kommandeur* of I/NJG 1, was an early convert to the He 219 and he demanded pre-production airplanes for his unit. He flew the type's operational debut on 11-12 June 1943, shooting down

five Lancasters in one sortie. His unit shot down 20 British aircraft – including 6 of the previously uncatchable Mosquitos – in July.

Built with an eye to jet propulsion, the He 219 was the first combat aircraft to have ejection seats for the crew. With de-icing, auto pilot, blind landing aids and armour plating, it carried a formidable armament of up to four 30 mm cannon and two 20 mm cannon in the nose or ventral gunpacks, plus two upward-firing 30 mm cannon.

Some German pilots claimed that had the He 219 been built in real numbers, the British bombers would have suffered unacceptable casualties. However, the He 219 did have a number of major drawbacks, not the least of which was that it was underpowered. At over 8 tonnes unloaded (and 15 tonnes fully fuelled and armed) the *Uhu* had an unimpressive rate of climb; loss of one engine during take-off or landing was incredibly dangerous. And many Bf 110 pilots refused convert, claiming that the cockpit misted over too much on landing in cold conditions.

'JAZZ MUSIC'

Upward-firing guns, dubbed *Schräge Musik* ('Slanting' or 'Jazz Music') were introduced by a number of units from the end of 1941. Oberleutnant Rudolf Schonert fitted two upward firing 7.92 mm MGs on his Do 17Z-10. Such weapons enabled a fighter to fly in formation with a target and to attack from beneath, rather than risk a shoot-out with an alert rear-gunner.

FIRING FROM BELOW

Three Do 217Js were fitted with upward-firing 20 mm cannon a year later, and the system became standard in NJG 5 by early 1943. However, although its use became widespread, it was not without hazard: Hauptmann Manfred Meurer, *Kommandeur* II/NJG 5, (63 victories) was killed when a Lancaster he shot down crashed onto his He-219.

In the last months of the war, the Germans introduced two jet night fighters. The single seat Arado Ar 234 bomber/ reconnaissance aircraft was fitted with radar and a ventral gun-pack to become the Arado Ar 234C-3/N two-seat night fighter. The radar operator was crammed into a tiny compartment behind the pilot. Neither man had much chance of bailing out in an emergency. The Ar 234 handled superbly at altitude, but its 'greenhouse' nose reflected searchlight beams all around the cockpit, which could be very distracting. Even so, with its safer single engine performance, the Arado was a better night fighter than the Messerschmitt Me 262B-1a/U1.

262 BY NIGHT

Two-seat versions of the Me 262 had been belatedly produced for training purposes, but by early 1945 they were being converted on the production line to night fighters. Its unreliable jet engines remained a menace, the two-seater being even harder to fly on one engine than the day fighter. Nevertheless, both jet night fighters were able to intercept Britsh Mosquitos. However, they were so fast that against lumbering night bombers they tended to overshoot.

Night Intruders

THE LUFTWAFFE WAS NOT the only air force to have night fighters in the skies over the Reich – RAF intruders found rich pickings preying on their German equivalents. Beaufighters and Mosquitoes fitted with advanced centimetric radar hovered on the fringes of British bomber streams and patrolled over known *Nachtjäger* bases.

The Germans were the first to use intruders, sending Dornier Do 217s and Junkers Ju 88s to infiltrate returning British bomber forces early in the war. The British returned the favour in the summer of 1943, and Beaufighters of No.141 squadron shot down 23 enemy night fighters in a matter of months.

But the Beaufighter had little performance advantage over its German equivalents. However, this was more than made up for by the arrival of night fighter versions of the de Havilland Mosquito, which began operations in August 1943. Almost impossible to catch as a bomber, it now struck fear into Luftwaffe hearts as a hunter.

Above: The first truly effective night fighter of the war, the Bristol Beaufighter was a tough, heavily-armed machine which became operational in September 1940. Equipped with AI Mk IV radar, it was the main reason why the Luftwaffe gave up the night Blitz.

Below: Although only a minority of the 7781 Mosquitos built were completed as night fighters, it first became operational in the summer of 1942, and began intruder missions over Germany the next year. Mosquitos accounted for more than 1500 Luftwaffe aircraft in three years.

Index

Page references in *italics* refer to illustrations.